Elementary and Intermediate Algebra

A Practical Approach
Volume One

D1537735

SECOND EDITION

Timothy Craine | Jeffrey McGowan | Thomas Ruben

CENGAGE
Learning·

Australia • Brazil • Japan • Korea • Mexico • Singapore • Spain • United Kingdom • United States

CENGAGE
Learning·

Elementary and Intermediate Algebra: A Practical Approach, Volume One, Second Edition

Elementary and Intermediate Algebra: A Practical Approach, 1st Edition
Timothy Craine | Jeffrey McGowan | Thomas Ruben

© 2004 Cengage Learning. All rights reserved.

Executive Editors:
Maureen Staudt
Michael Stranz

Senior Project Development Manager:
Linda deStefano

Marketing Specialist:
Courtney Sheldon

Senior Production/Manufacturing Manager:
Donna M. Brown

Production Editorial Manager:
Kim Frv

Sr. Rights Acquisition Account Manager:
Todd Osborne

For product information and technology assistance, contact us at
Cengage Learning Customer & Sales Support, 1-800-354-9706

For permission to use material from this text or product,
submit all requests online at **cengage.com/permissions**
Further permissions questions can be emailed to
permissionrequest@cengage.com

This book contains select works from existing Cengage Learning resources and was produced by Cengage Learning Custom Solutions for collegiate use. As such, those adopting and/or contributing to this work are responsible for editorial content accuracy, continuity and completeness.

Compilation © 2012 Cengage Learning
ISBN-13: 978-1-285-02649-7

ISBN-10: 1-285-02649-7

Cengage Learning
5191 Natorp Boulevard
Mason, Ohio 45040
USA

Cengage Learning is a leading provider of customized learning solutions with office locations around the globe, including Singapore, the United Kingdom, Australia, Mexico, Brazil, and Japan. Locate your local office at:
international.cengage.com/region.
Cengage Learning products are represented in Canada by Nelson Education, Ltd.
For your lifelong learning solutions, visit **www.cengage.com/custom.**
Visit our corporate website at **www.cengage.com.**

Printed in the United States of America

Brief Contents

Geometry and Numbers

The Ups and Downs of Wall Street

Investors pay close attention to how stock markets around the world are performing. In the United States the most closely watched market is the New York Stock Exchange, located on Wall Street in Manhattan. Every evening newscasters report on how the major stock indices such as the Dow Jones, the NASDAQ, and the S & P 500 performed that day. These numbers, which represent an average of many individual stocks, are usually reported in terms of change, that is, whether the stock price is up or down that day and by how many points. Thus investors are accustomed to thinking in terms of positive and negative numbers.

For many years individual shares traded on the New York Stock Exchange were sold in increments of $\frac{1}{8}$ of a dollar. A typical price for a share might be quoted as $42\frac{5}{8}$. At the beginning of the 21st century, however, the Exchange converted from fractions to decimals. Prices of stocks are now quoted to the nearest cent. (See Exploration on p. 42.)

1.1 Positive and Negative Numbers

AFTER STUDYING THIS SECTION YOU WILL BE ABLE TO

- Add, subtract, multiply, and divide signed numbers.
- Use models to represent signed numbers.

If you have a checking account, you probably receive a statement from the bank at the end of each month showing the total amount of money you deposited and the amount you withdrew from the bank by writing checks. The deposits may be considered **positive numbers** and the checks, **negative numbers**. If the total of the checks is more than the total of the deposits, you may end up with a negative balance, which means at least one of your checks will bounce.

Positive and negative numbers are also called signed numbers. Positive numbers may be shown with a raised plus sign (e.g., $^{+}3$) and negative numbers, with a raised "minus" sign (e.g., $^{-}4$).

One application of signed numbers is in chemistry, where particles may carry a positive or negative charge. A single positive charge and a single negative charge neutralize each other.

EXAMPLE 1

a. An oxide ion consists of 8 protons, with positive charges, and 10 electrons, with negative charges. Find the charge on an oxide ion.

b. An aluminum ion consists of 13 protons and 10 electrons. Find the charge on an aluminum ion.

Solution

a. This situation is represented in Figure 1. Notice how pairs of positive and negative charges are lined up. There are two negative charges that are not paired. The net charge for the oxide ion is $^{-}2$.

Figure 1

The combination of the charges may be written as a sum: $^{+}8 + {}^{-}10 = {}^{-}2$. (Read "positive 8 plus negative 10 equals negative 2.")

b. This situation is represented in Figure 2. There are three positive charges that are not paired. The net charge for the aluminum ion is $^{+}3$ because $^{+}13 + {}^{-}10 = {}^{+}3$.

Figure 2

EXAMPLE 2   Find the net charge when you combine the ions.
a. A calcium ion (charge $^+2$) with a sodium ion (charge $^+1$)
b. A sulfate ion (charge $^-2$) with a phosphate ion (charge $^-3$)
c. A sodium ion (charge $^+1$) with a chloride ion (charge $^-1$)

Solution   **a.** This combination may be written $^+2 + {}^+1 = {}^+3$. The net charge is $^+3$, as shown in Figure 3.

Figure 3

b. This combination may be written $^-2 + {}^-3 = {}^-5$. The net charge is $^-5$, as shown in Figure 4.

Figure 4

c. $^+1 + {}^-1 = 0$. The net charge is zero. One sodium ion neutralizes one chlorine ion. See Figure 5. These two ions are found in pairs in the compound sodium chloride, which is ordinary table salt.

Figure 5

Absolute Value

Every number has an **absolute value**. In Examples 1 and 2 the absolute value of each group of like charges may be thought of as the number of particles. Thus, in Example 1(a) the absolute value of $^+8$ is 8 and the absolute value of $^-10$ is 10. When these two charges are combined, pairs of positives and negatives cancel each other out, leaving a net charge of $^-2$. Its absolute value is 2.

A common way of writing absolute value in algebra is to use two vertical lines: ||. You will often see these absolute value statements written as

$$|^+8| = 8 \qquad |^-10| = 10 \qquad |^-2| = 2$$

Adding Signed Numbers

Examples 1 and 2 illustrate the addition rules for positive and negative numbers.

Adding Signed Numbers

To add (or combine) two signed numbers:

■   If the numbers have the *same* sign, *add* their absolute values and keep the sign.

(continued)

> ■ If the numbers have *opposite* signs, *subtract* their absolute values and take the sign of the number with the *larger* absolute value.

Example 3 illustrates how to use the addition rules.

EXAMPLE 3 Use the addition rules for signed numbers to find these sums:

a. $^-23 + {}^-15$
b. $^+426 + {}^-782$
c. $^+\frac{1}{2} + {}^+\frac{1}{4}$
d. $^+91.2 + {}^-43.913$

Solution
a. The numbers have the same sign. Add their absolute values ($23 + 15 = 38$) and keep the sign. The answer is $^-38$ because both numbers are negative.
b. The numbers have opposite signs. Subtract their absolute values ($782 - 426 = 356$) and then take the sign of the number with larger absolute value ($^-782$). The answer is $^-356$.
c. The numbers have the same sign. Add their absolute values ($\frac{1}{2} + \frac{1}{4} = \frac{2}{4} + \frac{1}{4} = \frac{3}{4}$) and keep the sign. The answer is $^+\frac{3}{4}$ because both numbers are positive.
d. The numbers have opposite signs. Subtract their absolute values ($91.2 - 43.913 = 47.287$) and then take the sign of the number with larger absolute value. The answer is $^+47.287$.

■ ■ ■

Note: In parts (a) and (b) the numbers are **integers**. Integers include positive and negative whole numbers as well as zero. In parts (c) and (d) we observe that the rules for adding signed numbers apply to fractions and decimals, not just to integers.

Using Calculators

On most calculators the raised plus sign ($^+$) is omitted. Positive numbers are entered without signs. In this book we will usually omit the plus sign; that is, we will write 7 rather than $^+7$.

There is a special key, $(-)$, for entering negative numbers.

Caution: Do not confuse the negative key with the subtraction key:

Although you may use a calculator to find the sum of two signed numbers, you should be able to do relatively simple problems such as $^-12 + 3$ using mental math and the rules for addition of signed numbers.

Calculators and computers often abbreviate absolute value as *abs*. On the TI-83 or 84, abs is found under the MATH NUM menu. If you enter ABS(8) the calculator will display 8. If you enter ABS(⁻8) it will also display 8.

The Number Line Model

As you saw in Examples 1 and 2, one model of signed numbers is charged particles. Another model for signed numbers is a number line. When a horizontal line is used, positive numbers are to the right of 0 and negative numbers are to the left of 0. See Figure 6.

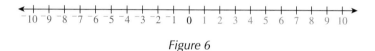

Figure 6

An example of an application that uses a vertical number line is temperature. Temperatures *above zero* are considered positive; temperatures *below zero* are negative. See Figure 7.

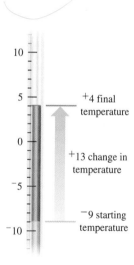

Figure 7

EXAMPLE 4   On a winter day the temperature at 6 A.M. was ⁻9°C. By noon the temperature had risen 13°. What was the temperature at noon?

Solution   The thermometer in Figure 7 shows the starting point and the change in temperature. The final temperature, indicated on the thermometer, is ⁺4°C. This result may also be obtained by applying the addition rules for signed numbers: ⁻9 + ⁺13 = ⁺4.

The number line model for addition involves three elements: starting position, change in position, and final position. The relationship among these three elements is summarized as follows.

Number Line Model for Addition

starting position *plus* change in position = final position

start + change = final

The number line model for subtraction involves these same three elements. An application of subtraction is shown in Example 5.

Number Line Model for Subtraction

final position *minus* starting position = change in position

final − start = change

EXAMPLE 5 On the same winter day, at noon the temperature was $^+4°$C. By midnight that night it had fallen to $^-12°$C. By how much had the temperature changed?

Solution The temperature dropped $16°$, so the change may be represented by $^-16$. You can verify this result by counting along the number line thermometer in Figure 8.

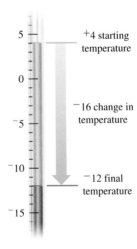

Figure 8

You can also use the number line model for subtraction to write

$$\text{final} - \text{start} = \text{change}$$

$$^-12 - {}^+4 = {}^-16$$

The change in temperature was $^-16°C$.

A Rule for Subtracting Signed Numbers

The answer to Example 5 is not found by combining the two temperatures. If we find the sum $^-12 + {}^+4 = {}^-8$, we clearly have an incorrect result, as a glance at the thermometer will show. Notice, however, that if the second number is changed to $^-4$, then we have $^-12 + {}^-4 = {}^-16$, which is the correct solution. In conclusion, the subtraction problem $^-12 - {}^+4$ gives the same result as the addition problem $^-12 + {}^-4$. The numbers $^+4$ and $^-4$ are called *opposites*, which suggests the following rule.

Subtracting Signed Numbers

To subtract two signed numbers, change the sign of the second number and change the operation to addition. Then follow the rules for the addition of signed numbers. *Think: a* minus *b = a* plus the opposite of *b*; that is

$$a - b = a + {}^-b$$

Example 6 illustrates the use of the rule for subtraction.

EXAMPLE 6 Apply the rule for subtraction.

  a. $^+7 - {}^+11$
  b. $^+7 - {}^-11$
  c. $^-7 - {}^+11$
  d. $^-7 - {}^-11$

Solution **a.** $^+7 - {}^+11 = {}^+7 + {}^-11$ *For opposite signs, subtract absolute values*

$$= {}^-4$$

  b. $^+7 - {}^-11 = {}^+7 + {}^+11$ *For the same signs, add absolute values*

$$= {}^+18$$

c. $^-7 - {}^+11 = {}^-7 + {}^-11$ *For the same signs, add absolute values*

$= {}^-18$

d. $^-7 - {}^-11 = {}^-7 + {}^+11$ *For opposite signs, subtract absolute values*

$= {}^+4$

■ ■ ■

Multiplying Signed Numbers

To multiply two signed numbers, we cannot apply the rule for addition. The next two examples allow us to discover the correct rule.

Note: In the first few chapters of this book we use the symbol $*$ for multiplication. It is the same symbol that appears on the screen of a TI-83 graphing calculator.

EXAMPLE 7   Look for a pattern in the following equations. Notice that the first number is decreasing by 1, but the second number is always 5. What numbers should replace the question marks?

$$4 * 5 = 20$$
$$3 * 5 = 15$$
$$2 * 5 = 10$$
$$1 * 5 = 5$$
$$0 * 5 = 0$$
$$^-1 * 5 = ?$$
$$^-2 * 5 = ?$$
$$^-3 * 5 = ?$$

Solution   The numbers on the right of the equal sign decrease by 5. Thus,

$$^-1 * 5 = {}^-5$$
$$^-2 * 5 = {}^-10$$
$$^-3 * 5 = {}^-15$$

■ ■ ■

From Example 7 it appears that when a positive number is multiplied by a positive number the product is positive, and when a negative number is multiplied by a positive number, the product is negative. What happens when a positive number is multiplied by a negative number, for example, $5 * {}^-3$? If we recognize that the order in which we multiply two numbers does not matter, we see that $5 * {}^-3 = {}^-3 * 5 = {}^-15$, as shown in Example 7. (The fact that $a * b = b * a$ is called the *commutative property of multiplication*.)

We may now ask what happens when two negative numbers are multiplied together. The next example addresses that question.

EXAMPLE 8

Look for a pattern in the following equations. Notice that the first number is decreasing by 1, whereas the second number is always $^-5$. What numbers should replace the question marks?

$$4 * {}^-5 = {}^-20$$
$$3 * {}^-5 = {}^-15$$
$$2 * {}^-5 = {}^-10$$
$$1 * {}^-5 = {}^-5$$
$$0 * {}^-5 = 0$$
$${}^-1 * {}^-5 = ?$$
$${}^-2 * {}^-5 = ?$$
$${}^-3 * {}^-5 = ?$$

Solution

The numbers on the right of the equal sign are increasing by 5. Thus,

$${}^-1 * {}^-5 = 5$$
$${}^-2 * {}^-5 = 10$$
$${}^-3 * {}^-5 = 15$$

From Example 8 we may conclude that when two negative numbers are multiplied together, their product is positive.

Examples 7 and 8 illustrate the rules for multiplying positive and negative numbers. Exercise 15 shows that the rules for division are similar.

Multiplying and Dividing Signed Numbers

If the signs are the same, the product or quotient is positive. If the signs are different, the product or quotient is negative.

positive $*$ positive $=$ positive	positive $\div$ positive $=$ positive
positive $*$ negative $=$ negative	positive $\div$ negative $=$ negative
negative $*$ positive $=$ negative	negative $\div$ positive $=$ negative
negative $*$ negative $=$ positive	negative $\div$ negative $=$ positive

There are special rules for multiplying and dividing with zero.

Multiplying and Dividing with Zero

- 0 multiplied by any number equals 0.
- 0 divided by any positive or negative number equals 0.
- Division by 0 is undefined.

Exercises 1.1

1. Write a sum for each of these charged-particle models.

   a.

   b.

2. Find the absolute value for each of the resulting charges in Exercise 1.

3. Use a charged-particle model to find each sum.

   a. $^-6 + {}^+7$ b. $^-8 + {}^+2$ c. $^-6 + {}^-2$

   d. $^+5 + {}^+4$ e. $^-6 + {}^+6$

4. Use the rule for addition to find each sum.

   a. $17 + {}^-8$ b. $^-321 + {}^-593$ c. $0 + {}^-6$

   d. $^-34.7 + {}^+71.8$ e. $^-62.3 + {}^-41.75$ f. $-\frac{1}{3} + \frac{1}{2}$

5. At 8:00 P.M. on a winter evening the temperature was $^-6°C$. By midnight the temperature had dropped 8°.

   a. What was the temperature at midnight?

   b. Represent this situation using the number line model for addition.

6. At 3:00 P.M. on a summer day, the temperature was 35°C. At 10:00 P.M. the temperature was 24°C.

   a. Find the change in temperature.

   b. Represent this situation with the number line model for subtraction.

7. Signed numbers may be applied to situations involving money. Think of deposits to your bank account as positive ($^+$) and checks or withdrawals as negative ($^-$). Alice has a beginning balance of $100 in her checking account. She writes a check for $250 and then deposits her paycheck, which is $475. She then withdraws $50 from an automatic teller machine (ATM).

   a. Find her balance after all these transactions.

   b. Represent this situation as a sum of all the transactions.

8. Signed numbers may be applied to elevations above ($^+$) or below ($^-$) sea level. Mt. Whitney is the highest spot in California, with an elevation of 14,494 feet above sea level. Death Valley has the lowest elevation in the state, 282 feet below sea level.

   a. Use positive or negative signs to represent the two elevations.

   b. Find the difference in elevations.

9. Apply the rule for subtraction to find each difference.

   a. $^+5 - {}^+13$ b. $^-37 - {}^+42$

   c. $^+11.8 - {}^+5.7$ d. $-\frac{2}{5} - \frac{^-1}{10}$

10. Explain the difference between these two keys on the calculator:

11. What happens when we use the negative key more than once? Experiment by entering

    etc. Describe what you observe.

12. Use the number line model for addition, start + change = final, to show that each pair of sums is the same. The first example is worked out for you.

Example: $^-3 + 9 = 9 + ^-3$
Solution: $^-3$ is the starting position, 9 is the change, 6 is the final position.

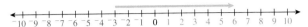

9 is the starting position, $^-3$ is the change, 6 is the final position.

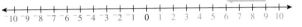

a. $^-6 + ^-2 = ^-2 + ^-6$ **b.** $2 + ^-7 = ^-7 + 2$

c. $2 + 6 = 6 + 2$

13. Use the number line model for subtraction, final − start = change, to find each difference. Then check using the rule for subtraction. The first example is worked out for you.
    Example: $^-7 − ^-2$
    Solution: $^-2$ is the starting position, $^-7$ is the final position, $^-5$ is the change.

$$^-7 − ^-2 = ^-7 + 2 = ^-5$$

a. $^-3 − 5$ **b.** $5 − ^-3$

c. $2 − 6$ **d.** $4 − ^-3$

14. Find each product or quotient. Then complete each statement with the correct word, positive or negative.
    a. $5 * 2$; positive $*$ positive $= ?$
    b. $5 * ^-2$; positive $*$ negative $= ?$
    c. $^-5 * 2$; negative $*$ positive $= ?$
    d. $^-5 * ^-2$; negative $*$ negative $= ?$
    e. $10 ÷ 2$; positive $÷$ positive $= ?$
    f. $10 ÷ ^-2$; positive $÷$ negative $= ?$
    g. $^-10 ÷ 2$; negative $÷$ positive $= ?$
    h. $^-10 ÷ ^-2$; negative $÷$ negative $= ?$

15. Think carefully about each of these temperature situations. Answer the questions and show how each example illustrates the rules for dividing signed numbers on page 9.
    a. The temperature at noon was 0°. Two hours later it was 6° above 0 ($^+6$). How fast did the temperature rise? (*Answer:* $^+6 ÷ ^+2 = ?$ so the temperature rose _____ degrees per hour.)
    b. The temperature at noon was 0°. Two hours later it was 6° below 0 ($^-6$). How fast did the temperature rise? Think of a falling temperature as a negative rise. (*Answer:* $^-6 ÷ ^+2 = ?$ so the temperature rose _____ degrees per hour.)
    c. The temperature at noon was 0°. Two hours before that (think negative 2) it was 6° below 0 ($^-6$). How fast did the temperature rise? (*Answer:* $^-6 ÷ ^-2 = ?$ so the temperature rose _____ degrees per hour.)
    d. The temperature at noon was 0°. Two hours before that it was 6° above 0 ($^+6$). How fast did the temperature rise? (*Answer:* $^+6 ÷ ^-2 = ?$ so the temperature rose _____ degrees per hour.)

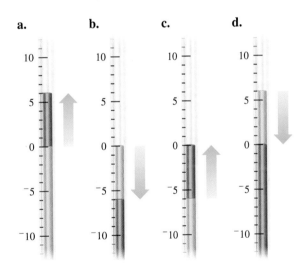

Skills and Review 1.1

16. Tisha eats $\frac{1}{2}$ of a whole pizza for lunch and $\frac{1}{3}$ of the same pizza for dinner. What fraction of the pizza did she eat in all? Use the diagrams to check your work.

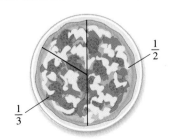

Notice that $\frac{1}{2}$ and $\frac{1}{3}$ are different-size slices of pizza and cannot be added in fraction form until the slices are broken up into equal-size slices. The diagram shows the same pizza broken into six equal slices.

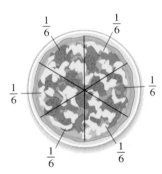

Equivalent fractions represent the same amount. Rewrite $\frac{1}{2}$ and $\frac{1}{3}$ with equivalent fractions using the new slice pattern in the diagram. Add the fractions.

17. **a.** Add: $\frac{1}{5} + \frac{1}{5} + \frac{1}{5} + \frac{1}{5} + \frac{1}{5}$

　　b. Explain why the answer to (a) is not $\frac{5}{25}$.

　　c. Multiply: $5 * \frac{1}{5} = \frac{5}{1} * \frac{1}{5}$.

　　d. Explain why the answers in (a) and (c) are the same.

18. Find each sum or difference without using a calculator.

　　a. $-\frac{1}{3} + \frac{3}{4}$ 　　　　　**b.** $-\frac{2}{3} - \frac{-1}{2}$

　　c. $^-.72 + ^-.08$ 　　　　**d.** $1.43 - .23$

19. Often word problems have key words that indicate mathematical operations. Use the chart in the next column to convert each word phrase into a mathematical phrase.

　　a. 10 m per second

　　b. $\frac{1}{2}$ of 4 miles

Operation	Symbol	Words used to indicate operation
Multiplication	× or *	Product, of, factor, multiple (*Note:* × will not often be used to indicate multiplication in this book because of its confusion with the variable x.)
Division	/ or — or ÷	Quotient, per, dividend, divisor
Addition	+	Sum, more, together, combine
Subtraction	−	Difference, less, left, remaining

　　c. 6 more than 68

　　d. 9 less than 81. (*Hint:* Think about what value is obtained; then write the mathematical phrase.)

20. One-half of one-half dollar is how much money? This question may be represented numerically as $\frac{1}{2} * \frac{1}{2}$. Perform the multiplication and describe your process for multiplying fractions.

21. Find each product or quotient without using a calculator.

　　a. $\frac{3}{5} * \frac{-7}{2}$ 　　**b.** $^-0.4 * ^-5$ 　　**c.** $^-1.8 \div 2$

22. Estimate 21.45 ounces $+ ^-7.8$ ounces $- 5.32$ ounces. Estimate by rounding each number to the nearest whole number.

23. How many seconds are in $1\frac{1}{2}$ hours? (*Hint:* 1 hour = 60 minutes and 1 minute = 60 seconds.)

24. How many ounces are in $\frac{3}{4}$ of a pint? (*Hint:* 1 pint = 16 ounces.)

25. Which number is greater, .1 or .07? Explain.

1.2 Rates and Ratios

AFTER STUDYING THIS SECTION YOU WILL BE ABLE TO

- Apply the concept of rate to problems involving distance and work.
- Represent rational numbers as fractions, decimals, and percents.

Distance, Rate, and Time

When something is moving, its **speed** is given in units such as miles per hour or kilometers per second. The speed, or **rate**, of a moving object may be found by dividing the distance it travels by the time it takes. Thus, rate is the **ratio** of the distance to the time.

$$\text{rate} = \frac{\text{distance}}{\text{time}}$$

EXAMPLE 1   Sam travels by walking, riding her bicycle, and driving her car.

a. On Monday Sam walks 12 miles in 4 hours.
b. On Tuesday she rides her bicycle a distance of 5 miles in $\frac{1}{3}$ hour.
c. On Wednesday she drives a car 48 miles in $\frac{2}{3}$ hour.

Find her rate for each trip.

Solution   A diagram can help you visualize what is happening in each case.

a. Distance = 12 miles and time = 4 hours. Assuming that her speed is constant, Sam is traveling 3 miles every hour, as shown in Figure 9.

$$\text{rate} = 12 \text{ miles} \div 4 \text{ hours} = 3 \text{ miles/hour}$$

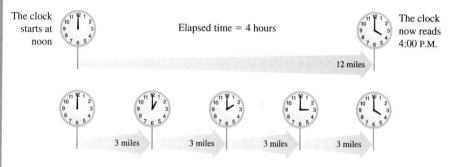

The clock starts at noon   Elapsed time = 4 hours   The clock now reads 4:00 P.M.

12 miles

3 miles   3 miles   3 miles   3 miles

Figure 9

Notice that the word "per" may be written with a forward slash (/), which is also used as a symbol for division. When you see 3 miles/hour, read "3 miles per hour."

b. Distance = 5 miles and time = $\frac{1}{3}$ hour. Figure 10 shows that Sam travels 5 miles in $\frac{1}{3}$ hour. Figure 11 shows her traveling at the same rate for an entire hour.

$$\text{rate} = \frac{5 \text{ miles}}{\frac{1}{3}\text{hour}}$$

$\frac{1}{3}$ of an hour = 20 minutes

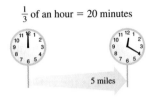

Figure 10

Remember, a fraction bar means division. Rewrite this as

$$\text{rate} = 5 \text{ miles} \div \tfrac{1}{3} \text{ hour}$$

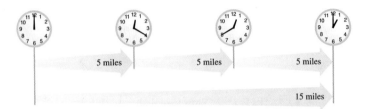

Figure 11   If Sam travels 5 miles every $\frac{1}{3}$ hour, she will travel 15 miles in 1 hour.

Now use the fact that dividing by a fraction (such as $\frac{1}{3}$) is the same as multiplying by its reciprocal ($\frac{3}{1}$).

$$\text{rate} = 5 \text{ miles} * \frac{3}{1 \text{ hour}} = 15 \text{ miles/hour}$$

c. Distance = 48 miles and time = $\frac{2}{3}$ hour. Figure 12 shows this, and Figure 13 shows that if Sam travels 48 miles in $\frac{2}{3}$ hour, she will travel 24 miles in $\frac{1}{3}$ hour and 72 miles in 1 hour.

$$\text{rate} = 48 \text{ miles} \div \tfrac{2}{3} \text{ hour} = 48 * \tfrac{3}{2} = 72 \text{ miles/hour}$$

Figure 12

Figure 13   24 miles every $\frac{1}{3}$ hour means 48 miles in $\frac{2}{3}$ hour, which is the same as in Figure 12.

Work, Rate, and Time

Situations involving how quickly a job can be completed are similar to those involving distance, rate, and time. In fact, just as we define speed as

$$\text{rate} = \frac{\text{distance}}{\text{time}}$$

we can also define **work rate**:

$$\text{work rate} = \frac{\text{work}}{\text{time}}.$$

Example 2 shows how to apply this concept.

EXAMPLE 2   Joe earns money for his college expenses by running a lawn-care business. He uses the concept of work rate to estimate how much time he'll need for a particular job.

a. His best mower can mow a lawn with an area of 8000 square feet in 25 minutes. What is its rate in square feet per minute?

b. One of Joe's customers is Mr. Brown. Joe can do all of the work required on Mr. Brown's lawn in 2 hours. What is Joe's work rate in jobs per hour?

c. Sometimes Joe employs his friend Frank as a helper. Working alone, Frank can do all of the work required on Mr. Brown's lawn in 3 hours. What is Frank's work rate in jobs per hour?

d. Suppose Joe and Frank work together on Mr. Brown's lawn. What is their combined work rate? About how long will it take them to do the job?

Solution   a. $$\text{rate} = \frac{\text{work}}{\text{time}} = \frac{8000 \text{ square feet}}{25 \text{ minutes}} = 320 \text{ square feet/minute}$$

b. $$\text{rate} = \frac{\text{work}}{\text{time}} = \frac{1 \text{ job}}{2 \text{ hours}} = \frac{1}{2} \text{ job/hour}$$

c. $$\text{rate} = \frac{\text{work}}{\text{time}} = \frac{1 \text{ job}}{3 \text{ hours}} = \frac{1}{3} \text{ job/hour}$$

d. If they are working together, it makes sense to *add* their individual work rates:

$$\text{Joe's rate} + \text{Frank's rate} = \frac{1 \text{ job}}{2 \text{ hours}} + \frac{1 \text{ job}}{3 \text{ hours}}$$

A common denominator for the two fractions is 6, so the combined rate is

$$\frac{3 \text{ jobs}}{6 \text{ hours}} + \frac{2 \text{ jobs}}{6 \text{ hours}} = \frac{5 \text{ jobs}}{6 \text{ hours}} = \frac{5}{6} \text{ jobs/hour.}$$

Because $\frac{5}{6}$ is a little less than 1, they can do almost the entire job in 1 hour. Together it will take them a little more than an hour to complete the job for Mr. Brown. Figure 14 shows this result.

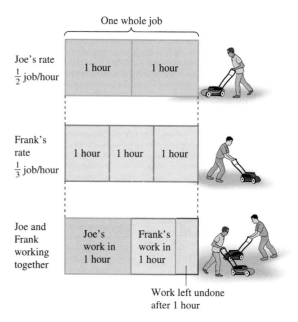

One whole job

Joe's rate
$\frac{1}{2}$ job/hour

| 1 hour | 1 hour |

Frank's rate
$\frac{1}{3}$ job/hour

| 1 hour | 1 hour | 1 hour |

Joe and Frank working together

| Joe's work in 1 hour | Frank's work in 1 hour | |

Work left undone after 1 hour

Figure 14

Symbols for Division and Fractions

As you can see from Examples 1 and 2, rates often involve fractions. You should be familiar with at least three different ways of symbolizing division and writing fractions. The symbol ÷ appears on calculator keys. The forward slash, /, appears on calculator and computer screen displays. Finally, the horizontal fraction bar, —, is commonly used in textbooks. The first of the two numbers being divided is called the **dividend** or **numerator**. The second of the two numbers is called the **divisor** or **denominator**. The dividend divided by the divisor gives the answer, or **quotient**.

$$\text{dividend} \div \text{divisor} = \text{dividend/divisor} = \frac{\text{dividend}}{\text{divisor}} = \text{quotient}$$

Division is not commutative. For instance, $6 \div 3 = 2$, but $3 \div 6 = .5$ (or $\frac{1}{2}$). Sometimes students confuse the order in which the dividend and divisor are written. This confusion arises from the fact that in performing a paper-and-pencil algorithm for long division, the divisor is written on the outside, to the left of the dividend, whereas in all other representations the dividend is written first.

$$\text{divisor}\overline{)\text{dividend}}^{\text{quotient}}$$

You may think of a common fraction as the quotient of the numerator and denominator. Thus, $\frac{2}{3}$ may be described as "two-thirds" or as "two divided by three."

Caution: When you use a calculator to multiply or divide fractions, you should enclose the fraction in parentheses. In part (c) of Example 1, for instance, $48 \div \frac{2}{3}$ appears on a calculator screen as $48/(2/3)$ and gives the correct quotient, 72. If the parentheses are omitted, as in $48/2/3$, the calculator will first divide 48 by 2 to give 24 and then divide the result by 3 to give an incorrect answer of 8.

Rational Numbers

A **rational number** is one that may be expressed as the quotient, or ratio, of two integers. Notice that the word "ratio" appears in the word "rational" to help remember this definition. There are three immediate consequences of this definition.

Properties of Rational Numbers

1. Every integer is a rational number because every integer may be written as a ratio in which the divisor is 1: $4 = \frac{4}{1}$, $0 = \frac{0}{1}$, and $^-7 = \frac{^-7}{1}$.
2. Every fraction is a rational number because it is already expressed as the quotient of two integers: $\frac{5}{3}$, $\frac{2}{5}$, and $\frac{^-3}{4}$.
3. The one integer that never appears in the denominator of a rational number is 0, because division by 0 is undefined. Thus $\frac{0}{1} = 0$, but $\frac{1}{0}$ is not a number.

Rational numbers may also be expressed as **decimals** or **percents**. To express a common fraction as a decimal, divide the numerator by the denominator. In general, use a calculator for this purpose.

EXAMPLE 3   Express each of these common fractions as a decimal.

   a. $\frac{13}{40}$

   b. $\frac{19}{22}$

   c. $\frac{7}{4}$

   d. $\frac{52}{9}$

   e. $\frac{3}{500}$

Solution   **a.** The calculator gives $\frac{13}{40} = .325$ (read "325 thousandths").

   b. The calculator gives $\frac{19}{22} \approx .8636363636$. This is an approximation, rounded to 10 decimal places, the most displayed by the calculator. In fact, $\frac{19}{22}$ is an example of a *repeating decimal*. Actually,

$$\frac{19}{22} = .8636363636363636363636363636363\ldots$$

(and so on, forever).

You may have seen a repeating decimal written with a bar over the digits that repeat, as in $\frac{19}{22} = .8\overline{63}$. For most purposes you will encounter in this textbook, a three-digit approximation may be used, so we can say $\frac{19}{22} \approx .864$.

Note: Be sure to use the symbol $\approx$ to indicate that two numbers are approximately equal. Use $=$ only to indicate exact equality.

c. $\frac{7}{4} = 1.75$. As in (a) the calculator gives an exact answer. $\frac{7}{4}$ is called an **improper fraction** because the numerator is larger than the denominator. It may also be expressed as the **mixed fraction**, or mixed number, $1\frac{3}{4}$.

d. $\frac{52}{9}$ gives another repeating decimal, $5.\overline{7}$. Or you may write $\frac{52}{9} \approx 5.778$. As a mixed fraction, $\frac{52}{9} = 5\frac{7}{9}$.

e. $\frac{3}{500} = .006$

Percents

Fractions and decimals may be expressed as percents. To express a fraction as a percent, first write it as a decimal. To express a decimal as a percent, move the decimal point two places to the right and use the percent symbol (%).

EXAMPLE 4 ■ Express each of the fractions in Example 3 as a percent.

Solution

a. $\frac{13}{40} = .325 = 32.5\%$

b. $\frac{19}{22} \approx .864 = 86.4\%$

c. $\frac{7}{4} = 1.75 = 175\%$

d. $\frac{52}{9} \approx 5.778 = 577.8\%$

e. $\frac{3}{500} = .006 = .6\%$

Notice that a percent may be greater than 100% (c, d) or less than 1% (e).

Common Equivalents

Although a calculator may be used to find decimal and percent equivalents of common fractions, you should know (and have a good intuitive feel for) some frequently encountered fractions. Three families of fractions with small denominators are displayed in the table.

A table of fraction-decimal-percent equivalents.

Fourths and Eighths	Fifths and Tenths	Thirds and Sixths
	$\frac{1}{10} = .1 = 10\%$	
$\frac{1}{8} = .125 = 12.5\%$		
		$\frac{1}{6} \approx .167 = 16.7\%$
	$\frac{1}{5} = \frac{2}{10} = .2 = 20\%$	
$\frac{1}{4} = \frac{2}{8} = .25 = 25\%$		
	$\frac{3}{10} = .3 = 30\%$	
		$\frac{1}{3} = \frac{2}{6} \approx .333 = 33.3\%$
$\frac{3}{8} = .375 = 37.5\%$		
	$\frac{2}{5} = \frac{4}{10} = .4 = 40\%$	
$\frac{1}{2} = \frac{2}{4} = \frac{4}{8} = .5 = 50\%$	$\frac{1}{2} = \frac{5}{10} = .5 = 50\%$	$\frac{1}{2} = \frac{3}{6} = .5 = 50\%$
	$\frac{3}{5} = \frac{6}{10} = .6 = 60\%$	
$\frac{5}{8} = .625 = 62.5\%$		
		$\frac{2}{3} = \frac{4}{6} \approx .667 = 66.7\%$
	$\frac{7}{10} = .7 = 70\%$	
$\frac{3}{4} = \frac{6}{8} = .75 = 75\%$		
	$\frac{4}{5} = \frac{8}{10} = .8 = 80\%$	
		$\frac{5}{6} \approx .833 = 83.3\%$
$\frac{7}{8} = .875 = 87.5\%$		
	$\frac{9}{10} = .9 = 90\%$	
$\frac{2}{2} = \frac{4}{4} = \frac{8}{8} = 1.00 = 100\%$	$\frac{5}{5} = \frac{10}{10} = 1.0 = 100\%$	$\frac{3}{3} = \frac{6}{6} = 1.000 = 100\%$

Rational Numbers and the Number Line

Rational numbers help fill in the gaps between the integers on the number line. In fact, between any two integers there are *infinitely* many rational numbers. However, there are some points on the number line that are not represented by rational numbers. We encounter irrational numbers in the next section.

EXAMPLE 5 ■ Sketch the location of each number in Example 3 on a number line.

Solution

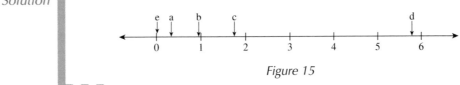

Figure 15

When comparing two numbers on a horizontal number line, the one to the left is smaller and the one to the right is greater. The symbols $<$ and $>$ may be used to express the relations less than and greater than. Thus $a < b$ means that a is to the left of b, and $a > b$ means that a is to the right of b on the number line.

EXAMPLE 6 Determine which symbol, $<$ or $>$, to insert between each pair of numbers to make true sentences.

   a. $^-1$ _____ 0

   b. 2 _____ $^-3$

   c. $\frac{7}{4}$ _____ $\frac{19}{22}$

   d. $\frac{3}{500}$ _____ $\frac{13}{40}$

Solution

   a. $<$ because $^-1$ is to the left of 0

   b. $>$ because 2 is to the right of $^-3$

   c. $>$ because $\frac{7}{4}$ (c in the figure in Example 5) is to the right of $\frac{19}{22}$ (b in the figure in Example 5)

   d. $<$ because $\frac{3}{500}$ (e in the figure in Example 5) is to the left of $\frac{13}{40}$ (a in the figure in Example 5)

Exercises 1.2

1. The Ramsey family drove from Hartford, Connecticut, to Washington, D.C., a distance of 342 miles, in 6 hours.

   a. Draw a picture to illustrate this situation.

   b. Find their average rate of speed.

2. The formula for finding rate when distance and time are known is

$$\text{rate} = \frac{\text{distance}}{\text{time}}$$

   a. Consider the case where the rate and time are known. At a rate of 60 miles/hour, what distance will you travel in 1 hour, 2 hours, and 3 hours?

   b. Find a formula for distance when rate and time are known.

   c. Use your formula to find how far an airplane can travel in 2.5 hours if its speed is 350 miles/hour.

3. Use the diagram in Example 1(b) to explain why dividing by $\frac{1}{3}$ is the same as multiplying by 3.

4. In Example 1(c), Sam travels 48 miles in $\frac{2}{3}$ hour. There are 60 minutes in 1 hour, so $\frac{2}{3}$ hour is the same as 40 minutes.

   a. Find Sam's speed in miles per minute.

   b. Use your answer in (a) to find her speed in miles per hour. Compare the result with the solution to the example.

5. Determine the work rate in each of these situations.

   a. Joseph can pick 250 apples in 2 hours. What is Joseph's work rate in apples per hour?

   b. Rachel can paint 2 houses in 8 days. What is Rachel's work rate in houses per day?

   c. Randy can repair 1 bicycle in 3 hours. What is Randy's work rate in bicycles per hour?

6. Study the table of common fraction-decimal-percent equivalents and describe any patterns you notice.

7. Name a common fraction that is equal or approximately equal to each of the percents.

a. 75%   **b.** 40%   **c.** 70%

d. 33.3%   **e.** 62.5%   **f.** 66.7%

8. Place the appropriate symbol (= or ≈) in each blank space.

a. $\frac{7}{12}$ ____ .583   **b.** $\frac{13}{16}$ ____ .8125

c. $\frac{18}{13}$ ____ 1.385   **d.** $\frac{8}{25}$ ____ .32

9. What happens on your calculator when you enter $1 \div 0$? Use the properties of rational numbers on page 17 to explain why your calculator gave what it did.

10. There are two ways to decide which of two fractions is greater: (1) by finding equivalent fractions with a common denominator, and (2) by finding decimal equivalents. For instance, if $\frac{3}{4}$ and $\frac{2}{3}$ are compared by method 1, we compare $\frac{9}{12}$ with $\frac{8}{12}$; by method 2 we compare .75 with the approximate value .667. In both cases we determine that $\frac{3}{4} > \frac{2}{3}$. Use both methods to determine which symbol, $<$ or $>$, to insert between each pair of fractions.

a. $\frac{1}{4}$ ——— $\frac{2}{5}$ **b.** $\frac{1}{2}$ ——— $\frac{4}{9}$

c. $\frac{13}{16}$ ——— $\frac{4}{5}$ **d.** $\frac{3}{8}$ ——— $\frac{5}{12}$

11. Locate these fractions on the number line.

a. $\frac{1}{3}$ **b.** $\frac{1}{4}$ **c.** $\frac{3}{4}$

d. $\frac{3}{8}$ **e.** $\frac{3}{10}$ **f.** $\frac{3}{100}$

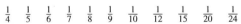

12. Decimal representations of fractions may be classified as repeating or terminating. For instance:

$\frac{1}{3} = .\overline{3} = .333333333333333\ldots$ *Repeating decimal*

$\frac{1}{2} = .5$ *Terminating decimal*

Classify each of these fractions. Then see if you can find a pattern that will help you predict which fractions are terminating and which are repeating.

$\frac{1}{4} \quad \frac{1}{5} \quad \frac{1}{6} \quad \frac{1}{7} \quad \frac{1}{8} \quad \frac{1}{9} \quad \frac{1}{10} \quad \frac{1}{12} \quad \frac{1}{15} \quad \frac{1}{20} \quad \frac{1}{24}$

13. A terminating decimal may be written as a fraction and then expressed in lowest terms. Here are two examples:

$$.45 = \frac{45}{100} = \frac{5 * 9}{5 * 20} = \frac{9}{20}$$

and

$$.642 = \frac{642}{1000} = \frac{2 * 321}{2 * 500} = \frac{321}{500}$$

Rewrite each decimal as a fraction in lowest terms.

a. .65   **b.** 1.24   **c.** .575

d. .400   **e.** .804

14. Many calculators have a feature that will write decimals as simplified common fractions. On the TI-83 and TI-84 this feature works for fractions with denominators less than or equal to 1000 and is found under the MATH menu. For example, if you type

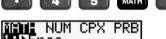

the answer 9/20 will appear on the screen.

Use the fraction-conversion feature to check your work for Exercise 13(a)–(e).

15. Use the fraction-conversion feature of a calculator on each of the decimals. Then describe what you observe.

a. .3   **b.** .33

c. .333   **d.** .3333

e. .3333333333   **f.** .333333333333

g. A student concluded from part (f) that $\frac{1}{3}$ is *exactly equal* to .333333333333. Do you agree? Explain your reasoning.

Skills and Review 1.2

16. Suppose you drive 1480 miles in 29 hours. Which is the best estimate of your rate of speed in miles per hour? (*Hint:* Round each number before finding an answer).

a. 700 miles/hour   **b.** 5 miles/hour

c. 70 miles/hour   **d.** 50 miles/hour

17. Two signed numbers are multiplied. Give a rule for determining the resulting sign.

18. Find each product and simplify if possible.

a. $2 * \frac{-1}{8}$ **b.** $\frac{-3}{5} * 10$ **c.** $\frac{-3}{2} * \frac{-4}{9}$

19. Find each quotient and simplify if possible.

    a. $\frac{-1}{3} \div \frac{5}{6}$ **b.** $0 \div 4$ **c.** $\frac{2}{3} \div {}^-4$

20. Without using a calculator, find each value.

    a. $5 + {}^+2 = 5 + 2$ **b.** $5 - {}^+2 = 5 - 2$

    c. $5 - {}^-2 = 5 + 2$ **d.** ${}^-5 + 2$

    e. ${}^-5 - 2$ **f.** ${}^-5 - {}^-2$

21. Use a number line to find each sum or difference.

    a. $6 + {}^-8$ **b.** ${}^-5 + 9$

    c. ${}^-2 - 4$ **d.** $3 - {}^-1$

22. Find each sum or difference without using a calculator.

    a. $48 - 72$ **b.** ${}^-.7 + {}^-.25$ **c.** ${}^-\frac{3}{5} - \frac{-1}{4}$

23. How many inches are in 4 yards? (*Hint:* 1 yard = 3 feet and 1 foot = 12 inches.) Explain how you found your answer and show your work.

24. Which number is less, .23 or .217?

25. Is $\frac{2}{3}$ closer to 0, $\frac{1}{2}$, or 1? Explain.

1.3 Exponents and Radicals

AFTER STUDYING THIS SECTION YOU WILL BE ABLE TO

- Raise numbers to integer powers.
- Write numbers in scientific notation.
- Find square roots of positive numbers.

Positive Integer Exponents

Repeated addition may be represented as multiplication. For instance, $5 * 3$ is the same as $5 + 5 + 5$. Similarly, repeated multiplication may be represented with an operation called exponentiation: 5^3 means the same as $5 * 5 * 5$. Read 5^3 as "5 raised to the third power" or "5 to the third." The **base** is 5 and the **exponent** is 3.

Typically we write the exponent as a **superscript**; there is no operation symbol between the base and the exponent. However, you should think of exponentiation as an operation just like addition or multiplication. On calculators there is usually a special key for this operation. On the TI-83 or 84 it appears directly above the division key; the symbol is the **caret** ($\wedge$). Thus, on a calculator you write 5^3 as $5 \wedge 3$.

EXAMPLE 1   Find each value, without using a calculator.

    a. 7^2

    b. 2^5

    c. $\left(\frac{1}{3}\right)^4$

    d. 10^1

    e. 1^{23}

Solution   **a.** $7^2 = 7 * 7 = 49$

b. $2^5 = 2 * 2 * 2 * 2 * 2 = 32$

c. $\left(\frac{1}{3}\right)^4 = \left(\frac{1}{3}\right) * \left(\frac{1}{3}\right) * \left(\frac{1}{3}\right) * \left(\frac{1}{3}\right) = \frac{1}{81}$

d. $10^1 = 10$

e. $1^{23} = 1$ (No matter how many times you multiply 1 by 1, the product is still 1.)

■ ■

Negative Bases

When a negative number is raised to a power, the result is positive or negative, depending upon whether the exponent is even or odd.

EXAMPLE 2   Find each value without using a calculator.

a. $(^-2)^1$

b. $(^-2)^2$

c. $(^-2)^3$

d. $(^-2)^4$

e. $(^-2)^5$

Solution   **a.** $(^-2)^1 = {}^-2$

b. $(^-2)^2 = {}^-2 * {}^-2 = 4$

c. $(^-2)^3 = {}^-2 * {}^-2 * {}^-2 = {}^-8$

d. $(^-2)^4 = {}^-2 * {}^-2 * {}^-2 * {}^-2 = 16$

e. $(^-2)^5 = {}^-2 * {}^-2 * {}^-2 * {}^-2 * {}^-2 = {}^-32$

■ ■

From the pattern shown in Example 2, we can make the following generalization.

Powers of Negative Bases

When a negative number is raised to an odd power, the result is negative.
When a negative number is raised to an even power, the result is positive.

Caution: When you wish to raise a negative number to a power, you must use parentheses. As we see in Example 2(d), $(^-2)^4 = 16$. If you enter $^-2 \wedge 4$ in your calculator, however, the result will be $^-16$ because $^-2^4$ is the opposite of 2^4, or $^-16$.

Zero as an Exponent

Exponentiation may be represented by repeated multiplication when the exponent is a positive integer. The definition of exponent can be extended to include other numbers. In this section we develop a definition for zero and negative integer exponents. In Chapter 9, we extend the meaning of exponentiation to include rational numbers as exponents.

What does it mean to raise a number to the zeroth power? For example, what is 2^0? You might be tempted to think that $2^0 = 0$, but that is not the definition mathematicians use. When any number (except 0) is raised to the zeroth power, the result is defined to be 1.

Definition   Zero Exponent

Let a be any number except 0. Then $a^0 = 1$.

The justification for this definition of a zero exponent is illustrated by the following activity. Take a sheet of paper and fold it in half. Open it, and observe that the creases divide the paper into two regions. Then fold it back and make a second fold (in the other direction). Unfold the paper and you have four regions. Figure 16 shows how the number of folds is related to the number of regions. The information shown in Figure 16 may be organized into a chart:

Number of Folds	Number of Regions
0	1
1	2
2	4
3	8
4	16
5	32

Note that powers of 2 appear in the chart:

Number of Folds	Number of Regions
0	1
1	$2 = 2^1$
2	$4 = 2^2$
3	$8 = 2^3$
4	$16 = 2^4$
5	$32 = 2^5$

Thus, it appears that number of regions = 2 raised to the power "number of folds," or $2^{\text{number of folds}}$. When the number of folds is 0, the number of regions is 1. So it makes sense to define $2^0 = 1$.

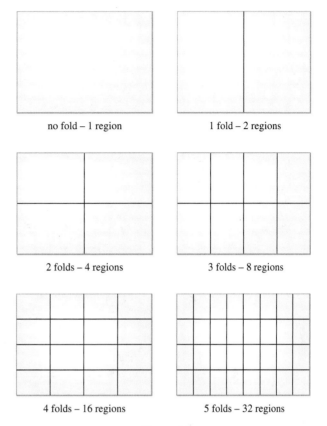

no fold – 1 region   1 fold – 2 regions

2 folds – 4 regions   3 folds – 8 regions

4 folds – 16 regions   5 folds – 32 regions

Figure 16

The definition of the zeroth power, like many others in mathematics, is based on looking at a pattern and making our definition fit the pattern. This process may now be extended to negative integer exponents.

Negative Integer Exponents

Let's look at the chart of the powers of 2 in a different way. Starting with $2^4 = 16$, we notice that when we reduce the exponent by 1, the result is half of the previous result:

$$2^4 = 16$$
$$2^3 = 8 = \tfrac{1}{2} \text{ of } 16$$
$$2^2 = 4 = \tfrac{1}{2} \text{ of } 8$$
$$2^1 = 2 = \tfrac{1}{2} \text{ of } 4$$

Now we continue the pattern to include zero and negative integer exponents:

$$2^0 = 1 = \tfrac{1}{2} \text{ of } 2$$

$$2^{-1} = \tfrac{1}{2} = \tfrac{1}{2} \text{ of } 1$$

$$2^{-2} = \tfrac{1}{4} = \tfrac{1}{2} \text{ of } \tfrac{1}{2}$$

$$2^{-3} = \tfrac{1}{8} = \tfrac{1}{2} \text{ of } \tfrac{1}{4}, \text{ etc.}$$

We note that according to this pattern, $2^{-3} = \tfrac{1}{8}$. Because $8 = 2^3$, we have $2^{-3} = \tfrac{1}{2^3}$. This pattern generalizes and gives us our definition for negative integer exponents.

Definition   Negative Integer Exponents

Let a be any number except 0 and let n be any positive integer. Then

$$a^{-n} = \frac{1}{a^n}$$

EXAMPLE 3   Find each value without using a calculator.

a. 3^{-2}
b. 12^{-1}
c. 4^{-3}
d. 2^{-6}
e. 891^0

Solution   **a.** $3^{-2} = \dfrac{1}{3^2} = \dfrac{1}{9}$

b. $12^{-1} = \dfrac{1}{12^1} = \dfrac{1}{12}$

c. $4^{-3} = \dfrac{1}{4^3} = \dfrac{1}{4*4*4} = \dfrac{1}{64}$

d. $2^{-6} = \dfrac{1}{2^6} = \dfrac{1}{2*2*2*2*2*2} = \dfrac{1}{64}$

e. $891^0 = 1$ by the definition of the zero exponent

$$87{,}215.9346$$

ten thousands
thousands
hundreds
tens
ones
tenths
hundredths
thousandths
ten thousandths

Figure 17 Place value in the decimal numeration system.

Powers of Ten and Scientific Notation

Our decimal numeration system is based on powers of ten, as shown in Figure 17. In this example,

$$87{,}215.9346 = 80{,}000 + 7{,}000 + 200 + 10 + 5 + .9 + .03 + .004$$
$$+ .0006$$
$$= 8 * 10^4 + 7 * 10^3 + 2 * 10^2 + 1 * 10^1 + 5 * 10^0 + 9 * 10^{-1}$$
$$+ 3 * 10^{-2} + 4 * 10^{-3} + 6 * 10^{-4}$$

Note that positive powers of 10 and 10^0 are located to the left of the decimal point. Negative powers of ten are located to the right of the decimal point. Adding the suffix "th" to the name for a power of ten is like taking the opposite of the exponent. For instance, one hundred is 10^2, whereas one-hundredth is 10^{-2}. Powers of 10 are used to express numbers in scientific notation.

Definition   Scientific Notation

A number is written in scientific notation if it is of the form $a * 10^b$, where a is an integer or decimal such that $1 \leq a < 10$ and b is an integer.

The exponent b gives an idea of approximately how large the number is.

To change a number in decimal form to scientific notation, move the decimal point so that you have a number between 1 and 10. Then count the number of places the decimal point has moved. Remember that a whole number has a decimal point immediately to its right.

EXAMPLE 4   Write each number in scientific notation.

a. The speed of light is 186,000 miles per second.
b. In 2011 the world's population reached 7 billion.
c. The radius of a hydrogen atom is .000000000053 m.

Solution   **a.** $186{,}000. = 1.86 * 10^5$ We moved the decimal point 5 places. We know that the exponent is positive because 186,000 is greater than 1. We could have written $1.86000 * 10^5$, but we usually drop unnecessary zeros after the decimal point.

b. $7{,}000{,}000{,}000. = 7 * 10^9$ We moved the decimal point 9 places. Again, the exponent is positive.

c. $.000000000053 = 5.3 * 10^{-11}$ We moved the decimal point 11 places. Because the number is less than 1, the exponent must be negative.

Note: In this book we use an asterisk (∗) for multiplication. In many texts you'll see a × used in scientific notation. Example 4(a) then would be written 1.86×10^5.

Calculators display scientific notation with an uppercase E. When you encounter E, read it as "times 10 to the power."

EXAMPLE 5 Use a calculator to find the answer. Then write the answer displayed by the calculator in both scientific notation and decimal notation.

a. Suppose that every day each of the world's 7 billion people had a nutritionally adequate diet with about 2500 calories. How many calories per day would the human population consume?

b. If a glacier moves .3 cm in 1 year, how far will it move in 1 day?

Solution **a.** Enter 7000000000 × 2500. The calculator shows 1.75E13, which is $1.75 \ast 10^{13}$. Move the decimal point 13 places to the right because the number is greater than 1: that gives 17500000000000 calories. Inserting commas makes the number easier to read: 17,500,000,000,000 calories, or 17.5 trillion calories.

b. Enter .3 ÷ 365 because there are 365 days in a year. The calculator displays $8.219178082E^-4$. That is approximately $8.22 \ast 10^{-4}$. Move the decimal point 4 places to the left because the number is less than 1 when the exponent is negative. The glacier moves .000822 cm in 1 day. You would need a microscope to observe this small distance.

Squares and Square Roots

The area of a figure is measured in square units. For instance, a square room that has a length of 20 feet and a width of 20 feet has an area of 400 square feet. Because feet are multiplied by feet we can also express square feet as feet². Similarly, when we find the volume of three-dimensional figures, we use cubic units. Cubic feet may be abbreviated feet³.

Because these exponents refer to squares and cubes, we often use the terms "squared" and "cubed" when raising numbers to the second and third powers. Thus we may say "x squared" for x^2 and "y cubed" for y^3.

Side = 4 cm

Figure 18

The square in Figure 18 has an area of 16 cm². The length of one side is 4 cm. We say "4 squared is 16"; using exponents, $4^2 = 16$. If we know the area of a square and want to know the length of the side, we can work backward. We reverse the process and say, "A **square root** of 16 is 4," or $\sqrt{16} = 4$.

A positive number such as 16 actually has two square roots, one positive (4) and one negative (⁻4). In this case, since the side of a square cannot be negative, we speak only of the positive root. The symbol $\sqrt{}$ is called a **radical** and is used to indicate the positive square root of a positive number. You will learn more about radicals later in the course.

The number 16 is called a **perfect square** because its positive square root is an integer. Other perfect squares with which you should be familiar are 1, 4, 9, 25, 36, 49, 64, 81, and 100.

EXAMPLE 6   Use mental math to find each of these square roots.

a. $\sqrt{36}$
b. $\sqrt{81}$
c. $\sqrt{25}$
d. $\sqrt{100}$

Solution   a. $6^2 = 36$; therefore, $\sqrt{36} = 6$.
b. $9^2 = 81$; therefore, $\sqrt{81} = 9$.
c. $5^2 = 25$; therefore, $\sqrt{25} = 5$.
d. $10^2 = 100$; therefore, $\sqrt{100} = 10$.

EXAMPLE 7   The shaded square in Figure 19 is formed by joining the midpoints of the sides of the square in Figure 18.

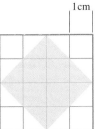

1 cm

Figure 19

a. Find the area of this square.
b. Find the length of one side of this square.

Solution   a. The area of the shaded square is exactly half of the original square. You can verify this by counting square centimeters from the original grid, as shown in Figure 20. There are four complete squares (1–4) and four pairs of triangles (5–8), each of which can be combined to form 1 cm². The area of the square is 8 cm².

b. You can estimate the length of a side of the square by drawing it on a centimeter square grid and using a ruler. The side is approximately 2.8 cm in length. The length of the side, which is $\sqrt{8}$, is not an integer because 8 is not a perfect square. Because 8 lies between two perfect squares, 4 and 9, it stands to reason that $\sqrt{8}$ is between $\sqrt{4}$ and $\sqrt{9}$, that is, greater than 2 but less than 3. A more precise approximation may be found with a calculator: $\sqrt{8} \approx 2.828427125$.

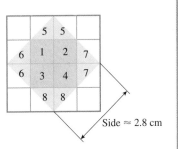

Side ≈ 2.8 cm

Figure 20

Irrational Numbers

The number $\sqrt{8}$ is called an **irrational** number. This means that it cannot be expressed as the ratio of two integers and there is no pattern of repeating digits in its decimal representation. The square root of any whole number that is not a perfect square is an irrational number. Thus, the following numbers are irrational: $\sqrt{2}, \sqrt{3}, \sqrt{5}, \sqrt{6}, \sqrt{7}$, and so on. Calculators can be used to get approximations of irrational numbers.

Another irrational number is $\pi \approx 3.141592654$. This number, called *pi*, is used to find the circumference and area of a circle, as you will see in the next section.

Although most square roots are irrational, if you know the perfect squares up through 100, you should be able to estimate the square root of any number between 0 and 100. You can check your estimate using a calculator.

EXAMPLE 8 Estimate these square roots.

a. $\sqrt{50}$

b. $\sqrt{20}$

c. $\sqrt{95}$

Solution
a. 50 is slightly greater than 49, so $\sqrt{50}$ is a bit more than 7. A good estimate is 7.1.

b. 20 is about halfway between 16 and 25. A good estimate is 4.5.

c. 95 is between 81 and 100 but closer to 100. A good estimate would be 9.7 or 9.8.

Exercises 1.3

1. Do not use a calculator.

   a. Use repeated addition to find $3 * 4$.

   b. Use repeated multiplication to find 3^4.

2. A student reasons that 5^3 is $5 * 3$. What mistake is the student making?

3. Find each value without using a calculator.

   a. 2^4 **b.** 1^{15} **c.** $\left(\frac{1}{4}\right)^2$

   d. $(^-3)^2$ **e.** $(^-3)^3$

4. Evaluate $(^-1)^2$, $(^-1)^3$, $(^-1)^4$, and $(^-1)^5$. What pattern do you notice?

5. On your calculator, experiment raising different numbers (except 0) to the zeroth power.

   a. What is the result?

   b. What do you conclude about raising any number except 0 to the zeroth power?

6. Without using a calculator, write each answer as a fraction and a decimal.

   a. 10^0 **b.** 10^{-1} **c.** 10^{-2}

   d. 10^{-3} **e.** 10^{-4}

7. Refer to Exercise 6.

   a. Plot each number on a number line.

   b. Continue evaluating negative powers of 10 (10^{-5}, 10^{-6}, 10^{-7}, etc.). To what number do you get closer?

   c. If you continue the process in (b), will you ever get a negative number? Explain.

8. Find each value without using a calculator.

   a. 5^{-2} **b.** 23^{-1} **c.** 3^{-4} **d.** 2^{-5}

9. Write each number in scientific notation.

   a. At freezing, the speed of sound is 1,089 feet/second.

   b. Jupiter's mean distance from Earth is 484 million miles.

   c. An aerosol particle has a diameter of .000000002 m.

10. a. Which number is greater, 1.2×10^7 or 1.2×10^{-15}?

   b. Write both numbers from part (a) in decimal notation.

   c. Does your answer in part (b) confirm your choice of the greater number?

11. Use a calculator to find each answer; then write the answer displayed by the calculator in both scientific notation and decimal notation.

   a. Some scientists predict the temperature of the earth's atmosphere will warm 3.5°F in the next 100 years. How much will it warm in 1 day?

   b. A typical daily diet for each of the 310 million U.S. residents should include 51 g of protein. How much protein should the entire population of the United States consume in one day?

12. Find each value without using a calculator.

   a. $\sqrt{4}$ **b.** $\sqrt{49}$ **c.** $\sqrt{4900}$ **d.** $\sqrt{.49}$

13. Which of the following statements does not describe $\sqrt{144}$?

   a. A number multiplied by itself is 144.

   b. A number squared is 144.

   c. The square root of 144 is 144 divided by 2.

   d. 144 divided by a number is the same number.

14. The square has an area of 36 cm².

   a. Find the length of each side of the square.

   b. Find the area of each triangle inside the square.

   c. Describe how you found the area of the triangles.

15. Estimate each square root and check your answer with a calculator.

   a. $\sqrt{10}$ **b.** $\sqrt{42}$ **c.** $\sqrt{80}$

Skills and Review 1.3

16. Round 64.268 tons to the nearest hundredth.

17. Express each number of minutes as a fraction of an hour and as a decimal. If possible simplify your fractions.

   a. 15 minutes   **b.** 0 minutes

   c. 30 minutes   **d.** 60 minutes

18. Place each number on a number line. (*Hint:* It may be helpful to write each number in the same form in order to determine placement.)

   a. $\frac{3}{2}$ **b.** .25   **c.** 212.5%

   d. $1\frac{1}{3}$ **e.** .875

19. There are 2.54 cm per 1 inch.

   a. How many centimeters are there in 7.6 inches?

   b. Show how you performed the calculation.

20. Write each number in the specified forms.

   a. $\frac{5}{6}$ as a decimal and a percent

   b. .3 as a fraction and a percent

   c. 20% as a fraction and a decimal

21. Simon can detail 10 cars in 5 days. What is his work rate in cars per day?

22. The first inch of a tape measure has been enlarged. Label each of the ticks with an appropriate fraction.

23. Without using a calculator, perform each calculation and include the appropriate units.

    a. 5 m/s ∗ 4.2 s

    b. 7 feet ÷ $\left(\frac{1}{3}\right)$ minute

    c. 10 cm/h ∗ 92.76 h

24. Write each verbal phrase as a numerical phrase and then evaluate.

    a. The sum of 2 and ⁻5

    b. The difference of 2 and ⁻5

    c. 1 decreased by 3

    d. 1 less than 3

    e. $\frac{1}{4}$ of 8

    f. 6 more than twice 3

25. The lowest elevation in the state of Louisiana is ⁻8 feet in New Orleans. The highest elevation is 535 feet on Driskill mountain. Find the difference in elevations.

1.4 Perimeter and Area

AFTER STUDYING THIS SECTION YOU WILL BE ABLE TO

- Find the perimeter of a two-dimensional figure.
- Apply formulas to find areas of rectangles, triangles, parallelograms, and trapezoids.
- Find the circumference and area of a circle.

In the previous section you counted small squares to find the area of a larger square. The same technique applies to rectangles. In Figure 21 a rectangle has been formed with 1-inch-square tiles. By counting the tiles we can determine that the area is 18 square inches. You may also find the area of the rectangle by multiplying the length (6 inches) by the width (3 inches). In fact, the formula for the area of a rectangle is given by area = length ∗ width, or $a = l \ast w$.

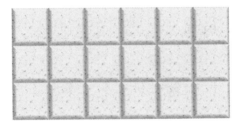

Figure 21

There are two measurements related to a two-dimensional geometric figure. The **perimeter** measures the distance around the outside of the figure. The **area** measures the amount of space inside the figure. Our first two examples illustrate the difference between these two concepts.

EXAMPLE 1 | You move into a new house with an L-shaped living room that has the dimensions shown in Figure 22. You need to put a strip of molding along each wall. Find the total length of the molding you need.

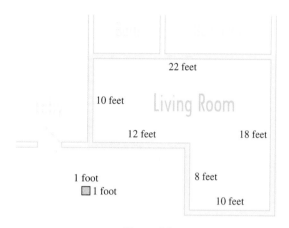

Figure 22

Solution | Add the lengths of the walls to find the perimeter:

22 feet + 18 feet + 10 feet + 8 feet + 12 feet + 10 feet = 80 feet

You will need 80 feet of molding.

EXAMPLE 2 | You plan to cover the floor of the living room in Example 1 with square tiles that are 1 foot on each side. How many tiles will you need? (See Figure 23.)

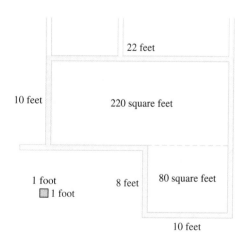

Figure 23

Solution

You could cover the room with squares that are 1 foot by 1 foot and count to find out how many there are. That would take a long time. A more efficient method is to split the room into two or more rectangular regions and find the area of each by multiplying length times width. The area of the larger rectangle is 220 square feet. The area of the smaller rectangle is 80 square feet. The total area of the room is 300 square feet. You will need 300 tiles.

■ ■ ■

The Commutative Properties of Addition and Multiplication

In Example 1, the order in which we add the sides does not make a difference. For instance, instead of starting with 22 feet and going around the figure in a clockwise direction, we could have started with 8 feet and gone in a counterclockwise direction:

$$8 \text{ feet} + 10 \text{ feet} + 18 \text{ feet} + 22 \text{ feet} + 10 \text{ feet} + 12 \text{ feet} = 80 \text{ feet}$$

We get the same sum. In other words, the *order* in which we add numbers does not affect the result. This is called the **commutative property of addition**.

Multiplication is also commutative. For instance, in calculating the area of the larger rectangle in Figure 23 you could multiply 22 feet by 10 feet or 10 feet by 22 feet. In either case, the area is 220 square feet. This is the **commutative property of multiplication**.

The commutative properties may be stated as follows:

The Commutative Properties

- Commutative property of addition:

  For any two numbers a and b, $a + b = b + a$.

- Commutative property of multiplication:

  For any two numbers a and b, $a * b = b * a$.

Formulas

In Example 2 you found the area of a rectangle by multiplying length times width. Formulas for the areas of other familiar geometric figures—triangles, parallelograms, and trapezoids—are shown in the following box.

Area Formulas

Figure	Formula	Abbreviation
Rectangle	area = length * width	$a = l * w$
Triangle	area = $\frac{1}{2}$ * base * height	$a = \frac{1}{2} * b * h$
Parallelogram	area = base * height	$a = b * h$
Trapezoid	area = $\frac{1}{2}$ * (base$_1$ + base$_2$) * height	$a = \frac{1}{2} * (b_1 + b_2) * h$

Note: In the last formula, the 1 and 2 are called **subscripts**. Base$_1$ is read "base sub 1" and refers to the first base. Base$_2$ is read "base sub 2" and refers to the second base.

The following examples illustrate the use of these formulas.

EXAMPLE 3 ▌ Use Figure 24 to explain the formula for the area of a triangle. (*Hint:* The height is always **perpendicular** to the base. Two lines are perpendicular when they form **right angles**.)

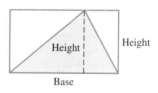

Base

Figure 24

Solution ▌ The area of the triangle is half the area of the rectangle that surrounds it. Notice that the base of the triangle is the same as the length of the rectangle. Also, the height of the triangle is the same as the width of the rectangle. Since the area of the rectangle is length * width, the area of the triangle must be $\frac{1}{2}$ * base * height.

■ ■

EXAMPLE 4 ■ Use Figure 25 to explain the formula for the area of a parallelogram.

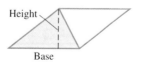

Base

Figure 25

Solution ▌ The parallelogram is made up of two triangles that are the same size and same shape. Each triangle has an area equal to $\frac{1}{2}$ * base * height. Therefore the area of the parallelogram is $2 * \frac{1}{2}$ * base * height, or simply base * height.
■ ■

EXAMPLE 5 ■ Use Figure 26 to explain the formula for the area of a trapezoid.

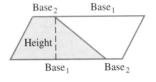

Figure 26

Solution ▌ Two trapezoids fit together to form a parallelogram. The area of the parallelogram is (base$_1$ + base$_2$) * height. Therefore, the area of the trapezoid is $\frac{1}{2}$ * (base$_1$ + base$_2$) * height, half the area of the parallelogram.
■ ■

EXAMPLE 6 ▌ **a.** Find the perimeter of the trapezoid in Figure 27.
b. Find the area of the trapezoid in Figure 27.

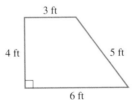

Figure 27

Solution ▌ **a.** To find the perimeter, add the lengths of the sides: 3 feet + 5 feet + 6 feet + 4 feet = 18 feet.
b. To find the area of the trapezoid, use the formula $A = \frac{1}{2}$ * (base$_1$ + base$_2$) * height. Note that the small square in the lower-left corner indicates that two sides are perpendicular, so 4 feet is the height. The bases are 3 feet and 6 feet. Thus, base$_1$ = 6 feet, base$_2$ = 3 feet, and height = 4 feet.
Substitute these values into the formula:

$$A = \tfrac{1}{2} * (\text{base}_1 + \text{base}_2) * \text{height}$$

$$A = \tfrac{1}{2} * (6 + 3) * 4 \qquad Substituting$$

$A = \frac{1}{2} * 9 * 4$ *Performing the operation inside parentheses first*

$A = 18$

The area is 18 square feet.

Circles

A circle is the set of all points in a plane that are a given distance from a point called the *center*. A **radius** is a line segment joining the center to a point on the circle. A **diameter** is a line segment that passes through the center and joins two points on the circle (see Figure 28).

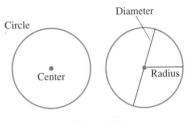

Figure 28

The perimeter of a circle is called the **circumference**. The ratio of the circumference to the diameter is the same for all circles. This ratio is a special number called pi, symbolized by the Greek letter π.

According to a calculator, $\pi \approx 3.141592654$. Recall that pi is an irrational number, so its digits continue forever with no apparent pattern. A commonly used approximation for π is 3.14.

Formulas for the circumference and area of a circle are given in the following box.

Circumference and Area of a Circle

Formula   **Abbreviation**

circumference $= \pi *$ diameter $= 2 * \pi *$ radius $C = \pi * d$ or $C = 2 * \pi * r$

area $= \pi *$ radius $*$ radius $= \pi *$ radius^2 $A = \pi * r * r$ or $A = \pi * r^2$

EXAMPLE 7   Carl is going to work out by running around a circular track with a radius of 70 yards. His goal is to run 5 miles. How many laps should he run (see Figure 29)? (1 mile = 1760 yards)

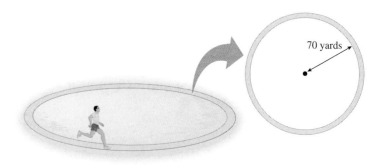

Figure 29

Solution

In order to solve this problem, Carl needs to know the length of one lap—that is, the circumference of the circle.

We can use the formula circumference $= 2 * \pi *$ **radius**. Using the approximation $\pi \approx 3.14$, $2 * \pi \approx 6.28$. Multiply 6.28 by **70** yards to get circumference ≈ 439.6 yards, or 440 yards.

If Carl wants to run 5 miles, that's $5 * 1760 = 8800$ yards. Because $8800 \div 440 = 20$, he'll have to run 20 laps to make his goal.

Note: Here is another method. Because the radius is 70 yards, the diameter must be twice that distance, or 140 yards. Using circumference $= \pi *$ diameter and $\pi \approx 3.14$, we get circumference ≈ 439.6 yards, or 440 yards, to the nearest yard.

Exercises 1.4

1. In Example 1 you found the perimeter of the figure. In Example 2 you found the area. Explain the difference between the two concepts.

2. In the figure each small square is one centimeter on a side. Find each value.

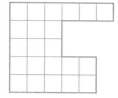

   a. Area   **b.** Perimeter

3. Use grid paper to draw two rectangles, each with an area of 24 square units but with different perimeters.

4. A rectangular field has a perimeter of 600 feet. Find two possible fields with different areas and find the areas.

5. The length of a rectangle is 4.5 cm and its width is 2.5 cm.

   a. Find its perimeter.

   b. Draw the rectangle on grid paper and estimate its area.

   c. Use the formula area $=$ length $*$ width to find its area exactly.

d. Compare your answer in (c) with the estimate from part (b).

6. You are told that the length of a rectangle is twice its width and that the width is 50 yards.

   a. Find the area of the rectangle.

   b. Find the perimeter of the rectangle.

   c. Suppose that the length of another rectangle is 10 yards more than twice its width. Assume that the width of this rectangle is also 50 yards. Answer parts (a) and (b) for this rectangle.

7. The Chang family owns a farm in the shape of a rectangle $\frac{1}{2}$ mile long and $\frac{1}{4}$ mile wide (see the figure).

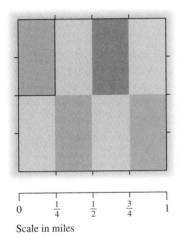

Scale in miles

a. What portion of the figure is shaded pink?

b. Use the formula $A = $ length $*$ width to find the area of the farm. Compare your answer with your answer in (a).

c. Find the perimeter of the farm.

d. Find the area of the farm in square rods and the perimeter in rods. (*Hint:* 1 mile = 320 rods.)

e. Find the area of the farm in acres. (*Hint:* 1 acre = 160 square rods.)

f. Check the answer in (e) by using the fact that there are 640 acres in 1 square mile.

8. Find the area and the perimeter of a rectangle that is $\frac{3}{4}$ mile long and $\frac{1}{3}$ mile wide.

9. A triangular patio has the dimensions shown in the figure.

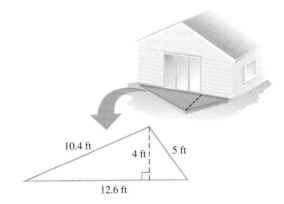

10.4 ft   4 ft   5 ft

12.6 ft

a. Find the area of the patio.

b. Find the perimeter of the patio.

10. In order to reduce the noise from above, the ceiling shown in the figure is covered with acoustic tiles.

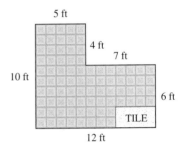

5 ft
4 ft
7 ft
10 ft
6 ft
TILE
12 ft

a. What is the area of the ceiling?

b. Each tile measures 2 feet by 4 feet. How many tiles are necessary to cover the ceiling?

11. Find the area of the trapezoid (see the figure).

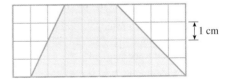

1 cm

a. Count squares (and parts of squares).

b. Use a formula.

12. Which of the figures have the same area? Which have the same perimeter? Explain.

a.

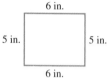

6 in.

5 in. / 4 in. / 5 in.

6 in.

b.

6 in.

4 in. | | 4 in.

6 in.

c.

6 in.

5 in. | | 5 in.

6 in.

d.

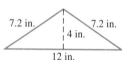

7.2 in. / 4 in. \ 7.2 in.

12 in.

13. In Example 7 why did Carl need to know the circumference of the circle rather than the area?

14. A couple owns a circular swimming pool with a radius of 10 feet (see the figure).

    a. They want to buy a cover for the pool. If pool covers are measured in square feet, what size cover should they purchase? Use $\pi \approx 3.14$.

    b. The couple also wants to place a fence around the pool. The fence is 4 feet from the edge of the pool (see figure). How many feet of fencing will they need to surround the pool?

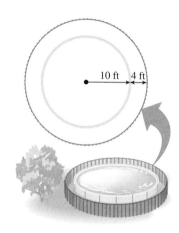

10 ft | 4 ft

15. Two students use different formulas to calculate the circumference of a circle. Lynn uses $C = 2 * \pi * r$. George uses $C = \pi * d$. Show that these two formulas produce the same circumference for a circle with a radius of 8.5 m.

Skills and Review 1.4

16. Sammy performs the sum $5 + 3 + 5 + 6 + 7 + 4$ mentally by finding pairs of numbers that add to 10.

    a. Find the sum by Sammy's method.

    b. Explain why Sammy's method works.

17. Suppose a young student knows that $7 * 5$ is 35 but doesn't know the product $5 * 7$.

    a. How can the student use the commutative property of multiplication to find the product?

    b. Explain how the commutative property can be used to reduce the number of facts in the multiplication table that need to be learned.

18. Perform the calculation $7 * 6 * 5$ mentally using the commutative property of multiplication to reorder for easier multiplication.

19. Find each value without using a calculator.

    a. $\sqrt{36}$ **b.** $\sqrt{100}$ **c.** $\sqrt{10,000}$

    d. $\sqrt{.81}$ **e.** $\sqrt{\frac{9}{25}}$

20. Evaluate without using a calculator and change your answers to scientific notation. Be sure to include the appropriate units.

    a. 700 feet $*$ 2000 feet $*$ 5000 feet

    b. $\dfrac{48,000,000 \text{ cm}^2}{60,000 \text{ cm}}$

21. What is the value of the digit 7 in the number 1,247,650.12?

22. Find each value without using a calculator.

    a. 4^3 **b.** $\left(\frac{5}{6}\right)^2$ **c.** 1^{12}

    d. $(^-3)^2$ **e.** 7^0

23. Without using a calculator, find 5^{-2}. Write your answer as a decimal.

24. Nicole reads 300 words per minute. What is her reading rate in words per second?

25. Which of the following numbers is not equal to 1.25?

    a. $1\frac{1}{4}$ **b.** $\frac{1.25}{1}$ **c.** $\frac{5}{4}$

    d. $1 \div \frac{4}{5}$ **e.** $\frac{7}{5}$ **f.** $\frac{10}{8}$

CHAPTER 1 ■ KEY CONCEPTS ■

Adding Signed Numbers   To add (or combine) two signed numbers, if the numbers have the *same* sign, *add* their absolute values and keep the sign. If the numbers have *opposite* signs, *subtract* their absolute values, and take the sign of the number with the *larger* absolute value. (Page 3)

Subtracting Signed Numbers   To subtract two signed numbers, change the sign of the second number and change the operation to addition. Then follow the rules for the addition of signed numbers. (Page 7)

Number Line Models for Addition and Subtraction   (Page 6)

$$\text{start} + \text{change} = \text{final}$$

$$\text{final} - \text{start} = \text{change}$$

Multiplying and Dividing Signed Numbers   (Page 9)

$$\text{positive} * \text{positive} = \text{positive} \qquad \text{positive} \div \text{positive} = \text{positive}$$

$$\text{positive} * \text{negative} = \text{negative} \qquad \text{positive} \div \text{negative} = \text{negative}$$

$$\text{negative} * \text{positive} = \text{negative} \qquad \text{negative} \div \text{positive} = \text{negative}$$

$$\text{negative} * \text{negative} = \text{positive} \qquad \text{negative} \div \text{negative} = \text{positive}$$

Multiplying and Dividing with Zero   0 multiplied by any number is 0. 0 divided by any positive or negative number is 0. Division by 0 is undefined. (Page 10)

Distance, Rate, and Time $\text{rate} = \dfrac{\text{distance}}{\text{time}}$. (Page 13).

Work, Rate, and Time $\text{work rate} = \dfrac{\text{work}}{\text{time}}$. (Page 15)

Rational Numbers   A rational number is one that can be expressed as the quotient or ratio of two integers. Rational numbers include integers and fractions and may be expressed as decimals or percents. (Page 17)

Common Fraction-Decimal-Percent Equivalents   These equivalents are shown in the table. (Page 19)

Positive Integer Exponents   Positive integer exponents may be used to represent repeated multiplication. For example, 5^3 means the same as $5 * 5 * 5$. (Page 22)

Zero Exponent   Let a be any number except 0. Then $a^0 = 1$. (Page 24)

Negative Integer Exponents   Let a be any number except 0 and let n be any positive integer. Then

$$a^{-n} = \frac{1}{a^n}$$

(Page 26)

Scientific Notation   A number is written in scientific notation if it is of the form $a * 10^b$ where $1 \leq a < 10$ and b is an integer. (Page 27)

Square Root   If we know the area of a square, the length of its side is called a square root of the area. For example, $\sqrt{16} = 4$ because $4^2 = 16$. (Page 28)

Irrational Numbers An irrational number cannot be expressed as the ratio of two integers and there is no pattern of repeating digits in its decimal representation. (Page 30)

Perimeter and Area The perimeter measures the distance around the outside of a two-dimensional figure. The area measures the amount of space inside the figure. (Page 32)

The Commutative Properties Addition: For any two numbers a and b, $a + b = b + a$. Multiplication: For any two numbers a and b, $a * b = b * a$. (Page 34)

Area Formulas (Page 35)

Figure	Formula	Abbreviation
Rectangle	area = length * width	$a = l * w$
Triangle	area = $\frac{1}{2}$ * base * height	$a = \frac{1}{2} * b * h$
Parallelogram	area = base * height	$a = b * h$
Trapezoid	area = $\frac{1}{2}$ * (base$_1$ + base$_2$) * height	$a = \frac{1}{2} * (b_1 + b_2) * h$

Circumference and Area of a Circle (Page 37).

Formula	Abbreviation
circumference = π * diameter = $2 * \pi$ * radius	$C = \pi * d$ or $C = 2 * \pi * r$
area = π * radius * radius = π * radius^2	$A = \pi * r * r$ or $A = \pi * r^2$

Exploration

The week of June 3, 2002, was not a good one for Wall Street. The changes in the Dow Jones Industrial Average (DJIA) for each day were as follows: Monday, $^-$215.46; Tuesday, $^-$21.95; Wednesday, 108.96; Thursday, $^-$172.16; Friday, $^-$34.97.

a. Find the net change in the DJIA for the week.

b. When the market opened on Monday, June 3, the DJIA stood at 9925.25. What was the DJIA at the close of trading on Friday, June 7?

c. Explain your answer to part (b) using a number line.

CHAPTER 1 ▪ REVIEW EXERCISES

Section 1.1 Positive and Negative Numbers

1. Use a charged particle model to find each sum.

   a. $^+3 + {}^+4$ **b.** $^+2 + {}^-5$

   c. $^-1 + {}^+3$ **d.** $^-4 + {}^-2$

2. Use the addition rules for signed numbers to find each sum.

   a. $^+71.2 + {}^-2.5$ **b.** $^-15.1 + {}^-56.76$

3. Use the rule for subtraction to find each difference.

a. $^+6 - ^+5$

b. $^+18 - ^-7$

c. $\frac{^-3}{8} - \frac{^+1}{4}$

d. $^-12.1 - ^-4.3$

4. At 8 A.M. a balloonist was floating over Badwater Basin at an elevation of 106 feet below sea level. By 11 A.M. the balloonist had risen 151 feet. What was the balloonist's elevation at 11 A.M.?

5. At 2 P.M. the balloonist in Exercise 4 was at an elevation of 86 feet. By 5 P.M. the balloonist had fallen to an elevation of $^-34$ feet. By how much had the balloonist's elevation changed?

6. Find each product.

a. $^+3 * ^+2$

b. $^+25 * ^-8$

c. $\frac{^-4}{5} * \frac{^+5}{6}$

d. $^-1.6 * ^-5$

7. Find each quotient.

a. $^+8 \div ^+4$

b. $^+102 \div ^-2$

c. $\frac{^-1}{10} \div \frac{^+3}{2}$

d. $^-3.9 \div ^-1.3$

Section 1.2 Rates and Ratios

8. Find each rate in kilometers per hour.

a. Kim drives 140 km in 2 h.

b. Phil jogs 3 km in $\frac{1}{4}$ h.

c. Laura walks 6 km in $\frac{3}{4}$ h.

9. Find each work rate.

a. Ed can carpet 400 square feet in 50 minutes. What is his work rate in square feet per minute?

b. Ed can complete a carpet job in 3 hours. What is Ed's work rate in jobs per hour?

c. Debbie can complete the same carpet job in 4 hours. What is Debbie's work rate in jobs per hour?

d. What is Ed and Debbie's combined work rate?

10. Express each fraction as a decimal. Round any decimals with more than three decimal places to the nearest thousandth.

a. $\frac{9}{5}$

b. $\frac{17}{30}$

c. $\frac{2}{35}$

11. Express each of the decimals in Exercise 10 as a percent.

12. Place each number on the number line.

a. $\frac{3}{4}$

b. 20%

c. $1\frac{3}{8}$

d. 1.2

e. $\frac{20}{5}$

Section 1.3 Exponents and Radicals

13. Find each value without using a calculator.

a. 4^3

b. 3^4

c. 8^1

d. $\left(\frac{1}{2}\right)^5$

e. 1^{36}

14. Find each value without using a calculator.

a. $(^-3)^1$

b. $(^-3)^2$

c. $(^-3)^3$

d. $(^-3)^4$

15. Find each value without using a calculator.

a. 2^{-4}

b. 15^{-1}

c. 58^0

16. Write each number in scientific notation.

a. 348,000,000

b. .00074

c. 5,772

17. Use a calculator to find each answer. Write your answer in both scientific notation and decimal notation.

a. $561,000 * 24,800$

b. $2.5 \div 5000$

18. Find each value without using a calculator.

a. $\sqrt{9}$

b. $\sqrt{64}$

c. $\sqrt{36}$

19. Estimate each square root.

a. $\sqrt{8}$

b. $\sqrt{37}$

c. $\sqrt{72}$

20. The area of the square is 48 square inches. Estimate the length of one side of the square.

Area
48 square inches

$s \approx ?$

Section 1.4 Perimeter and Area

In Exercises 21–23, use each figure to find the perimeter and area. Assume each square within the figures measures 1 cm by 1 cm.

21.

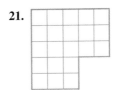

22.

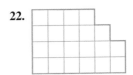

23.

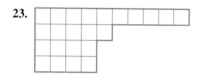

24. Use the commutative property of addition to reorder the following sum. Choose an order that will allow you to perform this sum mentally.

$$3 + 18 + 27 + 2$$

25. Use the commutative property of multiplication to reorder the multiplication. Choose an order that will allow

you to perform this multiplication mentally.

$$2 * 16 * 5$$

26. Find the perimeter and area of the following parallelogram.

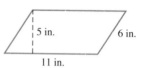

27. Find the circumference of a circle with a radius of 7 feet. Use $\pi \approx 3.14$.

CHAPTER 1 ■ TEST

1. Determine the sum $^-8 + 5$.

2. Determine the difference $^-7 - 3$.

3. Suppose the temperature at the North Pole went from $^-23°$C at 3 A.M. to $2°$C at noon. By how much had the temperature changed?

4. Determine each product or quotient.
   a. $12 \div ^-3$ **b.** $^-3 * 2$ **c.** $^-3 \div ^-12$

5. Larry drinks 64 ounces of water per day. Find his rate of drinking water in ounces per hour.

6. Express each fraction as a decimal and as a percent.
   a. $\frac{2}{5}$ **b.** $\frac{3}{4}$ **c.** $\frac{3}{10}$ **d.** $\frac{1}{3}$ **e.** $\frac{9}{4}$

7. Order the numbers from smallest to largest:

$$1\tfrac{5}{8}; \qquad 1.512; \qquad \tfrac{3}{2}; \qquad 145\%; \qquad 2^0$$

8. Find each value without using a calculator.
   a. 2^3 **b.** $(^-2)^3$ **c.** 2^{-3}
   d. 2^0 **e.** 1^{72}

9. Express each number in scientific notation.
   a. 115,000   **b.** .0000074

10. On your calculator, find .000000000032 mm $*$ 52,000 mm. Include the proper units and express the result as specified.

   a. Scientific notation form

   b. Decimal form

11. Estimate the square root $\sqrt{52}$ without using a calculator.

12. Determine the perimeter and area of the given figure. Assume each square within the figure measures 1 cm by 1 cm.

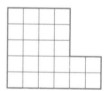

13. Use the commutative property of addition to reorder $14 + 33 + 2 + 16 + 7 + 8$ so that the sum can be found mentally.

14. The radius of a tire is 280 mm. Find the circumference of the tire. Use $\pi \approx 3.14$.

15. The area of a rectangular living room is 112 square feet and the room is 10 feet wide. What is the length of the living room?

2

Algebraic Expressions

2.1 ■ Grouping and the Order of Operations

2.2 ■ Expressions and Formulas

2.3 ■ The Coordinate Plane

2.4 ■ Representing Functions

Where on Earth Are We?

Global positioning system (GPS) technology has revolutionized the art of navigation. This system is based on 24 satellites, which orbit the earth at an altitude of 11,000 miles and send signals to receivers on or near the earth below. These signals are then used to determine the distance from a satellite to a receiver. Once the distance from a receiver to three or four of the satellites is known, a computer can find the location of the receiver within 100 m and with 95% accuracy.

GPS receivers are now standard equipment on commercial and military aircraft. They have helped explorers in remote regions of the world such as Antarctica and were used in the construction of the tunnel beneath the English Channel, which links England and France. The technology is now available for use in private cars in conjunction with a database of road maps. With GPS in your car you may never need to ask for directions!

GPS is based on a three-dimensional coordinate system similar to the two-dimensional system you study in this chapter. (See Exploration on p. 84.)

2.1 Grouping and the Order of Operations

AFTER STUDYING THIS SECTION YOU WILL BE ABLE TO

- Apply the commutative, associative, and distributive properties.
- Apply the order of operations.
- Apply special properties of 0, 1, and ⁻1.

In Chapter 1 you observed that letters may be used to represent numbers. In the formula for the circumference of a circle, $C = 2 * \pi * r$, for example, C represents the circumference and r represents the radius. Both C and r are **variables**, that is, they may assume many different values. On the other hand, the Greek letter π is a **constant**. It always represents the same number, approximately 3.14. Of course, 2 is also a constant, because its value is fixed.

The focus of this chapter is algebraic expressions. An **expression** is a meaningful arrangement of constants, variables, and special symbols.

The special symbols include operations such as addition, subtraction, multiplication, and division, as well as parentheses, ( ), used for grouping. In this section you learn how grouping is used in expressions.

The Associative Properties of Addition and Multiplication

In addition to being commutative, addition and multiplication are also *associative*.

EXAMPLE 1 | You need to build a fence around a triangular piece of land with the dimensions shown in Figure 1. Find the length of the fence.

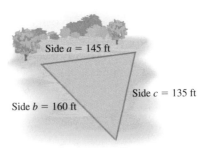

Side a = 145 ft

Side c = 135 ft

Side b = 160 ft

Figure 1

Solution | The length of the fence is the perimeter of the triangle, which is the sum of the lengths of the three sides. There are several ways to find the perimeter. Here are two of them:

1.   First add a and b then add the result to c.

$$(a + b) + c = (145 \text{ feet} + 160 \text{ feet}) + 135 \text{ feet}$$
$$= 305 \text{ feet} + 135 \text{ feet}$$
$$= 440 \text{ feet}$$

2.   First add b and c and then add the result to a.

$$a + (b + c) = 145 \text{ feet} + (160 \text{ feet} + 135 \text{ feet})$$
$$= 145 \text{ feet} + 295 \text{ feet}$$
$$= 440 \text{ feet}$$

Example 1 shows that three numbers added together may be grouped with parentheses in two different ways to get the same sum. In other words, $(a + b) + c = a + (b + c)$. This is called the **associative property of addition**, because the parentheses determine which numbers are to be associated. There is also an **associative property for multiplication**.

The Associative Properties

- Associative property of addition: For any numbers a, b, and c, $(a + b) + c = a + (b + c)$.
- Associative property of multiplication: For any numbers a, b, and c, $(a * b) * c = a * (b * c)$.

The Distributive Property

Another important property is the *distributive property*, as illustrated in Example 2.

EXAMPLE 2   A farmer has a rectangular field with dimensions 42 m and 20 m (Figure 2).

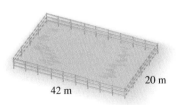

20 m

42 m

Figure 2

He decides to build a fence parallel to one of the sides, as shown in Figure 3. Find the area of the original field and of each of the two new fields.

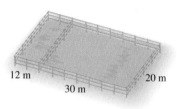

Figure 3

Solution
Use the formula for area of a rectangle, area = **length** * **width**.
In Figure 2,

$$\text{Area of original field} = 20 * 42 = 840 \text{ m}^2$$

In Figure 3,

$$\text{Area of field on left} = 20 * 12 = 240 \text{ m}^2$$

$$\text{Area of field on right} = 20 * 30 = 600 \text{ m}^2$$

Check: Because the total area has not changed, the sum of the areas of the two new fields should be the same as the area of the original field:

$$240 \text{ m}^2 + 600 \text{ m}^2 = 840 \text{ m}^2$$

■ ■

Example 2 illustrates an important property of multiplication and addition. Notice that the length of the original field, 42 m, is the sum of the lengths of the two new fields, 12 m + 30 m. Thus we can write $20 * (12 + 30) = 840$ and $(20 * 12) + (20 * 30) = 840$. Because the expressions are both equal to 840, they must be equal to each other:

$$20 * (12 + 30) = (20 * 12) + (20 * 30)$$

This is an example of the **distributive property of multiplication over addition**. In general we can say that $a * (b + c) = (a * b) + (a * c)$, as illustrated in Figure 4.

The Distributive Property of Multiplication over Addition

For all numbers a, b, and c, $a * (b + c) = (a * b) + (a * c)$.

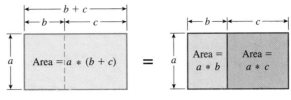

Figure 4

Here are some important facts about the distributive property.

1. The distributive property states that the *product, a* $* (b + c)$, is equal to the *sum,* $(a * b) + (a * c)$.

2. We use the words "expand" and "factor" in connection with the distributive property. If we start with the product, we **expand** $a * (b + c)$ to get $(a * b) + (a * c)$. If we start with the sum, we **factor** $(a * b) + (a * c)$ to get $a * (b + c)$.

3. We sometimes say that multiplication distributes over addition. Multiplication by a is distributed to both b and c.

4. Because subtracting a number is the same as adding its opposite (page 7), multiplication also distributes over subtraction; that is, $a * (b - c) = (a * b) - (a * c)$.

5. Because of the commutative property of multiplication, we can also write $(b + c) * a = (b * a) + (c * a)$. Thus, you can distribute from both the left and the right.

Examples 3 and 4 show how to use the distributive property.

EXAMPLE 3   Use the distributive property to expand each expression.

a. $4 * (20 + 5)$
b. $6 * (x + y)$
c. $3 * (a + b + c)$

Solution   **a.** $4 * (20 + 5) = (4 * 20) + (4 * 5)$. You can check this result by finding the value of each expression.

$$4 * (20 + 5) = 4 * 25 = 100$$

$$(4 * 20) + (4 * 5) = 80 + 20 = 100$$

b. $6 * (x + y) = (6 * x) + (6 * y)$
c. Multiplication distributes over all three terms, a, b, and c.

$$3 * (a + b + c) = (3 * a) + (3 * b) + (3 * c)$$

EXAMPLE 4 Use the distributive property to factor each expression.

a. $(5 * 97) + (5 * 3)$

b. $(8 * a) - (8 * b)$

Solution   **a.** $(5 * 97) + (5 * 3) = 5 * (97 + 3)$. You can check this result by finding the value of each expression.

$$(5 * 97) + (5 * 3) = 485 + 15 = 500$$
$$5 * (97 + 3) = 5 * 100 \quad = 500$$

b. $(8 * a) - (8 * b) = 8 * (a - b)$

■ ■ ■

The Order of Operations

You may have noticed that we used a lot of parentheses in the preceding examples. Some of these parentheses are not necessary if we take advantage of a rule called the **order of operations**.

> **The Order of Operations**
>
> **1.** Do operations inside grouping symbols first.
> **2.** Evaluate exponents and roots from left to right.
> **3.** Perform multiplication and division from left to right.
> **4.** Perform negations, then addition and subtraction from left to right.

This rule guarantees that whenever we evaluate an expression, everyone will arrive at the same answer. To be a successful algebra student, it is *extremely important* that you learn the order of operations, just as to be a successful driver you must learn the rules of the road. The order of operations is summarized in Figure 5.

First parentheses, then	( )
Exponents and roots, followed by	∧ √
Multiplication and division, and finally	* /
Negation, addition, and subtraction	⁻ + −

Figure 5   Use this chart to remember the order of operations.

EXAMPLE 5 Apply the order of operations to find the value of each of these expressions.

a. $2 * 3 + \frac{12}{4}$

b. $(10 - 3 * 6)^2$

c. $^-2^4 + (^-3)^4$

d. $\frac{\sqrt{16}}{3+1}$

Solution
a. There are no grouping symbols, exponents, or roots. Step 3 says to perform multiplication and division from left to right. Then step 4 says to perform the addition.

$$2 * 3 + \frac{12}{4} = 6 + 3$$
$$= 9$$

b. Do the operations inside the parentheses first. Inside the parentheses multiplication (step 3) comes before subtraction (step 4). The result is then raised to the second power.

$$(10 - 3 * 6)^2 = (10 - 18)^2$$
$$= \left(^-8\right)^2$$
$$= 64$$

c. There are two negation symbols, one inside parentheses and the other outside. Because exponents (step 2) come before negation (step 4), apply the exponents to positive 2 and negative 3. Then negate 16 and add the result to 81.

$$^-2^4 + \left(^-3\right)^4 = \,^-16 + 81$$
$$= 65$$

d. Remember that the horizontal fraction bar is a symbol of grouping. Apply operations in the numerator and denominator before performing the division.

$$\frac{\sqrt{16}}{3+1} = \frac{4}{4}$$
$$= 4 \div 4$$
$$= 1$$

Caution: Scientific and graphics calculators such as the TI-83 and TI-84 use the order of operations. Be careful, however—not all calculators do. If you have an unfamiliar calculator, test it first to see if it follows the rules. Enter 1 + 2 * 3. If the answer is 7, the calculator is following the order of operations. If the answer is 9, it is just taking the operations in order from left to right.

Special Properties of 0, 1, and ⁻1

Chapter 1 introduced the commutative property of addition and multiplication. This section introduced the associative and distributive properties. These three properties will be extremely useful in your study of algebra. In addition, there are three special numbers, 0, 1, and ⁻1, with special properties that are important to know.

Special Properties of 0

a. The sum of a number and its opposite is zero. For any number a, $a + {}^-a = 0$. *Example:* $6 + {}^-6 = 0$.

b. Zero added to any number gives the same number. For any number a, $0 + a = a$ and $a + 0 = a$. *Example:* $3 + 0 = 3$.

c. Zero times any number gives zero. For any number a, $0 * a = 0$ and $a * 0 = 0$. *Example:* $4 * 0 = 0$.

d. You cannot divide by 0. For any number a, $\frac{a}{0}$ is undefined; that is, it has no meaning. *Example:* $\frac{7}{0}$ is undefined. When you enter $7 \div 0$ on a calculator, you should get an error message. Try it.

Special Properties of 1

a. The product of a number and its reciprocal is 1. For any number a (except 0), $a * \left(\frac{1}{a}\right) = 1$. *Example:* $3 * \left(\frac{1}{3}\right) = 1$.

b. One multiplied by any number gives the same number. For any number a, $1 * a = a$ and $a * 1 = a$. *Example:* $1 * 7 = 7$.

c. $1*$ may be inserted in front of a left parenthesis. Thus $(a + b) = 1 * (a + b)$. *Example:* $(6 + x) = 1 * (6 + x)$.

d. $*1$ may be inserted behind a right parenthesis. Thus $(a + b) = (a + b) * 1$. *Example:* $(6 + x) = (6 + x) * 1$.

Special Properties of ⁻1

a. Negative 1 multiplied by any number gives the opposite of the number. For any number a, ${}^-1 * a = {}^-a$ and $a * {}^-1 = {}^-a$. *Example:* ${}^-1 * 7 = {}^-7$.

(continued)

b. A negation symbol in front of a left parenthesis may be replaced by $^-1*$. Thus $^-(a + b) = ^-1 * (a + b)$.
Example: $^-(6 + 1) = ^-1 * (6 + 1)$.

c. A subtraction symbol in front of a left parenthesis may be changed to addition if $^-1*$ is inserted. Thus $a - (b + c) = a + ^-1 * (b + c)$.
Example: $13 - (4 + 7) = 13 + ^-1 * (4 + 7)$. Recall that subtraction is the same as adding the opposite.

Examples 6 and 7 illustrate these properties.

EXAMPLE 6 Identify the special property of 0, 1, or $^-1$ used in each instance.

a. $^-3 + 3 = 0$
b. $1 * 7 = 7$
c. $\left(\frac{1}{5}\right) * 5 = 1$
d. $^-(3 + x) = ^-1 * (3 + x)$
e. $(6 + 3) = (6 + 3) * 1$

Solution **a.** Special property of 0 (a on page 52)
b. Special property of 1 (b on page 52)
c. Special property of 1 (a on page 52)
d. Special property of $^-1$ (b on page 53)
e. Special property of 1 (d on page 52)

■ ■ ■

EXAMPLE 7 Use the special properties and the distributive property to remove parentheses.

a. $(x - y) + (z + 7)$
b. $4 - (a + b)$
c. $^-(x + 4) + y$

Solution **a.** $(x - y) + (z + 7)$

$= 1 * (x - y) + 1 * (z + 7)$ *Using special property c of 1*

$= 1 * x - 1 * y + 1 * z + 1 * 7$ *Using the distributive property on page* 48

$= x - y + z + 7$ *Using special property b of 1*

b. $4 - (a + b)$

$= 4 + ^-1 * (a + b)$ *Using special property c of* $^-1$

$= 4 + ^-1 * a + ^-1 * b$ *Using the distributive property*

$= 4 + ^-a + ^-b$ *Using special property a of* $^-1$

The last expression may also be written as $4 - a - b$ using the rule for subtraction on page 7.

c. $^-(x + 4) + y$

$= {}^-1 * (x + 4) + y$ *Using special property b of $^-1$*

$= {}^-1 * x + {}^-1 * 4 + y$ *Using the distributive property*

$= {}^-x + {}^-4 + y$ *Using special property a of $^-1$*

The last expression may also be written as $^-x - 4 + y$ using the rule for subtraction.

■ ■ ■

With a bit of practice you should be able to combine steps to write:

a. $(x - y) + (z + 7) = x - y + z + 7$

b. $4 - (a + b) = 4 - a - b$

c. $^-(x + 4) + y = {}^-x - 4 + y$

However, in order to avoid errors, particularly with minus signs, it is important that you be aware of the special properties when you apply the distributive property to remove parentheses.

Exercises 2.1

1. A triangle has sides that measure 7.64 mm, 5.2 mm, and 4.8 mm.

   a. Make a sketch of the triangle and label the sides.

   b. An expression for the perimeter of the triangle is (7.64 mm + 5.2 mm) + 4.8 mm. Use the associative property of addition to group with parentheses in a different way.

   c. Evaluate the two expressions for the perimeter of the triangle to show that the sums are the same.

2. Recall from Section 1.4 that the area of a triangle is area $= (\frac{1}{2}) *$ base $*$ height.

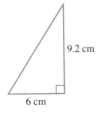

   a. An expression for the area is $(\frac{1}{2} * 6) * 9.2$. Group with parentheses in a different way.

   b. Do the two expressions give the same area? Explain.

   c. What is the property called that allows grouping multiplication in different ways?

3. A land developer wants to subdivide a rectangular parcel of land 220 feet by 891 feet into three smaller rectangular lots. See the accompanying figure.

Use the distributive property to show that the area of the original parcel is the same as the sum of the areas of the three lots.

4. Use the distributive property to expand each expression.

   a. $8 * (4 + 30)$

b. $6 * (200 - 5)$

c. Check your work by finding the value of each expression before and after rewriting.

5. Justin brags that he can perform many complicated multiplications in his head. For example, he says, "I can multiply $4 * 512$ by multiplying $4 * 500$ and adding $4 * 12$."

a. Use the distributive property to show what Justin did.

b. Use Justin's method to compute $11 * 403$ mentally.

6. Use the distributive property to expand each expression.

a. $2 * (L + W)$

b. $7 * (x - y)$

c. Substitute $x = 5$ and $y = 2$ into both expressions in part (b). Does your work check?

7. Factoring is the opposite of what process?

8. Use the distributive property to factor each expression.

a. $(4 * 61) + (4 * 9)$ **b.** $(9 * x) + (9 * y)$

c. $(23 * s) - (23 * t)$

9. Consider $3 - 4 \div 2$. Explain why it is necessary to follow the order of operations to evaluate this expression correctly.

10. Use the order of operations to evaluate each expression.

a. $3 + 5 * 2$ **b.** $6 - 2^3 * 4$

c. $\dfrac{4 - 6}{-8 + 2}$ **d.** $\sqrt{(5 - 2)^2}$

e. $(^-3)^2$ **f.** $^-3^2$

g. $\dfrac{5 + 43 * 1}{6}$ **h.** $13 - (2 + 9)$

11. a. Use the order of operations to evaluate

$$\frac{3 + 24 - 6}{6 - 2}$$

b. How would you enter this expression into your calculator to check your answer?

12. Identify the special property of 0, 1, or $^-1$ used in each instance.

a. $29 \div 0$ is undefined.

b. $^-3 * \left(\frac{-1}{3}\right) = 1$

c. $(5 + x) = 1 * (5 + x)$

d. $^-4.2 + 4.2 = 0$

13. Demonstrate the special properties of 0, 1, and $^-1$ with numbers of your choice.

14. Which of the expressions does not equal $^-(x + 7)$?

a. $^-1 * (x + 7)$ **b.** $(x + 7) * {}^-1$

c. $^-1 * x + 7$ **d.** $^-1 * x + {}^-1 * 7$

e. $x * {}^-1 + 7 * {}^-1$

15. Use the special properties and the distributive property to write each expression without parentheses.

a. $(a + b) - (8 + c)$ **b.** $^-(y + 6) + z$

c. $3 - (s + t)$

Skills and Review 2.1

16. A rectangle has a width of 6 feet and a length of 30 feet.

a. Sketch a figure and label the width and length.

b. Find the perimeter.

c. Find the area.

17. Recall that a formula for the circumference of a circle is $2 * \pi * r$. Find the circumference of a circle with a radius of 5 inches. Use $\pi \approx 3.14$. *Hint:* You may use the commutative property of multiplication to find the circumference without a calculator.

18. Find each value without using a calculator.

a. $2 * 5$ **b.** 2^5

19. Find each value without using a calculator.

a. 9^2 **b.** $\left(\frac{1}{2}\right)^3$

c. 1^5 **d.** 23^0

e. 3^{-4}

20. Find each value without using a calculator.

a. $^-7^2$ **b.** $(^-7)^2$

21. Write 2^{-10} in each format,

a. As a fraction with a positive exponent

b. In scientific notation

c. As a decimal

22. Find the missing decimal, fraction, or percent in each row of the table.

Decimal	Fraction	Percent
?	$\frac{1}{3}$	?
?	?	20%
.25	?	?

23. One wall of Cynthia's house has an area of 450 square feet. It takes Cynthia 9 hours to paint the wall.

 a. What is her work rate in square feet per hour?

 b. What is her work rate in square feet per minute?

 c. What is her work rate in walls per hour?

24. Which is greater, $\frac{2}{5}$ or $\frac{3}{8}$? How did you decide?

25. Evaluate $16 - {}^{-}3$. Use words to describe a change-in-temperature situation involving these numbers.

2.2 Expressions and Formulas

AFTER STUDYING THIS SECTION YOU WILL BE ABLE TO

- Find equivalent algebraic expressions by combining like terms.
- Translate verbal expressions into algebraic expressions.
- Apply the Pythagorean theorem to find the hypotenuse of a right triangle.

The statement that two expressions are equal is called an **equation**. A **formula** is an equation that shows how one variable depends upon one or more other variables. Formulas generally take the form: dependent variable = *expression*.

EXAMPLE 1 Use toothpicks to make a row of squares that share adjacent sides. See Figure 6. The number of toothpicks (T) you need depends upon the number of squares (S) in the row. Find a formula for T in terms of S.

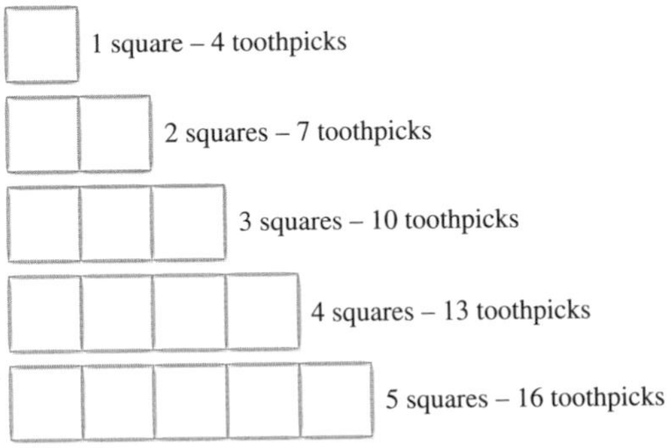

1 square – 4 toothpicks

2 squares – 7 toothpicks

3 squares – 10 toothpicks

4 squares – 13 toothpicks

5 squares – 16 toothpicks

Figure 6

Solution One formula is $T = 3 * S + 1$. Each time a new square is added, three more toothpicks are needed. If you have only $3 * S$ toothpicks, however, you will not be able to close up the left side, so one additional toothpick is needed. See Figure 7. You can check that this formula works by substituting values for S and

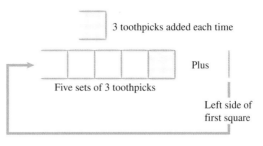

Figure 7

showing that you get the correct values for T:

when $S = 1$ when $S = 2$ when $S = 3$

$T = 3 * S + 1$ $T = 3 * S + 1$ $T = 3 * S + 1$

$T = 3 * 1 + 1$ $T = 3 * 2 + 1$ $T = 3 * 3 + 1$

$T = 3 + 1$ $T = 6 + 1$ $T = 9 + 1$

$T = 4$ $T = 7$ $T = 10$

Another formula is $T = (2 * S) + (S + 1)$. We obtain this formula by noticing that each square requires two horizontal toothpicks, one on top and one on the bottom. The number of vertical toothpicks is one more than the number of squares. So the total number of toothpicks is found by adding the number of horizontal toothpicks $(2 * S)$ to the number of vertical toothpicks $(S + 1)$. Again, this formula may be checked by substituting values for S:

when $S = 1$ when $S = 2$ when $S = 3$

$T = (2 * S) + (S + 1)$ $T = (2 * S) + (S + 1)$ $T = (2 * S) + (S + 1)$

$T = (2 * 1) + (1 + 1)$ $T = (2 * 2) + (2 + 1)$ $T = (2 * 3) + (3 + 1)$

$T = 2 + 2$ $T = 4 + 3$ $T = 6 + 4$

$T = 4$ $T = 7$ $T = 10$

Equivalent Expressions

In Example 1 two different formulas give the same result. That is because the expressions $3 * S + 1$ and $(2 * S) + (S + 1)$ are **equivalent**. Two expressions are equivalent if the results are the same no matter what values are substituted for the variable or variables.

The properties you have learned can be used to explain *why* the two expressions are equivalent. Start with

$(2 * S) + (S + 1)$ *Original expression*

$= ((2 * S) + S) + 1$ *Using the associative property of addition to change grouping*

$= ((2 * S) + (1 * S)) + 1$ *Using a special property of 1 to rewrite S as 1 * S*

$= ((2 + 1) * S) + 1$ *S is a common factor; use the distributive property*

$= (3 * S) + 1$ *Substituting 3 for $2 + 1$*

$= 3 * S + 1$ *Removing the parentheses because they are not needed*

Putting all the steps together, we conclude that $(2 * S) + (S + 1) = 3 * S + 1$ for all values of S.

Combining Like Terms

To show that the two formulas in Example 1 are equivalent, we used the distributive property to show that

$$2 * S + S = 2 * S + 1 * S = (2 + 1) * S = 3 * S$$

$2 * S$ and S are called **like terms** because they contain the same variable. Like terms may be combined by adding (or subtracting) the **coefficients**, that is, the constants that are multiplied by the variables. In this case the coefficients are 2 and 1. The 1 did not appear in the original expression but can always be thought of as being there, using a special property of 1.

The procedure of combining like terms is used so frequently that you may soon be able to write $2 * S + S = 3 * S$ without going through the intermediate steps. Furthermore, the multiplication symbol ($*$) may be omitted between a coefficient and a variable or between two variables. Thus, the process may be further streamlined by writing $2S + S = 3S$. Be sure, however, that if you take this shortcut you know what you are doing! It is better to take an extra step and get the right result than to make a mistake.

EXAMPLE 2 Simplify these expressions by combining like terms:

a. $5x + 8x$
b. $y - 7y$
c. $4a + 5 - 3a + 7$
d. $2x^2 + 3x - x^2 - 5x$

Solution **a.** $5x + 8x = 13x$ (*Think:* $5 + 8 = 13$.)
b. $y - 7y = {}^-6y$ (*Think:* $1 - 7 = {}^-6$.)
c. $4a + 5 - 3a + 7 = a + 12$ (*Think:* Combine the a terms: $4 - 3 = 1$. Combine constant terms: $5 + 7 = 12$.)
d. $2x^2 + 3x - x^2 - 5x = x^2 - 2x$ (*Think:* Combine the x^2 terms: $2 - 1 = 1$. Combine the x terms: $3 - 5 = {}^-2$.)

Caution: In the last expression x^2 and x are *not* like terms because for most values of x, x and x^2 are different numbers. Do not combine x and x^2 to get x^3.

Combining like terms is like combining fractions with the same denominator. For instance, you will recall that to add two fractions with the same denominator, you simply add the numerators:

$$\frac{2}{7} + \frac{3}{7} = \frac{2+3}{7} = \frac{5}{7}$$

When fractions do not have the same denominator, as in the case of $\frac{2}{5} + \frac{1}{4}$, however, you have to find a common denominator.

This principle extends to algebraic fractions, that is, those with variables in the numerator or denominator. The next example shows how the principle of combining like terms applies to fractions.

EXAMPLE 3   Simplify each of these expressions by combining like terms.

a. $\dfrac{5}{x} - \dfrac{2}{x}$

b. $\dfrac{a}{b} + \dfrac{3}{b}$

c. $\dfrac{x}{5} + \dfrac{2x}{5}$

d. $\dfrac{2}{5} + \dfrac{1}{4}$

e. $\dfrac{1}{x} + x + x^2 + x^{-1}$

Solution   **a.** The denominators are the same, so we combine like fractions.

$$\frac{5}{x} - \frac{2}{x} = \frac{5-2}{x} = \frac{3}{x}$$

b. The two fractions have the same denominator and can be combined. Because a and 3 are not like terms, they cannot be combined in the numerator.

$$\frac{a}{b} + \frac{3}{b} = \frac{a+3}{b}$$

c. The two fractions have the same denominator. The numerators are like terms and can be combined.

$$\frac{x}{5} + \frac{2x}{5} = \frac{x+2x}{5} = \frac{3x}{5}$$

d. The fractions do not have the same denominator. Once we find equivalent fractions with a common denominator, we can combine them.

$$\frac{2}{5} + \frac{1}{4} = \frac{8}{20} + \frac{5}{20} = \frac{13}{20}$$

e. Recall that $x^{-1} = \frac{1}{x}$. The two fractions with x in the denominator may be combined. As in Example 2(d), x^2 and x can't be combined because they are not like terms.

$$\frac{1}{x} + x + x^2 + x^{-1} = \frac{1}{x} + x + x^2 + \frac{1}{x} = \frac{1+1}{x} + x + x^2 = \frac{2}{x} + x + x^2$$

◼ ◼

Algebraic and Verbal Expressions

In solving word problems you will often need to rewrite a verbal expression as an algebraic expression. When doing so, look for key phrases that indicate mathematical operations.

EXAMPLE 4

A real estate developer is building homes in a new subdivision. The lots are rectangles with the same width, w feet, but different lengths. See Figure 8.

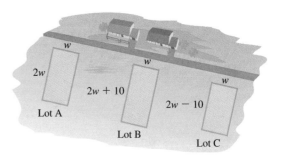

Figure 8

a. The length of lot A is twice the width. Find an expression for the perimeter of lot A.

b. The length of lot B is 10 feet more than twice the width. Find an expression for the perimeter of lot B.

c. The length of lot C is 10 feet less than twice the width. Find an expression for the perimeter of lot C.

d. Find the perimeter of each lot when $w = 120$ feet.

Solution

a. The key words are "twice the width." We are letting w represent the width, so we know that $2w$ represents twice the width. To find the perimeter add all the sides: $w + 2w + w + 2w$. Combine like terms to get $6w$ as a simplified expression for the perimeter of lot A.

b. The key words are "10 feet more than twice the width." Because $2w$ is twice the width, the length is $2w + 10$. To find the perimeter add all the sides:

$w + 2w + 10 + w + 2w + 10$. Combine like terms to get $6w + 20$ as a simplified expression for the perimeter of lot B.

c. The key words are "10 feet less than twice the width." Because $2w$ is twice the width, the length is $2w - 10$. To find the perimeter add all the sides: $w + 2w - 10 + w + 2w - 10$. Combine like terms to get $6x - 20$ as a simplified expression for the perimeter of lot C.

d. Substitute 120 feet for w in each expression for the perimeter.

$$\text{lot A: } 6w = 6 * 120 = 720 \text{ feet}$$

$$\text{lot B: } 6w + 20 = 6 * 120 + 20 = 720 + 20 = 740 \text{ feet}$$

$$\text{lot C: } 6w - 20 = 6 * 120 - 20 = 700 \text{ feet}$$

■ ■ ■

Caution: A common error made by many students in a problem such as Example 4(c) is to translate incorrectly the phrase "10 feet less than twice the width." Writing $10 - 2w$ instead of $2w - 10$ gives the opposite of the required expression. One way to avoid this error is to check the work by substituting a possible value of w into the expression.

For instance, suppose $w = 90$ feet. Then $2w - 10 = 2 * 90 - 10 = 180 - 10 = 170$ feet, a reasonable length. But $10 - 2w = 10 - 2 * 90 = 10 - 180 = {}^{-}170$. This isn't reasonable because the length of the lot can't be negative.

A Formula for Right Triangles

One of the most important formulas in geometry is named for the Greek mathematician Pythagoras, who lived in the sixth century B.C. However, the same formula was discovered by the Chinese and the Egyptians many centuries earlier.

In a **right triangle** the longest side is opposite the right angle and is called the **hypotenuse**. The Pythagorean theorem states that the area of a square built on the hypotenuse is equal to the sum of the areas of the squares built on the other two sides, as shown in Figure 9. We usually label the hypotenuse c and the other two sides a and b. Thus, $c^2 = a^2 + b^2$. This statement is called the Pythagorean theorem and is proved in Chapter 6. It leads us to a formula for the hypotenuse.

The Length of the Hypotenuse of a Right Triangle

In a right triangle with sides of length a, b, and c, if c is the length of the side opposite the right angle, then

$$c = \sqrt{a^2 + b^2}$$

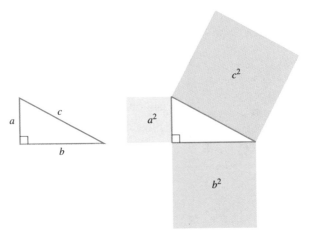

Figure 9

EXAMPLE 5 ▌ A rectangular lot is 120 feet long and 90 feet wide. Find the distance from one corner of the lot to the opposite corner.

Solution ▌ The diagram in Figure 10 shows that a right triangle is formed. We can use the formula for the hypotenuse to find c. Substitute $a = 90$ feet and $b = 120$ feet into the formula

$$c = \sqrt{a^2 + b^2} = \sqrt{90^2 + 120^2}$$

Here we must use the order of operations. The radical symbol groups the sum of a^2 and b^2 just like parentheses. So first we apply the powers and get $c = \sqrt{8100 + 14,400}$. Then we add $8100 + 14,400$, which gives $c = \sqrt{22,500}$. Finally, we find the square root of 22,500, which is $c = 150$. The distance between the two corners is 150 feet.

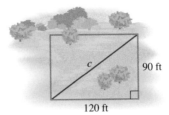

Figure 10

Exercises 2.2

1. Evaluate each expression for the given values of the variables.

   a. $3x - 5$ when $x = 2$

   b. $^-x + 1$ when $x = ^-3$

   c. $4x^2$ when $x = ^-1$

   d. $2\pi r$ when $r = \frac{3}{2}$ (use $\pi \approx 3.14$).

   e. $2L + 2W$ when $L = 4.5$ and $W = 3$

   f. $\sqrt{a^2 + b^2}$ when $a = 3$ and $b = 4$

2. Two formulas for the circumference of a circle are $C = 2 * \pi * \text{radius}$ and $C = \pi * \text{diameter}$.

   a. Check that these formulas are equivalent by substituting three numerical values for the radius. (*Hint:* diameter $= 2 * \text{radius}$.)

   b. Check that these formulas are equivalent by using the properties in Section 2.1 to derive one formula from the other.

3. Substitute the given values into each formula to find values of the indicated variables.

   a. $y = ^-2x + 6$; find y when $x = 3$.

   b. $y = 3x^2 - x$; find y when $x = ^-2$.

   c. The formula for the area of a rectangle is $a = l * w$. Find a when $l = \frac{5}{2}$ cm and $w = 8$ cm.

   d. The formula for the area of a trapezoid is $A = \frac{1}{2}(b_1 + b_2)h$. Find A when $b_1 = 5$ mm, $b_2 = 11$ mm, and $h = 6$ mm.

   e. The formula for the hypotenuse of a right triangle is $c = \sqrt{a^2 + b^2}$. Find c when $a = 6$ inches and $b = 8$ inches.

   f. The formula for the surface area of a cone is $S = \pi * r^2 + \pi * r * \sqrt{r^2 + h^2}$. Find S when $r = 3$ feet and $h = 4$ feet. Use $\pi \approx 3.14$.

4. The surface area of a rectangular box is the sum of the areas of its six rectangular faces, as shown in the figure. Let $w = $ width of the box, $l = $ length of the box, and $h = $ height of the box.

   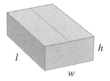

   a. Find a formula for the surface area (S) of the rectangular box in terms of w, l, and h.

   b. Find the surface area when $w = 8$ cm, $l = 10$ cm, and $h = 5$ cm.

5. The table shows the number of cups of flour (F) required to make S servings for a particular recipe.

   a. How many cups of flour are required to make 7 servings?

   b. How many cups of flour are required to make S servings?

   c. Write a formula for F in terms of S.

Servings (S)	Cups of Flour (F)
1	$\frac{1}{3}$
2	$\frac{2}{3}$
3	$\frac{3}{3} = 1$
4	$\frac{4}{3} = 1\frac{1}{3}$

6. Simplify each expression by combining like terms.

   a. $7a - 8a$ **b.** $11b + b$

   c. $3x + 5 - 2x + 9$ **d.** $6x^2 + 7x + x^2 - 6x$

7. A student concludes that $12x - 12x = 0x = x$. Demonstrate with $x = 1$ that $12x - 12x \neq x$.

8. Simplify each expression by combining like fractions.

   a. $\frac{3}{7} + \frac{2}{7}$ **b.** $\frac{3}{x} - \frac{1}{x}$

   c. $\frac{a}{y} + \frac{8}{y}$ **d.** $x^{-1} + \frac{2}{x}$

9. Assume the cost of operating a car is 13 cents per mile for fuel and an additional 30 cents per mile for wear and tear. Let $M = $ number of miles driven.

   a. Write a formula for the cost of operating the car in terms of M.

   b. Write an equivalent expression to the one found in part (a).

   c. What is the cost for each mile driven?

   d. What is the cost for driving 10 miles?

10. A length of a rectangle is 4 feet more than three times the width.

a. Let w represent the width. Find an expression for the length of the rectangle in terms of the width.

b. Draw and label a diagram.

c. Find an expression for the perimeter of the rectangle.

d. Find the value of the perimeter when the width is 35 feet.

11. The height of a parallelogram is 5 inches less than the base.

   a. Draw and label a diagram.

   b. Assign a variable for the length of the base. Then, write an expression for the height in terms of the base.

   c. Find an expression for the area of the parallelogram.

   d. Find the value of the expression when the base is 20 inches.

12. A triangular banner has a height that is one-eighth of the base. Let b represent the base.

   a. Find an expression for the height of the banner.

   b. Find an expression for the area of the banner.

   c. Find the area of the banner when the base is 80 cm.

13. The floor of a rectangular room measures 24 feet by 18 feet. What is the distance from one corner of the floor to the opposite corner?

14. A boat sails from Brisbane 40 km east and from that point, 30 km south.

   a. Draw and label a diagram showing the path of the boat.

   b. Find the boat's distance from Brisbane.

15. Suppose there are two alternative routes from Startville to Finishville. One route comprises two highways that form the legs of a right triangle and the other route is a secondary road, which is the hypotenuse of the triangle (see the figure).

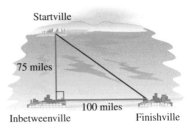

   a. Find the length of the secondary road.

   b. If you can average 50 miles per hour on the highways and 25 miles per hour on the secondary road, which route takes the least amount of time? Remember that time = distance/rate.

Skills and Review 2.2

16. a. Use the distributive property to expand $2(x - y)$.

   b. Use distribution to factor $2x - 2y$.

   c. How are expanding and factoring related?

17. Use the order of operations to evaluate $5 + 7 * (^-4)$.

18. Use the order of operations to evaluate

$$\frac{^-3 * 4^2}{2 - 6}.$$

19. Use the order of operations to evaluate

$$\frac{5 + \sqrt{(^-5)^2 - 4 * 1 * 6}}{2 * 1}$$

20. Use a special property of $^-1$ and the distributive property to write the expression without parentheses: $2 - (c + d)$.

21. The width of a rectangle is 5 inches. The length is 3 inches less than twice the width.

   a. Write an expression for the length of the rectangle.

   b. Evaluate your expression for the length.

   c. Find the area.

   d. Find the perimeter.

22. Recall that for any circle $\pi = $ circumference/diameter.

   a. Measure the circumference and diameter of a glass and use the formula above to approximate the value of π.

   b. Is it possible to get an exact value for π by measurement? Why or why not?

23. Find each value without using a calculator.

   a. 4^3 **b.** 3^0 **c.** 1^{39}

   d. 5^{-2} **e.** $(^-2)^4$

24. Find each absolute value.

    a. $|9|$ **b.** $|^-9|$

    c. $|0|$

25. Find each sum or difference.

    a. $8 + {}^-5$ **b.** ${}^-7 - 2$

    c. ${}^-6 + 4$ **d.** $3 - {}^-8$

2.3 The Coordinate Plane

AFTER STUDYING THIS SECTION YOU WILL BE ABLE TO

▪ Locate points in the coordinate plane.

▪ Apply the definitions of run and rise.

▪ Apply the distance formula.

In 1637 the French mathematician René Descartes invented a system for naming points in a plane. Today we refer to that system as the **coordinate plane**. We describe how the system works through a story about an imaginary town called Gridville.

    In Gridville the roads form a rectangular grid. Roads that run from south to north are called "avenues." Those that run from west to east are called "streets." The two major roads, called Avenue 0 and Street 0, intersect at the center of town, which is also called the **origin**.

    Avenues to the east of Avenue 0 have positive numbers. Avenues to the west of Avenue 0 have negative numbers. Streets to the north of Street 0 have positive numbers. Streets to the south of Street 0 have negative numbers (see Figure 11).

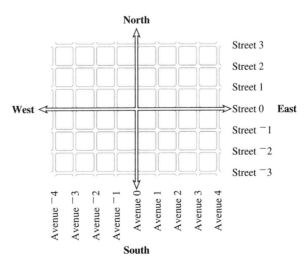

Figure 11

People who live in Gridville have an unusual method of describing locations. Each intersection of a street and an avenue is given a pair of numbers. The avenue number is always given first. Thus the intersection of Avenue ⁻1 and Street 2 is given by the pair (⁻1, 2). Instead of using house numbers, a resident of this town gives the pair for the nearest intersection. He or she figures that once you are at that intersection you should be able to find the house you are looking for quite easily.

The first number in the ordered pair is called the **x-coordinate**. The second number is the **y-coordinate**. Because the avenue (*x*) must be given before the street (*y*), order matters, and (*x*, *y*) is called an **ordered pair**. By knowing the ordered pair for a location, you also know what section of the town you are in. For instance, if both numbers are positive, your location is in the northeast quadrant, also known as the first quadrant. The names for the four quadrants are shown in Figure 12. The boundaries of the quadrants are Street 0, called the **x-axis**, and Avenue 0, called the **y-axis**.

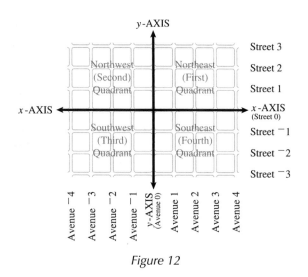

Figure 12

EXAMPLE 1 For each location, identify the quadrant or axis and locate the point on a map of Gridville.

   a. The public library is located at (⁻4, ⁻2).
   b. A grocery store is located at (⁻1, 3).
   c. The high school is located at (3, 2).
   d. The hospital is located at (1, ⁻2).
   e. There is a video-rental store at (0, ⁻3).

Solution **a.** Third quadrant
   b. Second quadrant
   c. First quadrant

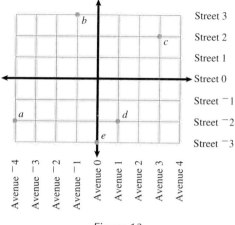

Figure 13

d. Fourth quadrant

e. *y*-axis

The locations are shown in Figure 13.

■ ■ ■

Coordinates on a Calculator

Throughout this book we use a graphing calculator to represent the coordinate plane. Let's begin by showing how to display the intersections in Gridville on the calculator screen.

First we must set the **window**. Press the ⎡WINDOW⎤ key and set the window variables for these values:

$$\text{Xmin} = ^-4.7 \quad \text{Xmax} = 4.7 \quad \text{Xscl} = 1$$

$$\text{Ymin} = ^-3.1 \quad \text{Ymax} = 3.1 \quad \text{Yscl} = 1$$

On a TI-83 or 84 a shortcut for this window is ZOOM 4 (ZDecimal).

Next, turn on the grid. On a TI-83 or 84 press ⎡2ND⎤ FORMAT and select GRIDON. The screen should look like the screen on the left in Figure 14. Press

Figure 14

GRAPH , and you should get the picture on the right in Figure 14. Each dot on the grid represents the intersection of a street and an avenue. Use the four direction keys to move the cursor around the screen. Notice that every time you move the cursor, either the *x*-coordinate or the *y*-coordinate will change by .1. That happens because in the Decimal window, the distance between adjacent pixels is .1.

Try to locate the five points from Example 1 and read their coordinates from the graph. Take some time to become familiar with how coordinates are related to points on the screen. As you do so, notice the following:

- If you move the cursor up or down, you will find that the value of *y* changes while the value of *x* remains the same.
- If you move right or left, the value of *x* changes while the value of *y* remains the same.
- When you move the cursor along the *x*-axis, *y* = 0.
- When you move the cursor along the *y*-axis, *x* = 0.

Run and Rise

There is a taxi service in Gridville. The dispatcher receives calls from riders and relays information to the drivers. Instead of telling drivers where to go, the dispatcher tells how to get there. The dispatcher and the drivers use two code words to communicate. *Run* means to travel along a street, and *rise* means to go along an avenue.

For example, suppose John, who works at the grocery store (located at $(^{-}1, 3)$), needs a ride home and that the closest available cab is at $(2, {}^{-}1)$. The dispatcher tells the driver "run $^{-}3$, rise 4." See Figure 15. Run $^{-}3$ means go three blocks in the negative direction (west) along a street. Rise 4 means go four blocks in the positive direction (north) along an avenue. A positive run would mean to go east. A negative rise would mean to go south.

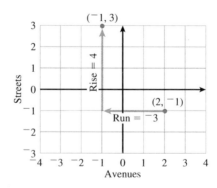

Figure 15

EXAMPLE 2   **a.** Suppose the driver is at $(^{-}2, 1)$ and the dispatcher tells her "run 5, rise $^{-}2$." To what location will the cab go?

b. One cab has just dropped off a teacher at the high school, $(3, 2)$. Now another rider is waiting at $(^-1, 1)$ to be picked up. What directions will the dispatcher give?

Solution

a. From Figure 16 you can see that the destination of the cab is $(3, ^-1)$. You can arrive at the same answer by using the number line model for addition (page 6). Recall that start + change = final. For the x-coordinate this means that $x_{start} + \mathbf{run} = x_{final}$:

$$^-2 + 5 = x_{final}$$

$$3 = x_{final}$$

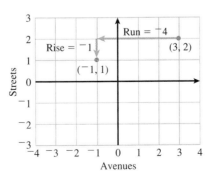

Figure 16

Similarly for y, $y_{start} + \mathbf{rise} = y_{final}$:

$$1 + {}^-2 = y_{final}$$

$$^-1 = y_{final}$$

b. From Figure 17 you can see that run $= {}^-4$ and that rise $= {}^-1$. You can arrive at the same answer by using the number line model for subtraction (page 6).

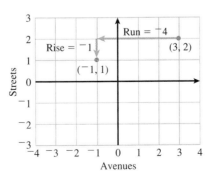

Figure 17

Recall that final − start = change. For the x-coordinates this means that

$$x_{\text{final}} - x_{\text{start}} = \text{run}$$

$$^-1 - 3 = \text{run} \qquad \textit{Substituting}$$

$$^-1 + {}^-3 = \text{run} \qquad \textit{Changing to addition}$$

$$^-4 = \text{run}$$

For the y-coordinates this means that

$$y_{\text{final}} - y_{\text{start}} = \text{rise}$$

$$1 - 2 = \text{rise} \qquad \textit{Substituting}$$

$$1 + {}^-2 = \text{rise} \qquad \textit{Changing to addition}$$

$$^-1 = \text{rise}$$

The solution to Example 2(b) suggests a general formula for run and rise. Call the starting point S, with coordinates (x_1, y_1), and the final point F, with coordinates (x_2, y_2). Then the run is the difference in the x-coordinates, that is, $x_2 - x_1$, and the rise is the difference in the y-coordinates, that is, $y_2 - y_1$.

Definition   Formula for Run and Rise

Suppose S and F are two points in the coordinate planes with coordinate $S = (x_1, y_1)$ and $F = (x_2, y_2)$. Then the **run** and **rise** from S to F are

$$\text{run} = x_2 - x_1$$

$$\text{rise} = y_2 - y_1$$

The Distance Formula

The emergency medical service (EMS) team for Gridville owns a helicopter, which it uses for emergencies. Unlike the taxicabs, the helicopter does not have to travel along the streets and avenues of Gridville. Instead, the helicopter takes the shortest path, "straight as the crow flies."

The management of EMS prepares contingency plans for every foreseeable emergency. They know, for instance, that Ms. Robinson, who lives at the intersection of Avenue $^-4$ and Street 2, has a serious heart condition and may need to be rushed to the hospital. They want to know in advance the distance the helicopter would have to travel.

EXAMPLE 3 Find the distance (in blocks) from Ms. Robinson's home at $(^-4, 2)$ to the hospital at $(1, ^-2)$.

Solution Straight as the crow flies means that the helicopter will travel along the hypotenuse of a right triangle as shown in Figure 18. Using the formulas for run and rise we have

$$\text{run} = x_2 - x_1 = 1 - {}^-4 = 1 + 4 = 5$$
$$\text{rise} = y_2 - y_1 = {}^-2 - 2 = {}^-2 + {}^-2 = {}^-4$$

The run is 5 blocks and the rise is $^-4$ blocks.

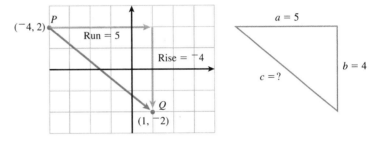

Figure 18

The length of a side of a triangle is always a positive number, so we can take the absolute values of the run and rise to find two sides of the right triangle. As shown in Figure 18 we have $a = 5$ and $b = 4$. Using the Pythagorean theorem (page 61), $c = \sqrt{a^2 + b^2}$. Substituting for a and b gives $c = \sqrt{5^2 + 4^2} = \sqrt{25 + 16} = \sqrt{41} \approx 6.403$. Thus, the helicopter will have to travel about 6.4 blocks to get Ms. Robinson to the hospital.

■ ■ ■

In Example 3 we were careful to distinguish between the rise of $^-4$ and its absolute value 4, which is the side b of the right triangle. Note that when we square 4 we get 16. If we square $^-4$ we get the same result because $(^-4)^2 = (^-4) * (^-4) = 16$. This suggests that we can find the distance between any two points in the coordinate plane directly from the run and the rise.

Definition   The Distance Formula

Suppose S and F are two points in the coordinate plane with coordinates $S = (x_1, y_1)$ and $F = (x_2, y_2)$. Then the distance from S to F is given by

(continued)

the formula

$$\text{distance} = \sqrt{\text{run}^2 + \text{rise}^2}$$

The distance may also be calculated directly from the coordinates:

$$\text{distance} = \sqrt{(x_2 - x_1)^2 + (y_2 - y_1)^2}$$

Notice that the distance formula is based on the Pythagorean theorem. If you have learned that $c = \sqrt{a^2 + b^2}$, then you should be able to remember that distance $= \sqrt{\text{run}^2 + \text{rise}^2}$.

EXAMPLE 4 Use the distance formula to find how far the helicopter will travel.

   a. From $(4, 2)$ to $(1, {}^-2)$

   b. From $({}^-4, {}^-3)$ to $(1, {}^-2)$

   c. From $(3, 2)$ to $({}^-3, 2)$

Solution   **a.** $\text{run} = x_2 - x_1 = 1 - 4 = {}^-3$

        $\text{rise} = y_2 - y_1 = {}^-2 - 2 = {}^-\mathbf{4}$

        $\text{distance} = \sqrt{\text{run}^2 + \text{rise}^2} = \sqrt{({}^-3)^2 + ({}^-4)^2} = \sqrt{9 + 16} = \sqrt{25} = 5$

       Caution: Once again, remember that when you square a negative number, you must put it in parentheses: $({}^-3)^2 = 9$, but ${}^-3^2 = {}^-9$, which is incorrect.

   b. $\text{run} = x_2 - x_1 = 1 - {}^-4 = 1 + 4 = \mathbf{5}$

        $\text{rise} = y_2 - y_1 = {}^-2 - {}^-3 = {}^-2 + 3 = 1$

        $\text{distance} = \sqrt{\text{run}^2 + \text{rise}^2} = \sqrt{5^2 + 1^2} = \sqrt{25 + 1} = \sqrt{26} \approx 5.099$

   c. $\text{run} = x_2 - x_1 = {}^-3 - 3 = {}^-\mathbf{6}$

        $\text{rise} = y_2 - y_1 = 2 - 2 = \mathbf{0}$

        $\text{distance} = \sqrt{\text{run}^2 + \text{rise}^2} = \sqrt{({}^-6)^2 + 0^2} = \sqrt{36 + 0} = \sqrt{36} = 6$

       Note: In this case, although the distance formula works, rise $= 0$, so it may be easier just to take the absolute value of the run.

Exercises 2.3

---

1. For each ordered pair, identify the quadrant or axis and locate the point on a graph of the coordinate plane.

  a. $({}^-3, 1)$ **b.** $({}^-2, {}^-4)$ **c.** $(3, 0)$

  d. $(2, 1)$ **e.** $(1, {}^-3)$

2. Give an example of an ordered pair in each location.

  a. Quadrant I

  b. Quadrant II

  c. Quadrant III

  d. Quadrant IV

e. On the x-axis
f. On the y-axis

3. Find the coordinates for the point on Street 4 that is halfway between Avenue $^-4$ and Avenue $^-6$.

4. Consider Avenue 2.

  a. List four ordered pairs on Avenue 2.

  b. What is the same about these ordered pairs?

  c. What is different about them?

5. Consider Street $^-3$.

  a. List four ordered pairs on Street $^-3$.

  b. What is the same about these ordered pairs?

  c. What is different about them?

6. On a graphing calculator, the cursor is located at $(^-2, 1)$. Suppose you move the cursor down.

  a. Which variable, x or y, changes?

  b. Does this variable increase or decrease?

7. On a graphing calculator, the cursor is located at $(^-3, ^-2)$. Suppose you move the cursor to the right.

  a. Which variable, x or y, changes?

  b. Does this variable increase or decrease?

8. Suppose you start at $(^-1, 2)$. Use the given run and rise to locate your final location.

  a. run 4, rise 2   **b.** run 0, rise $^-3$

  c. run 2, rise 0   **d.** run $^-3$, rise $^-4$

9. What are the run and rise needed to get from $(2, ^-5)$ to $(3, 4)$? What are the run and rise needed to get back to the starting position?

10. Plot $(0, 1)$. Use run 1 and rise 2 to plot the next point. Continue plotting new points using the same run and rise. What do you notice about the plotted points?

11. Given a starting point of $(1, ^-3)$ and a final point of $(^-2, ^-4)$,

  a. Graph the points on a coordinate plane.

  b. Find the run and rise and label your graph.

  c. Find the distance between the two points.

12. Find the distance between $(^-2.3, 4)$ and $(1.2, ^-3.4)$.

13. A point on a circle is $(0, 2)$, and the center of the circle is $(^-1, 6)$. Use the distance formula to find the radius of the circle.

14. Suppose a hospital wants to estimate the time it will take a helicopter to bring an injured patient to the hospital. The patient is at $(60, ^-20)$ and the hospital is at $(20, 10)$.

  a. Find the distance to the hospital.

  b. If the helicopter's average speed is 120 blocks per hour, find the time (in minutes) it will take to reach the hospital. (*Recall:* time = distance ÷ rate.)

15. Find the area of the triangle shown.

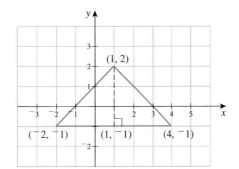

Skills and Review 2.3

16. For each statement, find an expression for the length in terms of the width. Let x represent the width.

  a. The length is 7 more than the width.

  b. The length is 3 times the width.

  c. The length is 4 less than twice the width.

  d. The length is 8 more than one-half the width.

17. Simplify each expression by combining like terms.

  a. $3y + 9y$ **b.** $6x - x$

  c. $^-2x - 4 + 5x + 7$ **d.** $5x^2 - x - 7x^2 + 2x$

18. Simplify the expression by first using the distributive property and then combining like terms: $^-(x + 2) - 6x$.

19. Evaluate $^-\frac{b}{2a}$ when $a = ^-2, b = 6$.

20. Recall that the area of a trapezoid is $A = \frac{1}{2}(b_1 + b_2)h$. Find the area when $h = 7$ cm, $b_1 = 3$ cm, and $b_2 = 8$ cm.

21. Use the order of operations to evaluate $(1 - 3 * 7)^2$.

22. Suppose your calculator shows 2.73E$^-5$. Write this number in each form.

  a. Scientific notation

  b. Decimal notation

23. Find each value without using a calculator.

  a. 2^5 **b.** $(^-3)^2$ **c.** $^-3^2$

  d. $\left(\frac{1}{5}\right)^2$ **e.** $(^-1)^{23}$

24. Find each quotient or product.

a. $^-48 \div ^-6$ **b.** $7 * ^-8$

c. $^-105 \div 5$ **d.** $\frac{^-3}{4} * \frac{5}{3}$

a. $5 - 8$ **b.** $^-5 + 8$

c. $5 - ^-8$ **d.** $^-5 - 8$

25. Find each sum or difference.

2.4 Representing Functions

AFTER STUDYING THIS SECTION YOU WILL BE ABLE TO

▪ Represent functions in four ways: verbally, symbolically, numerically, and graphically.

▪ Use a calculator to display tables and graphs.

We now look more closely at how two variables may be related to each other. We begin with an example.

EXAMPLE 1

Jamie has joined a health club. In addition to a monthly fee of $20, she will be charged $3 every time she uses the facility to work out. She plans to work out about 12 times each month. How much will it cost her to use the club for 1 month?

Solution

The cost of belonging to the health club for 1 month has two parts, an amount that varies according to how many times she uses the club during the month and a monthly membership fee that is fixed. These two components may be called *variable cost* and *fixed cost*, respectively. Jamie is interested in the total cost for the month, which may be computed using this relationship:

total cost = variable cost + fixed cost

The variable cost may be found by multiplying the number of times she uses the club, 12, by the cost for each visit, $3. Thus, the variable cost is **$36**. The fixed cost is given to be **$20**.

total cost = $36 + $20 = $56

Jamie will spend $56 for 1 month's membership in the club.

■ ■ ■

Functions

Of course, Jamie may not use the club exactly 12 times every month. Her actual cost will depend upon the number of times she uses the club. We can express this situation as a relationship between two variables.

EXAMPLE 2 Let y represent the total cost (in dollars) of 1 month's membership in the health club. Let x represent the number of times Jamie uses the health club. Write a formula that shows how y depends upon x.

Solution Again, use the relationship total cost = **variable cost** + **fixed cost**.

In Example 1, we found the variable cost by multiplying 12 visits times the rate $3 per visit. In this problem we don't know the number of visits, but we are representing it by the variable x, so x visits times $3 per visit gives a variable cost of $3x$. We know that the fixed cost is the same as before, $20, and that the variable y represents total cost. The formula $y = 3x + 20$ shows how y depends upon x.

■ ■ ■

When the value of one variable depends upon the value of another variable, we have a **function**. In this case y is a function of x. The value y is called the **output** (or **dependent**) **variable**, and the value x is the **input** (or **independent**) **variable**. The equation $y = 3x + 20$ is one way of representing this function. Because the equation takes the form dependent variable = expression, we may consider this equation to be a formula. (See Section 2.2.)

EXAMPLE 3 Complete this table using the formula $y = 3x + 20$ to show how y depends upon x.

x	y
0	
2	
4	
6	
8	
10	
12	

Solution In each case the value of y may be found by substituting for x in the formula.

x	y	
0	20	$= 3 * 0 + 20$
2	26	$= 3 * 2 + 20$
4	32	$= 3 * 4 + 20$
6	38	$= 3 * 6 + 20$
8	44	$= 3 * 8 + 20$
10	50	$= 3 * 10 + 20$
12	56	$= 3 * 12 + 20$

Most graphing calculators will display a table for you. On a TI-83 or TI-84, use [2ND] TBLSET to access the TABLE SETUP menu. Enter these values:

> TblStart = 0
> Δ Tbl = 2
> Indpnt: Auto
> Depend: Auto

This starts the table at x = 0.
This increments x by 2.
These commands tell the calculator
to make the table automatically.

Then enter Y1 = 3 ∗ X + 20 in the $\boxed{\text{Y=}}$ menu. $\boxed{\text{2ND}}$ TABLE will give you the desired table.

Note that the table illustrates an important property of functions. For each value of the independent variable, x, there is exactly one value of the dependent variable y. In other words, the value of x determines uniquely the corresponding value of y.

■ ■ ■

EXAMPLE 4 ■ Display the data in the table in Example 3 in a graph.

Solution Because neither x nor y can take on negative values, you need to show only the *first quadrant*. Choose a range and scale that will allow you to display values of x from 0 to 12 and values of y from 0 to 80.

On the left in Figure 19, paper with a centimeter grid is used to make the graph. On the x-axis 1 cm represents 2 visits. On the y-axis 1 cm represents 10 dollars.

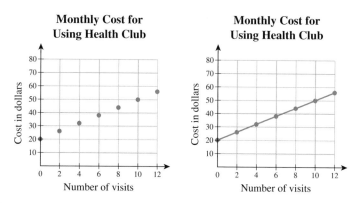

Figure 19

The x-axis is labeled with the name of its variable, Number of visits. Similarly, the y-axis is labeled Cost in dollars. The title, Monthly Cost for Using Health Club, appears above the graph.

From the graph in Figure 19, it appears that the data points lie in a line. In the graph on the right the line has been drawn. Chapter 4 provides more detail about equations of lines.

You may also use a calculator to display the graph drawn in Figure 19. Use the $\boxed{\text{Y=}}$ menu. Enter 3X + 20 for Y1. Use $\boxed{\text{WINDOW}}$ to set the range and scale.

One set of values that will work is:

$$Xmin = 0, \ Xmax = 47, \ Xscl = 5$$
$$Ymin = 0, \ Ymax = 80, \ Yscl = 10$$

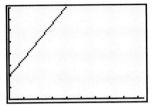

Figure 20

Figure 20 shows the graph that is displayed when $\boxed{\text{GRAPH}}$ is pressed. Because 47 creates a *friendly window* on the TI-83 and TI-84, 47 was chosen for Xmax. Friendly windows minimize the number of decimal places displayed when the $\boxed{\text{TRACE}}$ feature is used. Numbers that can be used to create friendly windows are shown in the table in Figure 21.

PIXELWIDTH	X_{min}	X_{max}	X_{scl}	Shortcut for Square Window
0.05	0	4.7	0.5	
0.1	⁻4.7	4.7	1	ZOOM 4 ZDecimal
0.1	0	9.4	1	
0.2	⁻9.4	9.4	2	ZOOM 4 ZDecimal ZOOM 3 Zoom Out ENTER
0.2	0	18.8	2	
0.5	⁻23.5	23.5	5	ZOOM 8 ZInteger ZOOM 2 Zoom In ENTER
0.5	0	47	5	
1	⁻47	47	10	ZOOM 8 ZInteger
1	0	94	10	
2	⁻94	94	20	ZOOM 8 ZInteger ZOOM 3 Zoom Out ENTER
2	0	188	20	
5	⁻235	235	50	
5	0	470	50	
10	⁻470	470	100	
10	0	940	100	

Figure 21   "Friendly" windows for TI-83 and TI-84 calculators.

To see how the graph is related to the table, press the $\boxed{\text{TRACE}}$ key. The calculator will display the point where X = 23.5 and Y = 90.5. Move the left arrow and watch the values of X and Y change. You should be able to find the ordered pairs (12, 56), (10, 50), etc., just as they appeared in the table in Example 3.

Pixels and Friendly Windows

The graphing screen on a calculator is made up of hundreds of pixels (*picture elements*), which may be turned on or off. The screen on a TI-83 is 95 pixels wide and 63 pixels high. Consequently, the width of one pixel is $\frac{1}{94}$ of the distance between Xmin and Xmax. The height of one pixel is $\frac{1}{62}$ of the distance between Ymin and Ymax.

As a result, some windows will give awkward-looking decimals for values of x and y. For example, when you set the Standard Window (ZOOM 6), Xmin $= {}^-10$, Xmax $= 10$, Ymin $= {}^-10$ and Ymax $= 10$. In this window the width of one pixel is approximately 0.2127659574 and the height is approximately 0.3225806452.

You may prefer to create a **friendly window** that will give pixel dimensions of at most one or two decimal places. The values of Xmin and Xmax suggested in Figure 21 will do just that.

The table in Figure 21 shows both four-quadrant windows in which the origin is at the center of the screen and first-quadrant windows in which the origin is at the lower-left corner of the screen. You can use a shortcut to get some of the windows with the ZOOM menu. Zoom In and Zoom Out will work if ZOOM FACTORS are both set at 2. (To set ZOOM FACTORS, use ZOOM MEMORY 4). ZInteger will always give a screen with PIXELWIDTH $= 1$ and PIXELHEIGHT $= 1$. The center of the screen depends upon the last location of the cursor. If necessary, activate ZOOM 6 Zstandard before pressing ZOOM 8 ZInteger.

Zoom 4 ZDecimal and Zoom 8 ZInteger produce square windows in which the width and height of the pixels are the same. An example of a square window is the one used in Figure 14 on page 67 to display street intersections in Gridville.

In the health club example shown in Figure 20, a square window is not appropriate. This is true in most problems involving applications. Once you have chosen friendly values for Xmin and Xmax, you can choose any appropriate values of Ymin and Ymax.

At first you may want to refer to Figure 21 when choosing a window. After a while you will probably remember that values of X like 4.7, 9.4, 47, and 94 will give you friendly windows.

EXAMPLE 5 Chose a friendly window that will include each set of points.

a. Data from the toothpick problem (Example 1, Section 2.2), where x is the number of squares and y is the number of toothpicks: $(1, 4)$, $(2, 7)$, $(3, 10)$, $(4, 13)$, $(5, 16)$.
b. Data from the real estate problem (Example 4, Section 2.2), where x is the width of lot A in feet and y is the perimeter of the lot: $(100, 600)$, $(120, 720)$, $(140, 840)$, $(150, 900)$.
c. Points that satisfy the equation $y = 3x + 5$: $({}^-4, {}^-7)$, $({}^-2, {}^-1)$, $(0, 5)$, $(2, 11)$, $(4, 17)$.

Solution **a.** All values of x and y are positive, so a first-quadrant window is appropriate. The largest value of x is 5 and the largest value of y is 16. For a friendly window we should have Xmax = 4.7 or Xmax = 9.4. Because 4.7 is too small, let's choose 9.4. One possible friendly window is Xmin = 0, Xmax = 9.4, Ymin = 0, Ymax = 20.

b. Again, all values are positive so we may choose a first-quadrant window. Because both x- and y-values are in the hundreds, we must be sure that Xmax is at least 150 and Ymax is at least 900. One possible friendly window is Xmin = 0, Xmax = 188, Ymin = 0, Ymax = 1000.

c. Here we have both positive and negative values of x and y, so a four-quadrant window is in order. One possibility is Xmin = $^-$4.7, Xmax = 4.7, Ymin = $^-$10, Ymax = 20. Just make sure that all the values of x and y that you want to show lie within the window.

Four Representations for Functions

You have seen four ways of representing the function that shows how the cost for 1 month's membership at the health club depends upon the number of times Jamie uses the facility:

- Verbally: A description of the situation in words: She is charged a monthly fee of $20 and $3 for each visit.
- Symbolically: A formula, $y = 3x + 20$, as found in Example 2
- Numerically: A table of values, as found in Example 3
- Graphically: A graph, as found in Example 4

The **rule of four** states that any function may be represented in these four ways: verbally, symbolically, numerically, and graphically. In our study of functions throughout this course, we will be using these four different representations and exploring the connections among them.

EXAMPLE 6 To convert from Celsius to Fahrenheit temperatures, multiply the Celsius temperature by 1.8. Then add 32°. Show how the rule of four can be applied to this function.

Solution The situation has already been described *verbally*. The rule works because 0° on the Celsius scale is the freezing point of water, which corresponds to 32° on the Fahrenheit scale. Furthermore, each Celsius degree is 1.8 times as great as a Fahrenheit degree.

For a formula, let y represent Fahrenheit temperature and x represent Celsius temperature. The rule described in words can be represented *symbolically* by the formula $y = 1.8 * x + 32$.

To represent the function *numerically*, you may create a table.

x (Celsius)	y (Fahrenheit)
⁻10	14
0	32
10	50
20	68
30	86

A traveler from the United States to a country where Celsius is used might want a copy of the table for quick reference. Or he or she could learn this poem:

```
30 is hot
20 is pleasing
10 is cool, and
0 is freezing!
```

Finally, we may represent the function *graphically* as in Figure 22. Notice that the graph includes points outside the first quadrant because both Celsius and Fahrenheit temperatures can take on negative values. An appropriate friendly window for the calculator would be Xmin = ⁻94, Xmax = 94, XScl = 20, Ymin = ⁻100, Ymax = 100, and YScl = 20.

Converting Celsius to Farenheit Temperatures

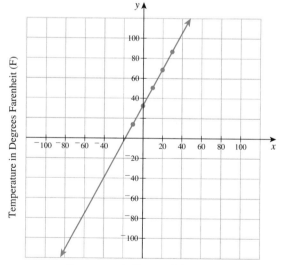

Figure 22

Exercises 2.4

1. From your reading of Section 2.4, explain the meaning of the terms *fixed cost* and *variable cost*.

2. Gertrude needs to rent a car for 1 day. She will be charged a daily fee of $40.00 in addition to 6 cents for every mile she drives. Assign the variables by letting x = the number of rental miles she drives and y = the total cost. This situation can modeled by the equation $y = .06x + 40$.

   a. Which part of the formula represents the variable cost?

   b. Which part of the formula represents the fixed cost?

   c. What is the total cost if Gertrude drives 100 miles?

3. A plumber charges $75.00 for house calls plus $42.00 for every hour he works.

   a. Let t represent the time (in hours) the plumber works and c represent the cost for his services.

   b. Write a formula for c in terms of t.

   c. Is this formula a function? Explain.

   d. What is the output if the input is 2 hours?

Use the following situation for Exercises 4–6: An office supply company delivers paper that costs $10.00 for each box. They charge $25.00 for delivery.

4. a. Let x represent the number of boxes and y be the total cost. Write a formula for y in terms of x.

   b. Which is the independent variable and which is the dependent variable?

   c. Make a table by hand for values of 0, 2, 4, 6, and 8 boxes of paper.

   d. Enter the formula from part (a) into the $\boxed{Y =}$ menu on the calculator. Press $\boxed{2\text{ND}}$ TBLSET. Start the table at 10 and increment the number of boxes by 2. Press $\boxed{2\text{ND}}$ TABLE to display a table, and record your calculator's table values in the table you started in part (c).

5. a. Do x-values of 0 or less make sense in this situation? Explain.

   b. Use the values in the table from Exercise 4(d) to make a graph by hand. Be sure to label the axes and title the graph.

   c. Do the ordered pairs on your graph appear to fall on a line? If so, connect the points.

   d. What does the ordered pair (14, 165) represent?

6. Now display the graph on your calculator.

   a. Enter the formula from Exercise 4(a) into the $\boxed{Y =}$ menu on the calculator.

   b. Enter the following values in the $\boxed{\text{WINDOW}}$ menu: Xmin = 0, Xmax = 47, Xscl = 5, Ymin = 0, Ymax = 500, Yscl = 100.

   c. Press $\boxed{\text{GRAPH}}$. Use the $\boxed{\text{TRACE}}$ feature to find the cost when 15 boxes of paper are shipped.

   d. Replace your current-window Xmax setting with double its value and view the graph. Why does the graph appear different?

7. Consider the function $y = 2x + 5$. We wish to produce a calculator graph that will include the following table of values.

x	y
$^-15$	$^-25$
$^-10$	$^-15$
$^-5$	$^-5$
0	5
5	15
10	25
15	35

   a. Pick a friendly window for viewing these values. (See the chart in Figure 21 on page 77.)

   b. Display the graph and describe what it looks like.

   c. Use $\boxed{\text{TRACE}}$ to find the value of y when $x = {}^-4$.

8. Display the function $y = 2x + 5$ from Exercise 7 with the Standard Window, Xmin = $^-10$, Xmax = 10, Xscl = 1, Ymin = $^-10$, Ymax = 10, Xscl = 1. *Hint:* You may use Zoom 6 to obtain this window.

   a. Describe in what ways the graph is similar to the graph from Exercise 7 and in what ways it is different.

   b. Press $\boxed{\text{TRACE}}$ and move the cursor to the right. What do you notice?

   c. Is it possible to use $\boxed{\text{TRACE}}$ to find the exact value of y when $x = {}^-4$? Explain.

   d. Why is the Standard Window not considered to be friendly?

9. Example 6 gave a formula for converting Celsius temperatures to Fahrenheit temperatures. Here is a verbal description of how to convert from Fahrenheit to Celsius: To find a Celsius temperature, subtract 32° from

the Fahrenheit temperature and multiply the result by $\frac{5}{9}$. Now represent this situation three other ways:

a. Write a formula for Celsius temperature in terms of Fahrenheit temperature.

b. Make a table of values by hand that includes Fahrenheit temperatures of 10°, 30°, 50°, 70°, and 90°. Round Celsius temperatures to the nearest .1°.

c. Make a graph by hand.

10. Represent the same situation as Exercise 9 with your calculator.

a. Produce a table of values with Fahrenheit temperatures of 10°, 30°, 50°, 70°, and 90°.

b. Give a friendly window setting for graphing the function.

c. Draw the calculator's graph with scales and labels.

11. The simple interest on an investment is 6% of the principal invested. Recall that to find 6% of a number you may multiply by .06.

a. Assign variables to represent the principal and the interest.

b. Represent this function symbolically with a formula giving interest in terms of the principal.

c. Represent this function numerically with a table of values for investments of $500, $1000, $1500, $2000, and $2500.

d. Represent this function graphically.

12. The number of gallons of paint required to cover the walls of a room is found by dividing the square footage of the walls by 350. Represent this function by a formula, a table of values, and a graph for square footages of 1000, 2000, 3000, and 4000. Be sure to assign your variables before you write a formula.

13. Assume a new product costing $10,000 depreciates the same amount each year. Its remaining value can be found by subtracting the product of $1500 and the years of service from $10,000.

a. Represent this function by a formula, a table of values, and a graph.

b. What range of years makes sense in this situation?

c. What is the range of values for the product?

d. How do your answers from parts (b) and (c) help you choose window settings?

14. An art collector has a $300 painting, which she believes will appreciate 10% of its original value each year. The value of the painting, then, is $300 plus $30 for each year she owns the painting.

a. Write a formula for the value of the painting.

b. Make a table of values.

c. Draw a graph by hand or create a graph on your calculator.

15. a. Describe the difference between a four-quadrant window and a first-quadrant window.

b. For which of these functions is a four-quadrant window appropriate? For which is a first-quadrant window appropriate?

- The cost of office supplies (Exercises 4–6)
- $y = 2x + 5$ (Exercises 7–8)
- The formula for converting temperatures from Fahrenheit to Celsius (Exercises 9–10)
- The paint required to cover the walls of a room (Exercise 12)

Skills and Review 2.4

16. Graph, by hand, the ordered pairs $(^-1, 3)$ and $(2, ^-4)$ and connect the points.

a. Find the run and rise from $(^-1, 3)$ to $(2, ^-4)$. Label your graph.

b. Find the distance between the ordered pairs.

c. How do the run and rise relate to the distance between the ordered pairs?

17. Start at $(^-4, 6)$. Use a run of 2 and a rise of $^-3$ to find your next location.

18. Find the hypotenuse of a right triangle whose other sides measure 30 feet and 40 feet.

19. A handheld computer has a rectangular viewing screen. The length is 1.4 inches more than the width.

a. Let x represent the width of the computer screen, in inches. Find an expression for the perimeter of the screen.

b. Find the perimeter of the computer screen when the width is 3.8 inches.

20. Evaluate $(a + 3)(6 - b)$ when $a = 4$ and $b = 8$.

21. Consider the expressions $50 - 4x$ and $^-4x + 50$.

a. Show that the expressions are equivalent by the commutative property.

b. Show equivalence by substituting three values into each expression.

22. Use the order of operations to evaluate

$$\frac{2 + 5 * 4^2}{6 - 8}.$$

23. Estimate $\sqrt{41}$.

24. Write $^-6.15 * 10^{-4}$ in decimal notation.

25. Find the rate in miles per hour for each situation.

    a. Uta walks 6 miles in 2 hours.

    b. Ben jogs 6 miles in 1 hour.

    c. Tanya runs 6 miles in $\frac{2}{3}$ hour.

    d. Roberto bicycles 6 miles in $\frac{2}{5}$ hour.

CHAPTER 2 ▪ KEY CONCEPTS ▪

Expression An expression is a meaningful arrangement of constants, variables, and symbols for operations and grouping. (Page 46)

The Associative Properties Addition: for any numbers a, b, and c, $(a + b) + c = a + (b + c)$. Multiplication: for any numbers a, b, and c, $(a * b) * c = a * (b * c)$. (Page 47)

The Distributive Property For all numbers a, b, and c, $a * (b + c) = (a * b) + (a * c)$. (Page 48)

The Order of Operations (Page 50).

a. Do operations inside grouping symbols first.

b. Evaluate exponents and roots from left to right.

c. Perform multiplication and division from left to right.

d. Perform negation, then addition and subtraction, from left to right.

Special Properties of 0 (Page 52).

a. For any number a, $a + {}^-a = 0$.

b. For any number a, $0 + a = a$ and $a + 0 = a$.

c. For any number a, $0 * a = 0$ and $a * 0 = 0$.

d. For any number a, $\frac{a}{0}$ is undefined; that is, it has no meaning.

Special Properties of 1 (Page 52).

a. For any number a (except 0), $a * (\frac{1}{a}) = 1$.

b. For any number a, $1 * a = a$ and $a * 1 = a$.

c. $1*$ may be inserted in front of a left parenthesis. Thus $(a + b) = 1 * (a + b)$.

d. $*1$ may be inserted behind a right parenthesis. Thus $(a + b) = (a + b) * 1$.

Special Properties of $^-1$ (Page 52).

a. For any number a, $^-1 * a = {}^-a$ and $a * {}^-1 = {}^-a$.

b. A negation symbol in front of a left parenthesis may be replaced by $^-1*$. Thus $^-(a + b) = {}^-1 * (a + b)$.

c. A subtraction symbol in front of a left parenthesis may be changed to addition if $^-1*$ is inserted. Thus $a - (b + c) = a + {}^-1 * (b + c)$.

Equations and Formulas The statement that two expressions are equal is called an equation. A formula is an equation that shows how one variable depends upon one or more other variables. (Page 56)

Equivalent Expressions Two expressions are equivalent if the results are the same no matter what values are substituted for the variable or variables. (Page 57)

Like Terms Like terms contain the same variable raised to the same power. Like terms may be combined by adding (or subtracting) the **coefficients**, that is, the constants that are multiplied by the variables. For example, $3x + 4x = 7x$. *Caution:* x and x^2 are *not* like terms. (Page 58)

The Pythagorean Theorem The Pythagorean theorem states that in a right triangle with sides of length a, b, and c, if c is the length of the side opposite the right angle, then $c^2 = a^2 + b^2$ and $c = \sqrt{a^2 + b^2}$. (Page 61)

The Coordinate Plane Every point in the plane is represented by an ordered pair of numbers (x, y). The first number is the x-coordinate; the second number is the y-coordinate. (Page 65)

Run and Rise Suppose P and Q are two points in the coordinate plane with coordinates $P = (x_1, y_1)$ and $Q = (x_2, y_2)$. Then the run and rise from P to Q are

$$\text{run} = x_2 - x_1$$
$$\text{rise} = y_2 - y_1 \qquad \text{(Page 70)}$$

The Distance Formula If P and Q are two points in the coordinate plane with coordinates $P = (x_1, y_1)$ and $Q = (x_2, y_2)$, the distance from P to Q is given by the formula

$$\text{distance} = \sqrt{\text{run}^2 + \text{rise}^2} \qquad \text{(Page 71)}$$

Functions on a Graphing Calculator Use $\boxed{Y=}$ to enter the function in symbolic form. Use $\boxed{2\text{ND}}$ TBLSET and $\boxed{2\text{ND}}$ TABLE to display the function numerically. Use $\boxed{\text{WINDOW}}$ and $\boxed{\text{GRAPH}}$ to display the function graphically and $\boxed{\text{TRACE}}$ to show the values of x and y for points on the graph. (Page 76)

Friendly Windows Friendly windows for the TI-83 calculator are shown in Figure 21. (Page 77)

The Rule of Four Any function may be represented in these four ways: verbally, symbolically, numerically, and graphically. (Page 79)

Exploration

An automobile near Chambersburg, Pennsylvania, is equipped with a GPS receiver. It receives a signal from a satellite located above the Pacific Ocean midway between Los Angeles, California, and Honolulu, Hawaii. The center of the earth is at the origin of a coordinate system with distances measured in miles. The coordinates of the automobile are $x_1 = 661$, $y_1 = {}^-3033$, and $z_1 = 2522$. The coordinates of the satellite are $x_2 = {}^-9654$, $y_2 = {}^-8692$, and $z_2 = 7500$.

a. Find the differences in the x-, y-, and z-coordinates:

$$x_2 - x_1 = ?$$
$$y_2 - y_1 = ?$$
$$z_2 - z_1 = ?$$

b. Use the three-dimensional distance formula

$$\text{distance} = \sqrt{(x_2 - x_1)^2 + (y_2 - y_1)^2 + (z_2 - z_1)^2}$$

to find the distance from the automobile to the satellite.

c. Given the fact that the satellite is 11,000 miles directly above the surface of the earth, is your answer to part (b) reasonable? Explain.

CHAPTER 2 ▪ REVIEW EXERCISES

Section 2.1 Grouping and the Order of Operations

1. Use the associative property of addition to regroup with parentheses and find the sum. (Do not use a calculator.)
   a. $6 + (124 + 58)$ **b.** $(189 + 43) + 17$

2. Does the associative property hold for subtraction? Give an example to support your answer.

3. Use the associative property of multiplication to regroup with parentheses and find the product. (Do not use a calculator.)
   a. $(7 * 8) * 5$ **b.** $\frac{1}{3} * (3 * 467)$

4. Does the associative property hold for division? Give an example to support your answer.

5. Use the distributive property to expand.
   a. $3 * (40 + 7)$ **b.** $4 * (90 - 2)$
   c. $6 * (8 + 10)$ **d.** $2 * (x + y)$
   e. $9 * (a - b)$ **f.** $8 * (x - y)$

6. Use the distributive property to factor.
   a. $(4 * 52) + (4 * 8)$ **b.** $(3 * 9) + (3 * 81)$
   c. $(5 * x) + (5 * y)$ **d.** $(7 * a) - (7 * b)$

7. Apply the order of operations to evaluate each expression.
   a. $8 + 4 \div 4$ **b.** $3 + 5^2 - (7 + 2)$
   c. $\frac{\sqrt{5 + 20} - 7}{2}$

8. Write the keystrokes necessary to correctly evaluate the given expression on your calculator:
$$\frac{5 + 11}{6 - 8}$$

9. Fill in the blanks.
   a. $4 + ? = 0$ **b.** $\frac{23}{?}$ is undefined
   c. $? * 17 = 17$

10. Name the special property of 1 or $^-1$ that makes each equation true.
    a. $(x + y) = 1 * (x + y)$
    b. $x - (y + z) = x + {}^-1 * (y + z)$

11. Demonstrate, with numbers, each of the four special properties of 0.

12. Demonstrate, with numbers, each of the four special properties of 1.

13. Demonstrate, with numbers, each of the three special properties of $^-1$.

Section 2.2 Expressions and Formulas

14. Evaluate each formula with the given substitution.
    a. $C = 2 * \pi * r$ for $r = 2$ inches. You may use $\pi \approx 3.14$.
    b. $r = \frac{d}{t}$ for $d = 3$ feet, $t = 6$ seconds.
    c. $A = \pi * r^2$ for $r = 4$ feet.
    d. run $= x_2 - x_1$ for $x_2 = 5$, $x_1 = {}^-1$
    e. distance $= \sqrt{(x_2 - x_1)^2 + (y_2 - y_1)^2}$ for $x_2 = {}^-6$, $x_1 = 0$, $y_2 = 5$, $y_1 = {}^-3$

15. Determine if each pair of expressions is equivalent by substituting the values $x = 4, 3, {}^-2$.
    a. $5 * x - 2$ and $6 * x - (x + 2)$
    b. $\sqrt{x^2 + 2 * x + 1}$ and $x + 1$
    c. $(x - 1) * (x + 1)$ and $x^2 - 1$

16. One formula for the area of a trapezoid is $A = \frac{1}{2} * (b_1 + b_2) * h$; another formula is $A = \frac{1}{2} * b_1 * h + \frac{1}{2} * b_2 * h$. Use the distributive property to show that the two expressions are equivalent.

17. Simplify each expression by combining like terms.
    a. $6y + 9y$ **b.** $4x - x$
    c. $a^2 - 3a + 2a^2 - 9a$

18. Simplify each expression by combining like terms.
    a. $\frac{3}{a} + \frac{8}{a}$ **b.** $\frac{5}{a} - \frac{2}{3} + \frac{7}{a} + \frac{1}{9}$
    c. $\frac{2}{y} + \frac{x}{y}$ **d.** $x - \frac{1}{x^2} + x^2 + x^{-2}$

19. Rewrite each verbal expression as an algebraic expression. Let x represent the unknown number.
    a. A number increased by 5
    b. 4 more than a number
    c. 4 less than a number
    d. The difference between a number and 2
    e. Twice a number

f. One-third of a number

g. The product of 7 and a number

h. The quotient of a number and 6

i. A number divided by 3

j. 4 more than 3 times a number

k. 4 less than 3 times a number

20. A rectangle's length is 3 yards more than 4 times its width.

    a. Let x represent the width of the rectangle, in yards. Find an expression for the perimeter of the rectangle.

    b. Find the value of this expression when $x = 15$ yards.

21. Use the Pythagorean theorem to find the hypotenuse of a right triangle whose base is 6 cm and height is 17 cm.

Section 2.3 The Coordinate Plane

22. On the coordinate plane, locate the following points and identify the quadrant or axis where each lies.

    a. $(^-2, 3)$ b. $(0, 5)$ c. $(1, 4)$

    d. $(^-1, ^-2)$ e. $(2, ^-4)$

23. Explain why the x-coordinates of all the ordered pairs on a vertical line are the same. *Hint:* Draw a vertical line and label several ordered pairs.

24. Draw a horizontal line through the y-axis at $(0, 3)$; what can you say about the y-coordinates of each ordered pair on that line?

25. Compute the run and rise between the given ordered pairs.

    a. $(1, ^-2)$ and $(^-3, 4)$ b. $(2, 6)$ and $(^-2, ^-3)$

26. Start at the point $(^-1, 0)$. If you move a run of 5 and a rise of $^-2$, at what point will you end?

27. Apply a run of $^-2$ and a rise of 1 to find the ending location if you start at $(3, ^-4)$.

28. Use the shortcut ZOOM 4 ZDecimal to find the value of the WINDOW variables Xmin = ?, Xmax = ?, Xscl = ?, Ymin = ?, Ymax = ?, and Yscl = ?

29. Describe what the WINDOW settings Xmin = $^-10$, Xmax = 10, Ymin = $^-10$, and Ymax = 10 will do to the window of your GRAPH screen.

30. Find the distance between the points $(2, 0)$ and $(^-1, ^-4)$.

31. Given the two ordered pairs $(2, ^-1)$ and $(^-6, 7)$:

    a. Write the keystrokes necessary to enter your distance calculation on your calculator.

    b. Approximate the distance shown on your calculator.

Section 2.4 Representing Functions

For Exercises 32–36, use the following situation: The No-mystery Airline Company charges $100 plus .25 per mile of travel.

32. How much will it cost to travel 800 miles on Nomystery Airline?

33. Let x represent the number of miles of travel and let y represent the cost (in dollars) of the travel.

    a. Write a formula that shows how y depends upon x.

    b. What is the independent variable?

    c. What is the dependent variable?

34. By hand, create a table of values with inputs of $x = 0$, 100, 200, 300, and 400 miles.

35. By hand, create a graph that includes the values from Exercise 34.

36. Consider representing the same function on your calculator.

    a. How is the formula from Exercise 33(a) entered into your Y = menu?

    b. Choose table settings in 2ND TBLSET so that the table shown in 2ND TABLE includes your table of values from Exercise 34.

    c. Choose a friendly window for viewing a graph that includes the table of values from Exercise 34.

CHAPTER 2 ▪ TEST

1. Use the associative property of addition or multiplication to regroup with parentheses and find the sum. (Do not use a calculator.)

    a. $^-8 + (^-2 + 51)$ b. $(9 * 5) * 6$

    c. $(9 + ^-73) + 73$

2. Use the distributive property to either expand or factor the following expressions.

    a. $5 * (3 - 8)$ b. $(6 * a) + (6 * b)$

    c. $7 * (a + b)$ d. $(2 * x) - (2 * y)$

3. Apply the order of operations to evaluate each of the expressions.

   a. $\sqrt{16-7}+3$ **b.** $(12-9\div3)^2$

   c. $(^-2)^4 - \sqrt{4}*6$

4. Use the special properties of 0, 1, or $^-1$ to fill in the blanks.

   a. $?+{}^-7={}^-7$ **b.** $?*6=0$

   c. $5*?=1$ **d.** $6*?={}^-6$

5. Evaluate each formula with the given substitution.

   a. $y=5*x+6$ for $x=3$

   b. $A=\frac{1}{2}*b*h$ for $b=4$ cm, $h=10$ cm

6. Determine if the expressions $x+4*x$ and $x*(1+4)$ are equivalent by substituting the values $x=5,\ 2,\ {}^-3$.

7. One formula for the amount of money in an account is $A=P*(1+r*t)$. Use the distributive property to find an equivalent formula.

8. Simplify each expression by combining like terms.

   a. $11x-5x$ **b.** $\frac{1}{2}+\frac{4}{x}-\frac{3}{8}-\frac{1}{x}$

   c. $^-6a+3+7a-8$ **d.** $\frac{3}{a}+\frac{8}{a}$

9. Soccer fields are rectangular in shape. The length of the field is 135 feet more than the width of the field.

   a. Let w represent the width of the field, in feet. Find an expression for the perimeter of the field.

   b. Find the perimeter of the soccer field if the width is 225 feet.

10. Suppose a cornerback has scored a touchdown by returning an interception from the corner of his goal line to the goal line at the opposite corner of the field. Use the dimensions in the figure in the next column to find the distance he ran.

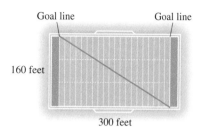

11. On the coordinate plane, locate the following points and identify their quadrants or axes.

    a. $(^-4,1)$ **b.** $(2,0)$

    c. $(1,{}^-3)$

12. Compute the run and rise between the given ordered pairs.

    a. $(0,3)$ and $(^-1,5)$ **b.** $(^-3,4)$ and $(1,5)$

13. What is the distance between the ordered pairs $(^-1,{}^-5)$ and $(5,3)$?

For Exercises 14–16, use the following situation: A phone company provides long-distance service for \$4.95 per month plus \$.07 per minute for each long distance call.

14. Write a formula for the monthly cost of long-distance service in terms of the number of minutes of calls. *Note:* Be sure to assign the variables you use.

15. On your calculator, create a table of values that includes inputs of $x=0,\ 20,\ 40,\ 60,$ and 80 minutes.

16. On your calculator, create a graph that includes the table of values from Exercise 15.

3

Linear Equations

3.1 ■ Solving Simple Equations

3.2 ■ Simplifying Expressions to Solve Equations

3.3 ■ The Problem-Solving Process

3.4 ■ Arithmetic Sequences (Optional)

A Matter of Balance

Photosynthesis is the process by which plants harness the sun's energy to produce sugar from water and carbon dioxide. It is one of the most important biological phenomena, for without photosynthesis, life as we know it would not exist. This process may be described as a chemical equation in words: water + carbon dioxide = oxygen + glucose.

Scientists prefer to write this equation using chemical formulas indicating the elements comprising each of these substances. Water is H_2O, because one molecule of water contains 2 hydrogen atoms and 1 oxygen atom. Carbon dioxide is CO_2, because its molecule contains 1 carbon atom and 2 oxygen atoms. Oxygen molecules each contain 2 atoms of the element oxygen, so oxygen is written O_2. Glucose, the most simple of sugars, has the most complex formula: $C_6H_{12}O_6$. The equation for photosynthesis may then be written $H_2O + CO_2 = O_2 + C_6H_{12}O_6$.

There is something wrong with this equation, however. There are only 2 hydrogen atoms on the left side but 12 hydrogen atoms on the right side. Chemical equations must be balanced, just as we maintain the balance of an algebraic equation when we perform the same operation on both sides. In this chapter you will learn more about how the principle of balance is used to solve algebraic equations. (See Exploration on p. 118.)

3.1 Solving Simple Equations

AFTER STUDYING THIS SECTION YOU WILL BE ABLE TO

- Solve simple linear equations with a variable on one side of the equation.
- Solve simple linear equations with a variable on both sides of the equation.
- Solve word problems leading to simple linear equations.

In Chapter 2 you learned to use variables to form algebraic expressions. In this chapter you learn how to solve equations. Recall from Section 2.2 that an *equation* is a statement that two *expressions* are equal. Solving an equation involves finding what value or values of the variables make that statement true. Example 1 shows a problem situation that leads to an equation.

EXAMPLE 1 John's mechanic is replacing the timing chain on his car. The part costs $95 and she charges $60 per hour for labor. If the total cost for the repair was $200, how long did the mechanic work? Write an equation to solve the problem.

Solution In order to write an equation, we need an expression for the cost of repairs. To write an expression we must answer the question, "What should the variable be?" Look at what the problem is asking: "How long did the mechanic work?" This suggests a variable will be needed for time. We let t represent the number of hours she worked.

Recall from Section 2.4 that **total cost = variable cost + fixed cost**. The total cost is known to be **$200**. The variable cost is the hourly rate times the number of hours she works, or **60t**. The fixed cost is the cost of the part, **$95**. Putting all this together gives an equation:

$$\$200 = \$60 \text{ per hour} * t + \$95$$

or, more simply,

$$200 = 60t + 95.$$

Once we have an equation, the next step is to solve it. We need to use the following fact.

Basic Principle of Equation Solving

If we are given an equation, we can add the same term on both sides or multiply by the same number on both sides and still have a valid equation.

This principle works because if two things are equal, we think of them as *the same*, and if we do the same thing to things that start the same, they will end up the same. The only exception is division by zero, which is never allowed.

EXAMPLE 2 ■ Solve the equation in Example 1.

Solution ┃ Start with the equation

$$200 = 60t + 95$$

Our goal is to get a valid equation with t all by itself on one side. Think about the order of operations. The expression on the right side says "take t, multiply it by 60 and then add 95." To find t, reverse the steps, first eliminating 95 and then eliminating 60 from the right side of the equation.

To eliminate 95 from the right side of the equation, use the **basic principle of equation solving** and *add* $^-95$ on both sides:

$$200 + {}^-95 = 60t + 95 + {}^-95$$

Combining constant terms on each side gives

$$105 = 60t$$

To eliminate 60 from the right side of the equation, we again use the basic principle of equation solving and *multiply* on both sides by the reciprocal of 60, that is, $\frac{1}{60}$:

$$\tfrac{1}{60} * 105 = \tfrac{1}{60} * 60t$$

and because

$$\tfrac{1}{60} * 60t = \tfrac{60}{60}t = t$$

we get $t = \frac{105}{60} = 1.75$ hours. The answer is in hours, because that is how we measured time.

Note: We could have described the first step as *subtracting* 95 on both sides as well as adding $^-95$. Likewise we could have described the second step as *dividing* by 60 as well as multiplying by $\frac{1}{60}$. You may think of subtraction as adding an opposite and division as multiplying by a reciprocal.

■ ■ ■

EXAMPLE 3 ┃ Suppose we place equilateral triangles that are 2 feet on each side together, as in Figure 1, to make quadrilaterals. How many triangles will it take to get a quadrilateral with a perimeter of 54 feet?

Solution ┃ Notice that only two sides from each new triangle are added to the perimeter, and one side of a previous triangle is lost, so we add 2 to the perimeter for each new

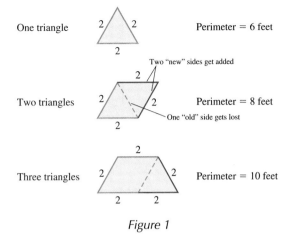

Figure 1

triangle. We are asked to solve for the number of triangles, so we should give that a variable name. Let N represent the number of triangles. Because we add 2 to the perimeter for each new triangle and the first perimeter is 6 feet, we can check the formula

$$\text{perimeter} = 4 + 2 * N$$

against the values in Figure 1 and see if it works.

We want to know how many triangles will give a **perimeter** of **54** feet. Substituting 54 for perimeter gives us the equation

$$54 = 4 + 2 * N$$

We can solve the same way we solved the equation in Example 2, by getting a constant term on one side and the variable on the other.

$54 = 4 + 2N$	
$+\ ^-4 = +\ ^-4$	*Adding $^-4$ on both sides*
$50 = 2N$	*Combining constant terms*
$\frac{1}{2} * 50 = \frac{1}{2} * 2N$	*Multiplying by $\frac{1}{2}$ on both sides*
$25 = N$	$\frac{1}{2} * 50 = 25$ *and* $\frac{1}{2} * 2 = 1$

We can check our work using a calculator. We enter the left and right sides of the equation separately in the $\boxed{\text{Y}=}$ screen (Figure 2), where X stands in for N. Because we suspect that $N = 25$ and because Y1 $= 54$, we need to find a friendly window from Figure 21 on page 77 that will work; it looks as if Xmin $= 0$, Xmax $= 47$ will work, and we can let Ymin $= 0$ and Ymax $= 100$. Figure 3 shows the resulting graph.

Press the $\boxed{\text{TRACE}}$ key and move the cursor to where the two lines intersect. When you reach that point you will see X $= 25$ and Y $= 54$ displayed at the

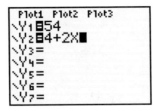

Figure 2

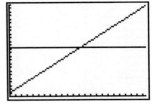

Figure 3

bottom of the screen. This shows that the point (25, 54) lies on both lines and that X = 25 is a solution to the equation 54 = 4 + 2X. See Figure 4.

It looks as if it will take 25 triangles to build a quadrilateral with a perimeter of 54 feet. We can check by substituting 25 into our formula for perimeter:

$$\text{perimeter} = 4 + 2 * N = 4 + 2 * 25$$

$$= 4 + 50$$

$$= 54$$

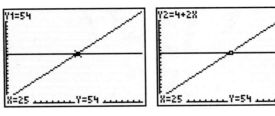

Figure 4

In Examples 1–3 our procedure was first to add (or subtract) the same number on both sides and then to multiply (or divide) the same number on both sides. When the variable appears on both sides of an equation, however, we have an additional first step, as Example 4 shows.

EXAMPLE 4 Recall Jamie's health club from Examples 1 and 2 of Section 2.4. An expression for the amount (in dollars) she will have to pay for one month is $3x + 20$, where x is the number of times she visits the club. There is another health club she is considering where she would pay a monthly fee of $2 and a charge of $6 for each visit. The cost of belonging to that club is $6x + 2$. Knowing how many times per month she would use a health club, Jamie figures that the cost of the two clubs will be the same. How many times per month does Jamie plan on using a health club?

Solution In effect, we need to find a value of x that makes the two expressions $3x + 20$ and $6x + 2$ equal each other. Thus, we have the equation

$$3x + 20 = 6x + 2$$

To solve this equation, we first add an x-term to both sides to eliminate $3x$. The x-term we add is ^-3x, that is, the opposite of $3x$.

$$3x + 20 = 6x + 2 \qquad \textit{Original equation}$$

$$\underline{+\,{}^-3x \qquad +\,{}^-3x} \qquad \textit{Adding } {}^-3x \textit{ on both sides}$$

$$20 = 3x + 2 \qquad \textit{Combining like terms}$$

$$\underline{+\,{}^-2 \qquad +\,{}^-2} \qquad \textit{Adding } {}^-2 \textit{ on both sides}$$

$$18 = 3x \qquad \textit{Combining constant terms}$$

$$\tfrac{1}{3} * 18 = \tfrac{1}{3} * 3x \qquad \textit{Multiplying by } \tfrac{1}{3} \textit{ on both sides}$$

$$6 = x \qquad \tfrac{1}{3} * 18 = 6, \textit{ and } \tfrac{1}{3} * 3 = 1$$

Jamie plans to visit a health club about 6 times a month.

We can check our work by substituting $x = 6$ into both sides of the equation. When checking an equation, we write a question mark (?) above the equal sign until we reach a statement where the left and right sides are equal.

$$3x + 20 = 6x + 2 \qquad \textit{Original equation}$$

$$3 * 6 + 20 \stackrel{?}{=} 6 * 6 + 2 \qquad \textit{Substituting 6 for } x$$

$$18 + 20 \stackrel{?}{=} 36 + 2$$

$$38 = 38 \qquad \textit{OK!}$$

We can also check our answer using a calculator, as in Example 3, by entering $Y1 = 3X + 20$ and $Y2 = 6X + 2$ and using $\boxed{\text{TRACE}}$ to find the point of intersection.

■ ■ ■

Some equations involve fractions. The next example shows how these may be solved.

EXAMPLE 5 Solve the equation

$$\frac{2}{3}x + \frac{1}{2} = \frac{11}{2}$$

Solution Don't let the fractions scare you! Think of this as an equation similar to Example 3, $54 = 4 + 2N$. The first step is to add (or subtract) the same number on both sides. In this case the logical choice is to eliminate $\frac{1}{2}$ from the left side.

$$\frac{2}{3}x + \frac{1}{2} = \frac{11}{2} \qquad \textit{Original equation}$$

$$\underline{+\,{}^-\frac{1}{2} \qquad +\,{}^-\frac{1}{2}} \qquad \textit{Adding } {}^-\frac{1}{2} \textit{ on both sides}$$

$$\frac{2}{3}x = \frac{10}{2} \qquad \textit{Combining constants}$$

To get x alone, we can multiply on both sides by the reciprocal of $\frac{2}{3}$, that is, $\frac{3}{2}$.

$$\frac{3}{2} * \frac{2}{3}x = \frac{3}{2} * \frac{10}{2}$$ *Multiplying by $\frac{3}{2}$ on both sides*

$$\frac{6}{6}x = \frac{30}{4}$$ *Multiplying numerator times numerator and denominator times denominator*

$$x = \frac{15}{2} = 7\frac{1}{2} = 7.5$$

The solution to this equation may be checked by substituting $\frac{15}{2}$ for x in the original equation:

$$\frac{2}{3}x + \frac{1}{2} = \frac{11}{2}$$ *Original equation*

$$\frac{2}{3} * \frac{15}{2} + \frac{1}{2} \overset{?}{=} \frac{11}{2}$$ *Substituting $\frac{15}{2}$ for x*

$$5 + \frac{1}{2} \overset{?}{=} \frac{11}{2}$$

$$5\frac{1}{2} = 5\frac{1}{2}$$ *OK!*

Exercises 3.1

1. In Example 2 we solved for t in the equation $200 = 60t + 95$. If the total cost of the repair is \$245, we get a slightly different equation. Solve for t in the equation $245 = 60t + 95$ to find the time the mechanic worked with the new total cost.

2. In Example 3 we solved for N and checked our answer to the equation $54 = 4 + 2N$. Solve for N and check your answer to the equation $108 = 4 + 2N$.

3. Solve $8 = 2x - 6$ for x.

4. Solve $\frac{1}{2}z - 5 = 6$ for z.

5. Solve $1.8b - 3.4 = {}^-10.2$ for b. Write your repeating decimal as a fraction by using the fraction feature on your calculator. (See Exercise 14 of Section 1.2).

6. A camper has collected 25 logs for an overnight fire. Suppose he burns 4 logs every hour. A formula for L, the number of logs remaining after t hours, is $L = 25 - 4t$.

a. Enter the equation $Y1 = 25 - 4X$ in your calculator's ⎡Y=⎤ menu. Note that Y takes the place of L and X takes the place of t.

b. Use the window settings Xmin $= 0$, Xmax $= 9.4$, Xscl $= 1$, Ymin $= 0$, Ymax $= 30$, and Yscl $= 5$. Press ⎡GRAPH⎤ and observe that the graph is a line.

c. Press ⎡TRACE⎤ and move the cursor to estimate for what value of X (time) the number of logs (Y) is zero.

d. Solve the equation $0 = 25 - 4t$ to find exactly how much time it takes for the logs to run out.

e. The camper begins his fire at 11:00 P.M. At what time of day does he run out of wood?

7. Solve $11x = 20x - 18$ for x.

8. A carpenter and his helper decide to have a nail hammering contest. The carpenter is so confident that he can beat his helper that he lets him count the 30 nails he hammered in practice. They set a timer and both begin hammering nails. The carpenter hammers nails at

the rate of 50 per minute, whereas the helper hammers only 40 nails per minute.

a. Complete the table of values.

Time (minutes)	Nails Hammered by Carpenter	Nails Hammered by Helper
0	0	30
1	50	70
2	100	110
3		
4		
5		

b. Let t represent the number of minutes that have passed since they start the timer. Write an expression for the number of nails hammered by each person in terms of t.

c. Set the expressions in (b) equal to each other and solve to find the time it will take the carpenter to equal the helper's nail hammering.

d. If you were the helper, how long would you want the contest to last to guarantee your victory?

9. In Example 4, we solved the equation $3x + 20 = 6x + 2$. The basic principle of equation solving (p. 89) says that as long as we add the same amount on both sides of an equation or multiply by the same amount on both sides we still have a valid equation. Therefore, we can arrive at the same solution by performing the steps in a different order. Describe what was done next to each step in solving this equation.

$3x + 20 = 6x + 2$	*Original equation*
$3x + 20 + {}^-20 = 6x + 2 + {}^-20$	*?*
$3x = 6x + {}^-18$	*Combining like terms*

$3x + {}^-6x = 6x + {}^-18 + {}^-6x$	*?*
${}^-3x = {}^-18$	*Combining like terms*
$\dfrac{{}^-3x}{{}^-3} = \dfrac{{}^-18}{{}^-3}$	*?*
$x = 6$	*Solution*

What does the solution $x = 6$ stand for in this real-life problem?

10. Solve ${}^-7x + 3 = 4x - 5$ for x.

11. Solve $\frac{1}{3}x - 7 = 9 + x$ for x.

12. Show that $x = 3$ checks as the solution to the equation $60 + 5x = 20x + 15$.

13. Solve $\frac{1}{3}x - \frac{2}{3} = x - \frac{1}{2}$ for x.

14. An employee is offered a choice between two vacation plans. The number of days off is given by the expressions $.5m + 1$ for plan A and $.4m + 3$ for plan B, where m is the number of months employed.

a. Write an equation by setting the two expressions equal to each other.

b. Solve the equation in order to find the number of months the employee needs to work before the plans give the same number of days off.

c. Which plan would you prefer if you worked less than 12 months at the company? Explain.

15. The monthly charges for an Internet provider are $12 plus $2 for each hour of use. Another provider charges $15 plus $1.50 for each hour of use.

a. Write an expression for each provider's charges.

b. Write an equation by setting the two expressions equal to each other.

c. Solve the equation.

d. Interpret the solution in the context of the problem.

Skills and Review 3.1

16. Make a table of values and graph the function $y = 2x + 1$. Do not use a calculator.

17. The amount a person spends at the movies is $7 for a ticket plus $5 for each pound of candy. Let sweets represent the number of pounds of candy and cost represent the amount spent for a ticket and candy. A formula for the cost in terms of sweets is $cost = 7 + 5 * sweets$.

a. How is this function entered into the $\boxed{Y=}$ menu?

b. Use the Table feature on your calculator to determine the cost when sweets $= \frac{1}{4}, \frac{1}{2}, \frac{3}{4}, 1$, and 2 pounds. Organize your results in a table.

c. Use the table values from part (b) to draw a graph by hand.

18. Data from the previous movie problem are: (.25, 8.25), (.5, 9.5), (.75, 10.75), (1, 12), and (2, 17).

    a. In what quadrants do these points appear?

    b. Choose a friendly window that includes these points.

19. Find the run and rise when you start at $(2, {}^{-}5)$ and end at $({}^{-}1, 3)$.

20. Find the distance between the points $(0, 4)$ and $(3, 9)$.

21. Evaluate the expression $3x - 4y$ when $x = \frac{-1}{3}$ and $y = 2$.

22. Evaluate without using a calculator:

$$\frac{12 + 4}{7 - {}^{-}5}$$

23. Evaluate $3 + 8 \div 2 * \frac{1}{4} - 2^3$ without a calculator.

24. Evaluate $5 + 3 * \sqrt{36}$ without a calculator.

25. Which expression is not equal to 5^{-2}?

    a. $\frac{1}{25}$ **b.** $^{-}25$

    c. .04   **d.** $\frac{1}{5^2}$

3.2 Simplifying Expressions to Solve Equations

AFTER STUDYING THIS SECTION YOU WILL BE ABLE TO

- Simplify expressions by removing parentheses and combining like terms.
- Solve equations that require the expression on one or both sides to be simplified.

In the previous section you learned to use the basic principle of equation solving to solve equations. In this section you solve more complex equations. These require that the expressions on one or both sides of the equation be simplified before adding the same number or multiplying by the same number on both sides of the equation. Example 1 illustrates this situation.

EXAMPLE 1 A train heading east passes a train heading west on a parallel track, and both engineers start blowing their whistles to say hello. The eastbound train is going 75 miles/hour and the westbound train is going 60 miles/hour. If the sound of the whistles carries for 20 miles, how long will it be before the engineers cannot hear each other's whistles?

Solution Because the whistles can be heard for 20 miles, the question is really asking how long until the trains are 20 miles apart. If we draw a picture (Figure 5), we can

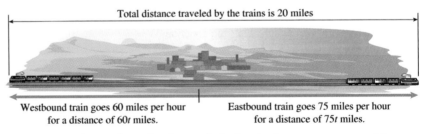

Total distance traveled by the trains is 20 miles

Westbound train goes 60 miles per hour for a distance of 60*t* miles.

Eastbound train goes 75 miles per hour for a distance of 75*t* miles.

Figure 5 The eastbound train travels farther in the same amount of time.

see that this will happen when the *sum* of the distances traveled by the two trains is 20 miles. The unknown is the time until the distance equals 20 miles, so we should give that a variable name, say, t.

We know distance $=$ **rate** $*$ **time**, so in t hours the eastbound train travels **75t** miles and the westbound train travels **60t** miles. We want the sum of these distances to equal 20 miles, which gives the equation

$$20 = 75t + 60t$$

The expression on the right side must be simplified. We combine the t terms and get

$$20 = 135t$$

Then we divide both sides by 135 and get

$$t = \frac{20}{135} = \frac{4}{27} \approx .15$$

So it will be about .15 hours, or 9 minutes, until the trains are 20 miles apart and the engineers cannot hear each other's whistles.

■ ■ ■

In Example 1 we simplified the expression on the right side by combining like terms. In Example 2 we need to use the distributive property to remove parentheses on one side of the equation.

EXAMPLE 2 One cellular phone plan charges a flat fee of $10 per month plus 5 cents per minute, and another adds 100 minutes to the number of minutes you use and then charges 7 cents per minute. For how many minutes of use will the cost of the two plans be equal?

Solution The formula for the cost of the first plan is

$$10 + .05t$$

where t is the number of minutes used. The cost of the second plan is

$$.07(t + 100)$$

To find out for how many minutes of use the cost will be the same, we equate the two costs:

$$10 + .05t = .07(t + 100)$$

To solve this equation, we need to simplify the expression on the right side.

$10 + .05t = .07(t + 100)$ *Original equation*

$10 + .05t = .07t + 7$ *Simplifying the right side by removing parentheses*

$$+^-.05t \qquad +^-.05t$$ *Adding* $^-.05t$ *on both sides*

$$10 = .02t + 7$$ *Combining t terms*

$$+^-7 \qquad +^-7$$ *Adding* $^-7$ *on both sides*

$$3 = .02t$$ *Combining constant terms*

$$\frac{3}{.02} = \frac{.02t}{.02}$$ *Multiplying on both sides by* $\frac{1}{.02}$ *(or dividing by .02)*

$$150 = t$$ $3 \div .02 = 150$ *and* $.02 \div .02 = 1$

If the phone is used for 150 minutes, the cost of the two plans is the same.

■ ■

In both Examples 1 and 2 we found it necessary to simplify an expression on one side of the equation before applying the basic principle of equation solving. In Example 1, we simplified the expression $75t + 60t$ by combining like terms. We replaced $75t + 60t$ with the *equivalent expression* $135t$. In Example 2, we simplified the expression $.07(t + 100)$ by applying the distributive property to remove parentheses. We replaced $.07(t + 100)$ with the equivalent expression $.07t + 7$.

Example 3 shows an expression that needs several steps to simplify.

EXAMPLE 3 ■ Is there a shorter way to write the expression $7(2x + 3) - 2x + 4 - 4x$?

Solution First, use the distributive property to remove the parentheses around $2x + 3$. Then simplify.

$$7(2x + 3) - 2x + 4 - 4x$$

$$= 14x + 21 - 2x + 4 - 4x$$ *Using the distributive property*

$$= 14x - 2x - 4x + 21 + 4$$ *Grouping like terms using the commutative property*

$$= 8x + 25$$ $14x - 2x - 4x = 8x$ *and* $21 + 4 = 25$

■ ■

In Example 3, nothing more can be combined in the expression $8x + 25$. We say that $8x + 25$ is in **simplified form**. In manipulating an expression to put it in simplified form, the special properties of 1 and $^-1$ are useful, as Example 4 shows.

EXAMPLE 4 ■ Simplify the expression $3(x + 2) - (x - 1) + 5$.

Solution First, use the distributive property to eliminate any parentheses involved with a multiplication. Remember that subtracting an expression in parentheses is really like multiplying each term by $^-1$.

$$3(x + 2) - (x - 1) + 5$$

$$= 3x + 6 + {}^-x + 1 + 5 \qquad \textit{Using the distributive property}$$

$$= 3x - x + 6 + 1 + 5 \qquad \textit{Using the commutative property to collect like terms}$$

$$= 2x + 6 + 1 + 5 \qquad \textit{Combining the variable terms}$$

$$= 2x + 12 \qquad \textit{Combining the constant terms}$$

The expression $2x + 12$ is in simplified form because $2x$ and 12 cannot be combined.

We may want to write fewer steps.

$$3(x + 2) - (x - 1) + 5 = 3x + 6 + {}^-x + 1 + 5$$
$$= 2x + 12$$

If we do so, we still need to be conscious of the steps left out.

Our solution states that the expressions $3(x + 2) - (x - 1) + 5$ and $2x + 12$ are equivalent. This means that they have the same value no matter what values are substituted for X. You may demonstrate this with the TABLE feature of the calculator.

In the $\boxed{\text{Y=}}$ menu, enter the expressions as Y1 and Y2:

$$Y1 = 3(X + 2) - (X - 1) + 5$$
$$Y2 = 2X + 12$$

Then press $\boxed{\text{2ND}}$ TBLSET and let TblStart $= 0$ and ΔTbl $= 1$. Independent and dependent variables should both be set at AUTO. Finally press $\boxed{\text{2ND}}$ TABLE and notice that for all the values of X displayed, the expressions are equal (Figure 6).

■ ■ ■

X	Y1	Y2
0	12	12
1	14	14
2	16	16
3	18	18
4	20	20
5	22	22
6	24	24

Figure 6

We may now summarize what we have learned in the previous examples as a procedure for simplifying expressions.

Procedure for Simplifying an Expression

Step 1   Use the special properties of 1 and $^-1$ if necessary.

Step 2   Remove all parentheses using the distributive property.

Step 3   Group like terms using the commutative property.

Step 4   Combine like terms.

Now that we know how to simplify an expression, we may apply this skill in solving a more complex linear equation. Example 5 requires that both sides be simplified.

EXAMPLE 5 ■ Solve for x in this equation: $2(9 + x) = 4(2x + 1) - (7 - x)$.

Solution

$2(9 + x) = 4(2x + 1) - (7 - x)$	*Original equation*
$18 + 2x = 4(2x + 1) - (7 - x)$	*Simplifying the left side using the distributive property*
$18 + 2x = 4(2x + 1) + {}^-1(7 + {}^-1x)$	*Simplifying the right side using the special properties of ${}^-1$*
$18 + 2x = 8x + 4 - 7 + x$	*Simplifying the right side by removing parentheses using the distributive property*
$18 + 2x = 8x + x + 4 - 7$	*Simplifying the right side by grouping like terms*
$18 + 2x = 9x - 3$	*Simplifying the right side by combining like terms*
$\underline{+{}^-2x \quad\quad +{}^-2x}$	*Adding ${}^-2x$ on both sides*
$18 = 7x - 3$	
$\underline{+3 \quad\quad +3}$	*Adding 3 on both sides*
$21 = 7x$	
$\dfrac{1}{7} * 21 = \dfrac{1}{7} * 7x$	*Multiplying on both sides by $\frac{1}{7}$*
$3 = x$	

This may seem like a lot of steps to solve one equation. With practice, we may leave out some steps when we write our solution, but we must still be aware of each step and the justification for each. We can help ourselves do this with the following abbreviations:

LS Simplifying the expression on the left side of the equation.

RS Simplifying the expression on the right side of the equation.

 A Adding the same quantity on both sides (or subtracting, because adding a negative is the same as subtracting).

 M Multiplying both sides by the same quantity (or dividing, because multiplying by a reciprocal is the same as dividing).

Here is a streamlined version of the preceding solution using these abbreviations.

$$2(9 + x) = 4(2x + 1) - (7 - x)$$
$$18 + 2x = 8x + 4 - 7 + x \qquad \text{LS, RS}$$
$$18 + 2x = 9x - 3 \qquad\qquad \text{RS}$$

$$\underline{-2x} \quad \underline{-2x}$$
$$18 = 7x - 3 \qquad\qquad A$$
$$\underline{+3} \quad \underline{+3}$$
$$21 = 7x \qquad\qquad A$$
$$\frac{21}{7} = \frac{7x}{7} \qquad\qquad M$$
$$3 = x \qquad\qquad LS, RS$$

You should check that $x = 3$ is indeed a solution by substituting 3 for x in the original equation.

■ ■ ■

We summarize the steps needed to solve linear equations with the following procedure.

Procedure for Solving Linear Equations

Step 1   If necessary, simplify the expression on the left side.

Step 2   If necessary, simplify the expression on the right side.

Step 3   If necessary, add the same terms on both sides until you have a variable term on one side and a constant term on the other side.

Step 4   If necessary, multiply both sides by the reciprocal of the coefficient of the variable in order to get the variable alone.

Let's apply this procedure to a word problem that requires simplification on both sides of an equation.

EXAMPLE 6   A rectangle and an equilateral triangle have the same perimeter. The length of the rectangle is three times the width. Each side of the triangle is 10 feet more than the width of the rectangle. Find the dimensions of both figures.

Solution   Let w represent the width of the rectangle (in feet). Then $3w$ is an expression for the length. The perimeter of the rectangle is $w + 3w + w + 3w$. Each side of the triangle is $w + 10$ feet. Because the three sides are equal, the perimeter of the triangle is $3(w + 10)$. See Figure 7.

Because the two perimeters are equal, we have the equation $w + 3w + w + 3w = 3(w + 10)$. To solve this equation, we need to simplify the expressions on both sides of the equation.

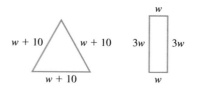

Figure 7

$$w + 3w + w + 3w = 3(w + 10)$$
$$8w = 3(w + 10) \qquad LS$$
$$8w = 3w + 30 \qquad RS$$
$$\underline{-3w \qquad -3w}$$
$$5w = 30 \qquad A$$
$$\frac{5w}{5} = \frac{30}{5} \qquad M$$
$$w = 6 \qquad LS, RS$$

The width of the rectangle is 6 feet. The length of the rectangle is $3w$, or 18 feet. Therefore, the perimeter of the rectangle is $6 + 18 + 6 + 18 = 48$ feet. Each side of the triangle is $w + 10 = 16$ feet. So, the triangle's perimeter is $3 * 16 = 48$ feet. Our solution to the equation checks with the conditions given in the problem.

Exercises 3.2

1. What property is shown in this figure?

2. Consider the four rectangles in this figure.

   a. Write an expression for the area of each rectangle.
   b. Write the areas of the rectangles as a sum.

   c. Simplify to find an equivalent sum. Be sure to combine only like terms.

3. Group the like terms and simplify the expression:

   $$\frac{3}{5}x + 2 - \frac{1}{10}x - 6$$

4. Identify and correct the error in each of the simplifications.

   a. $5 + 3(x - 11) = 5 * 3x - 33$
   $$= 15x - 33$$

   b. $^{-}2(b + 4) = ^{-}2b + 4$

5. Simplify $6(x + 5) + 2x - 7$.

6. Review the procedure for simplifying an expression and describe each step used to simplify $7a - (2a + 5) + 1$.

$7a - (2a + 5) + 1$	*Original expression*
$7a + {}^-1(2a + 5) + 1$	*?*
$7a + {}^-2a + {}^-5 + 1$	*?*
$5a + {}^-4$	*?*
$5a - 4$	*Using the rule for subtraction*

7. Simplify each expression.

  a. $c^2 + 3c - 2c^2 + 8c - 5$

  b. ${}^-(x + 2) - 3x + 7$

  c. $2 \text{ inches}^2 + 5 \text{ inches} + 7 \text{ inches}^2$

  d. $2(3x - 7) - (x - 4) + 5$

  e. $\frac{5}{3}(x - 6) + x - 4$

8. Solve each equation for x. Use the abbreviations on page 100 to keep track of what you did at each step.

  a. $8(4 - 2x) + 10 = 5x$

  b. $(2x - 1) - (4x + 3) = 8$

9. Solve each equation for x.

  a. $2 - 3x + 15 = 4 + x - 6$

  b. $7 = 4x - 3 - 7x - 11$

  c. $.6x + 2 - 1.1x = 2.6$

  d. $\frac{1}{4}(2x + 5) - x = \frac{1}{2}(5x - 2)$

10. Show that $x = {}^-3$ checks as a solution to the equation $3x + 5 - 6x = 2(4 - x)$.

11. Suppose two cars leave the same spot traveling in opposite directions. One car travels 40 miles per hour and the other travels 55 miles per hour. Use (a)–(c) to find how long it will be before the cars are 57 miles apart.

  a. Let t represent the number of hours of travel. Write an expression for the distance each car travels.

  b. Write an equation showing that the sum of the distances is 57 miles.

c. Solve the equation for t to find the time that these cars travel.

12. Two insects are 100 feet apart at 11:00 A.M. The insects move toward each other, with the junior insect traveling 8 feet per minute and the older insect traveling 12 feet per minute. At what time will they meet?

In Exercises 13–15, use the fact that the sum of the measures of the three angles in any triangle is 180°.

13. In a triangle, the measure of angle B is 10° more than that of angle A and the measure of angle C is twice that of angle A.

  a. Let x represent the measure of angle A. Write expressions for the measures of angle B and angle C. Label the diagram in the figure with your expressions for angles A, B, and C.

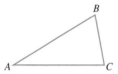

  b. Write an equation showing that the sum of the measures of these three angles is 180°.

  c. Solve the equation for x to find the measure of angle A.

14. In a triangle often used in trigonometry, angle B measures twice angle A and angle C measures three times angle A.

  a. Let x represent the measure of angle A. Draw a diagram and label each angle with an expression for its measure.

  b. Write an equation for the sum of the angles.

  c. Solve the equation and find the measure of each angle.

15. In another triangle, angle B measures 5° more than twice angle A and angle C measures 15° less than angle A. Find the measure of each angle.

Skills and Review 3.2

16. Solve for x: $5x - 6 = 2x + 12$.

17. Verify that $x = 1$ is a solution to the equation $2x - 5 = {}^-10x + 7$.

18. The weekly savings (S) for an employee is given by the formula $S = .03P + 20$, where P is his weekly pay. Find his pay if he saves $35.00.

19. Are the expressions $\frac{1}{3}x + \frac{8}{5}$ and $\frac{5x+24}{15}$ equivalent? Explain.

20. Let $y = -\frac{2}{3}x + 20$.

   a. Use the table feature on your calculator to find five ordered pairs that satisfy this equation.

   b. Find a friendly window that will include the ordered pairs from part (a).

   c. Use the friendly window from part (b) to graph the function on your calculator. Copy the graph.

21. Recall from Exercise 9 on page 81 that the formula

$$C = \frac{5}{9}(F - 32)$$

converts Fahrenheit temperatures to Celsius. Find the Celsius temperature when the Fahrenheit temperature is $14°$.

22. Evaluate $\frac{1}{3}x^2 + 5$ when $x = 6$.

23. Use the order of operations to evaluate

$$-8 + \frac{(-1)^{19} + 6}{9 - 10}$$

How you would enter this expression on your calculator to check your work?

24. Write the decimal number .000521 in scientific notation.

25. Below are steps for simplifying the expression

$$\frac{-16 \text{ ft}}{\sec^2}(2 \sec)^2 + \frac{50 \text{ ft}}{\sec}(2 \sec) + 150 \text{ ft}.$$

Explain what was done at each step.

$$\frac{-16 \text{ ft}}{\sec^2}(2 \sec)^2 + \frac{50 \text{ ft}}{\sec}(2 \sec) + 150 \text{ ft} \qquad \textit{Original expression}$$

$$= \frac{-16 \text{ ft}}{\sec^2}(4 \sec^2) + \frac{50 \text{ ft}}{\sec}(2 \sec) + 150 \text{ ft} \quad ?$$

$$= \frac{-64 \text{ ft} * \sec^2}{\sec^2} + \frac{100 \text{ ft} * \sec}{\sec} + 150 \text{ ft} \quad ?$$

$$= -64 \text{ ft} + 100 \text{ ft} + 150 \text{ ft} \qquad\qquad ?$$

$$= 186 \text{ ft}$$

3.3 The Problem-Solving Process

AFTER STUDYING THIS SECTION YOU WILL BE ABLE TO

■ Describe a seven-step process for solving problems.

■ Apply the seven-step process to a variety of problems.

A Guide for Solving Problems

Throughout this book we emphasize that algebraic equations may be used to model real-world applications. Knowing how to solve equations, however, is just part of the problem solving process. An effective problem solver needs to be able to read a problem and set up an appropriate equation or equations. It is helpful, therefore, to have a *rough guide*, a series of steps that can help us organize our work toward a solution.

Seven Steps for Problem Solving

Step 1   *Understand* the problem. The best way to do this is to read the statement of the problem *carefully* before you begin to solve it.

Step 2   *Visualize* the problem. The right way to carry out this step depends on what type of problem you are trying to solve. For some problems, especially those involving geometry and distance-rate-time problems, you will probably want to draw a picture of some sort. It might not be possible to draw a picture that will help you, but you can still try to *visualize* the problem by thinking of it as happening right in front of you.

Step 3   *Assign* variable(s). If you are going to use algebra to help you solve a problem, you will need to have variables to work with. You should assign a variable to the quantity for which you are solving (which will usually be easy to spot as a question in the original problem) and possibly to other quantities that are unknown at the start of the problem. A picture might help you work out what the variables should be.

Step 4   *Write equation(s).* Use any information from the first two steps to write one or more equations involving the variables you assigned in step 3.

Step 5   *Solve* equation(s). Use the techniques we have discussed so far to solve any equations you wrote in step 4.

Step 6   *Answer* the question. Go back to the original problem and answer the question. It is important to remember that just writing $x = 3$, for example, will probably not answer the question asked in the original problem.

Step 7   *Check* your answer. Does your answer make sense? Go back to the original problem and make sure your answer works.

Applying the Seven Steps

Examples 1–4 illustrate how to use the seven steps for problem solving. Example 1 is an application of the distance formula.

EXAMPLE 1   Suppose a helicopter in Gridville (see Section 2.3) travels from the police station on Avenue $^-2$ Street 1 to pick up an officer who lives on the corner of Avenue 2 and Street 3. From there, it picks up a second officer at Avenue 1, Street $^-1$ and then returns to the police station. How far did the helicopter fly?

Solution   ■   Use the seven steps to help solve this problem.

Step 1   To *understand* this problem, we go back to Section 2.3 where Gridville is described and read the description carefully. Recall that the streets and avenues of Gridville are laid out in a grid on the coordinate plane, with avenues running north-south and streets running east-west. Each corner is labeled with two numbers, the first for the avenue and the second for the street. A helicopter flies in a straight line, so it does not fly along avenues and streets but takes the shortest path. The distance it travels is given by the distance formula, which is

$$\text{distance} = \sqrt{\text{run}^2 + \text{rise}^2}$$

Step 2   Now that we understand the problem, we can try to *visualize* the problem. In this case we draw a figure, making sure to include all the information we have (see Figure 8). Drawing a picture lets us see that the helicopter's flight path is a triangle and that the total distance the helicopter flies is the *perimeter* of this triangle.

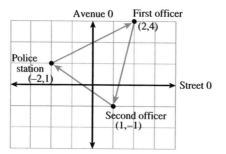

Figure 8   The arrows indicate the flight path of the helicopter.

Step 3   The next step is to *assign* variables. Because we are asked to find the distance, it might seem that the best assignment would be d equals the distance the helicopter travels, but if we look carefully at the way the distance formula works, we see that it can be used only to compute the distance traveled for each leg of the helicopter's flight and not for all of them together. So, let's call the three distances d_1, d_2, and d_3, with d_1 the distance from the police station to the first officer, d_2 the distance from the first officer to the second officer, and d_3 the distance from the second officer back to the police station.

Step 4   Now we are ready to use the distance formula to *write equations* for the three variables for which we want to solve. Looking back at Figure 8 to work out the run and rise for each trip, we have

$$d_1 = \sqrt{4^2 + 2^2}$$
$$d_2 = \sqrt{(^-1)^2 + (^-4)^2}$$
$$d_3 = \sqrt{(^-3)^2 + 2^2}$$

Step 5   The next step, *solving* the equations, is straightforward. We need only to simplify inside the square roots and then compute the square roots.

$$d_1 = \sqrt{4^2 + 2^2} = \sqrt{20} \approx 4.5$$
$$d_2 = \sqrt{(^-1)^2 + (^-4)^2} = \sqrt{17} \approx 4.1$$
$$d_3 = \sqrt{(^-3)^2 + 2^2} = \sqrt{13} \approx 3.6$$

Step 6   The second-to-last step is to *answer* the question. You might think you have already done this, because you have written down three distances, d_1, d_2, and d_3. But if you look back at the original question, you were asked to find how far the helicopter flew and not how far the helicopter flew for each leg of its trip. The answer to the question is given by the *total* distance flown, so we need to add the distances d_1, d_2, and d_3, which gives

$$\text{total distance} \approx 4.5 + 4.1 + 3.6 = 12.2$$

The solution can be stated, The helicopter flew approximately 12.2 blocks.

Step 7   Finally, you should complete the last step by *checking* your answer. In this case, you can use Figure 8 to estimate the length of each side of the triangle and check that your answer looks right.

Our second example is a problem involving perimeter.

EXAMPLE 2   The organizers of the county fair want to fence in a rectangular area for vendors. Each vendor will set up a booth on the inside of the fence. They need 900 feet of fence to accommodate all the vendors and they want the rectangle to be twice as long as it is wide. What should the dimensions of the rectangular area be?

Solution

Step 1   To *understand* this problem, we need to decide exactly what we are being asked. Because the fence will form a rectangle, 900 feet will be the perimeter of the rectangle. The dimensions are the length and the width, so we need to be able to find a rectangle with length twice its width and perimeter 900 feet.

Step 2   To *visualize* the situation, we draw a picture of a rectangle and move immediately to step 3.

Step 3   We can *assign* variables by labeling the rectangle (see Figure 9).
        We let x represent the width of the rectangle. Because the length of the rectangle must be twice the width, we may let $2x$ represent the length.

Step 4   We may now *write an equation*. The perimeter of 900 feet is the sum of all the sides, so $900 = x + 2x + x + 2x$.

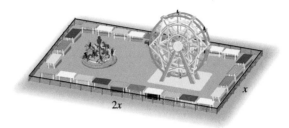

Figure 9 The length of the rectangle should be twice the width.

Step 5 To *solve* the equation, we combine like terms and then divide on both sides by 6.

$$900 = 6x$$
$$\frac{900}{6} = \frac{6x}{6}$$
$$150 = x$$

Step 6 To *answer* the question, we need to give both the length and width of the rectangle. Because $x = 150$, and x stands for width, we know the width is 150 feet. The length is $2x = 2 * 150 = 300$, so the length is 300 feet. Both answers must include the unit (feet) to have any meaning.

Step 7 Let's *check*: does this answer make sense? If we add all the sides, the perimeter is $150 + 300 + 150 + 300 = 900$ feet, so we have found the correct answer.

■ ■ ■

Example 3 is an application of fixed and variable costs.

EXAMPLE 3 Rashid subscribes to a cell-phone service that charges a flat fee of $12.95 per month plus 2 cents for each minute he uses the phone. He knows that he can afford only $30 per month for his telephone bill. How much time will he be able to spend each month on the phone?

Solution **Step 1** Let's see if we *understand* the problem situation. Rashid has $30 to spend. The more he talks, the more he spends. We are asked to find how much time he will be able to spend on the phone. Because he is charged by the minute, the answer should be in minutes. Even if he never picks up the phone, he still has to pay the flat fee of $12.95.

Step 2 Can we *visualize* this problem? If a picture does not immediately come to mind, we may be able to relate this situation to a similar one, Jamie's health club (Section 2.4). There we used the formula

total cost = variable cost + fixed cost

represented by the picture in Figure 10.

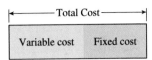

Figure 10

Step 3   We know we have to find time, so we may *assign* the variable *t* to represent the number of minutes Rashid uses the phone in one month.

Step 4   We may *write an equation* with the information in steps 1, 2, and 3. The total cost is $30. The fixed cost is the flat fee, $12.95. The variable cost depends upon *t*. Because he is charged 2 cents ($.02) per minute, the cost is .02*t* for *t* minutes. Putting it all together we have

$$\text{total cost} = \text{variable cost} + \text{fixed cost}$$

$$30 = .02t + 12.95$$

Step 5   We may now *solve* the equation.

$$30 = .02t + 12.95$$

$$\underline{{}^{-}12.95 + {}^{-}12.95} \qquad \textit{Adding }{}^{-}12.95\textit{ on both sides}$$

$$17.05 = .02t \qquad \textit{Combining constant terms}$$

$$\frac{17.05}{.02} = \frac{.02t}{.02} \qquad \textit{Dividing on both sides by .02}$$

$$852.5 = t \qquad 17.05 \div .02 = 852.5$$

Step 6   The *answer* to our question is that Rashid will be able to use the phone 852.5 minutes each month. For a month with 30 days, that works out to about 28.4 minutes a day, just under half an hour. Rashid will have to budget his time carefully!

Step 7   We may *check* our answer by going back to the original problem. If he talks for 852.5 minutes at 2 cents per minute, the variable cost will be $.02 * 852.5 = $17.05. Adding that to the fixed cost of $12.95 gives the $30 Rashid can afford.

Our last example is a distance-rate-time problem.

EXAMPLE 4   Ruth leaves her house at 9 A.M., driving west along Route 7, which runs right past her house. She drives at a steady 40 miles per hour. An hour after she leaves, her husband Jacob realizes that she forgot the slides she will need for the presentation, so he takes off after her, driving at a steady rate of 60 miles per hour. When will Jabob catch Ruth?

Solution   **Step 1**   Here is what we should *understand* from reading the problem: We are asked to find *when* Jacob catches Ruth, so we need to solve for time. We know that Jacob drives faster than Ruth, but he starts later so he has less time. They both start from the house, and when he catches up to her they will both have traveled the same distance.

Step 2   To *visualize* this problem you may want to act it out with a classmate. Have Ruth leave the house before Jacob does and have Jacob move at a faster speed until they meet. The diagram in Figure 11 represents the situation.

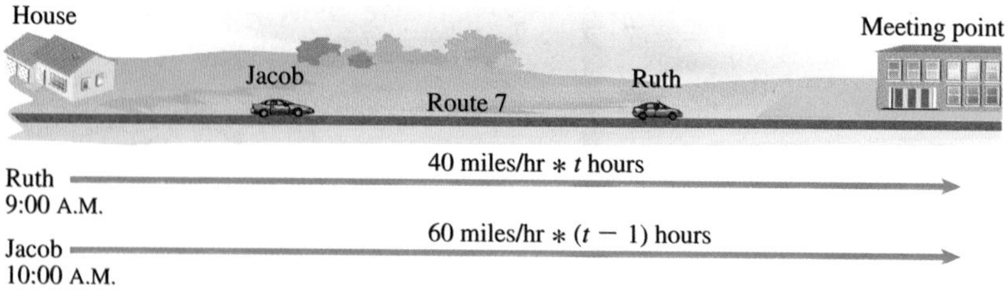

Figure 11

Step 3   Let's *assign* t as the variable to represent Ruth's time, that is, time elapsed since 9 A.M. Jacob leaves 1 hour later, so his time is 1 hour less, that is, $t - 1$.

Step 4   The diagram in Figure 11 may help us to *write an equation.*
distance = *rate * time*, so Ruth's distance is **40t** and Jacob's distance is **60($t - 1$)**. Because these two distances are the same, we have the equation

$$40t = 60(t - 1).$$

Step 5   Simple algebraic manipulation lets us *solve* this equation for t.

$$60(t - 1) = 40t \qquad \textit{Original equation}$$

$$60t - 60 = 40t \qquad \textit{Distributive property}$$

$$\underline{-60t \qquad -60t} \qquad \textit{Subtracting 60t on both sides}$$

$$^-60 = {}^-20t \qquad \textit{Combining t terms}$$

$$\frac{^-60t}{-20} = \frac{^-20t}{-20} \qquad \textit{Dividing by } {}^-20 \textit{ on both sides}$$

$$3 = t \qquad \frac{^-60t}{-20} = 3 \textit{ and } \frac{^-20t}{-20} = t$$

Step 6   The question asked what time it would be when Jacob catches Ruth, not how long it would take. So to *answer* the question, we need to convert the elapsed time, $t = 3$ hours on Ruth's stopwatch, to the actual time of day. Ruth left at 9 A.M., so 3 hours later it is noon.

Step 7   We can *check* this answer calculating the distances Ruth and Jacob travel. Ruth traveled for $t = 3$ hours at a rate of 40 miles per hour for a distance of $40 * 3 = 120$ miles. Jacob traveled $t - 1 = 2$ hours at a rate of 60 miles per hour for a distance of $60 * 2 = 120$ miles. As expected, they traveled the same distance.

Exercises 3.3

1. Summarize the seven steps for problem solving.
2. Review Example 1 and outline the work performed for each of the seven steps for problem solving.
3. Review Example 2 and outline the work performed for each of the seven steps for problem solving.
4. In Example 3, how many hours per month will Rashid use the phone?
5. In Example 4, does the solution $t = 3$ complete the problem-solving process? Explain.

Exercises 6 and 8 explore various approaches to visualizing a problem. Exercises 7 and 9 then ask you to apply those results to continue solving the problems.

6. The sum of two numbers is 11. Ten times the smaller number minus 5 times the larger number is 8. What are the two numbers?
   a. Step 1: Understand the problem by completely reading the problem. Then state what the problem is looking for.
   b. Step 2: Visualize the problem by using guess and check on pairs of numbers that sum to 11. Make a table. Do your guesses come close to meeting the second condition of the problem? Explain.
   c. Step 3: Let x represent the smaller number. Explain why $11 - x$ represents the larger number.
7. Continue the seven steps for problem solving to find the two unknown numbers from Exercise 6.
8. The length of a rectangle is four times the width. What are the dimensions of the rectangle if the perimeter is 100 m?
   a. Complete step 2 of the problem-solving process by drawing a picture of the information given in the problem.
   b. What additional information did your picture help you gather?
9. Complete the problem-solving steps to find the dimensions of the rectangle in Exercise 8.

10. The perimeter of a rectangle is 98 feet. The width of the rectangle is 5 feet more than one-third the length. Use the seven steps for problem solving to find the width and length of the rectangle.
11. Steve wants to record his music professionally. A studio charges an up-front fee of $500 plus $12 for each minute of recording. How many minutes can he record for $1200?
12. Each month Rachel has spring water delivered to her apartment. She rents a water dispenser for $6.25 per month. Each jug of water costs $3.70. She budgets $25 per month for water and the dispenser. How many jugs of water can she buy each month?
13. Two trains pass each other going in opposite directions. The first train travels 5 miles per hour faster than the second train. What is the average speed of each train if they are 370 miles apart after 2 hours?
   a. Complete step two of the seven steps for problem solving by completing the table below.

	Rate (miles/hour)	Time (hours)	Distance (miles)
Train A			
Train B			
Total			

   b. Complete the remaining problem-solving steps to find the average speed of each train.
14. Two cyclists begin from the same place at the same time riding toward the same final destination. One cyclist averages 20 miles per hour and the other averages 26 miles per hour. After how many minutes will the two cyclists be 10 miles apart?
15. Kyle and Missy buy a total of 52 lottery tickets. Missy buys 8 less than twice the number of tickets that Kyle buys. How many tickets did each buy?

Skills and Review 3.3

16. Simplify.
   a. $2x - (x + 6)$
   b. $5(3x - 7) - 4x - 2$
   c. $(x^2 - 5) - 4(2x + 7) + (x^2 - 6x)$
   d. $x + x^{-2} + 5 + \frac{3}{x^2} - 6x$

17. Simplify

$$6\left(x - \tfrac{9}{2}\right) - (4 - 1)$$

18. Solve for x if $2x + 3 = 11$.

19. Solve for x: $^-(3 + x) - 6 = 1 + (4x - 30)$.

20. Solve for x: $\tfrac{1}{3}x - 5 = \tfrac{1}{2}x + 4$.

21. Solve for y when $x = ^-4$ if $5x - 7y = 22$.

22. Suppose a person travels 10 miles/hour in one direction and another person travels 12 miles/hour in the opposite direction. How long will it be before they are 110 miles apart?

23. Evaluate $x^2 + 2x - 3$ when $x = ^-1$.

24. Evaluate using the order of operations.

a. $\dfrac{^-2 - (^-5)}{^-3 - 6}$

b. $\dfrac{\sqrt{(^-3)^2 - 4 * 1 * (^-4)}}{2 * 1}$

25. Find the run and rise going from $(2, ^-6)$ to $(7, ^-3)$.

3.4 Arithmetic Sequences (Optional)

AFTER STUDYING THIS SECTION YOU WILL BE ABLE TO

- Determine if a sequence of numbers is an arithmetic sequence.
- Find the formula for the nth term in an arithmetic sequence.
- Use the formula to find terms in an arithmetic sequence.

A sequence is a list of numbers that show some pattern or rule. The numbers in a sequence are called terms. If you can figure out the rule, you can find more terms.

EXAMPLE 1 Find the pattern for each sequence and then find the next three terms.

a. 12, 15, 18, 21, . . .

b. 100, 94, 88, 82, . . .

c. 3, 6, 12, 24, . . .

d. 8, 10, 8, 10, . . .

Solution

a. The rule appears to be add 3 to each term to find the next term. The next three terms are 24, 27, and 30.

b. The rule appears to be subtract 6 from each term to find the next term. The next three terms are 76, 70, and 64.

c. The rule appears to be multiply each term by 2 to find the next term. The next three terms are 48, 96, and 192.

d. The rule appears to be add 2, then add $^-2$, then add 2, then add $^-2$, etc. The next three terms are 8, 10, and 8.

The sequences in Example 1(a) and (b) above are called **arithmetic sequences**. In these sequences a term is found by adding or subtracting the same number to the previous term. The number added or subtracted is called the **com-**

mon difference. In (a) the common difference is 3, and in (b) the common difference is $^-6$.

The sequences in (c) and (d) are not arithmetic sequences. In (c) each term is found by multiplying the previous term by 2. It is an example of a **geometric sequence**. In (d), the terms alternate between 8 and 10, and the differences flip back and forth between 2 and $^-2$. Because the differences are not the same, (d) does not qualify as an arithmetic sequence.

Formulas for Arithmetic Sequences

Variables may be used to describe an arithmetic sequence. The terms are usually designated by the letter a. Because there is more than one term, subscripts are used: a_1 represents the first term, a_2 represents the second term, a_3 represents the third term, and so on, until a_n represents the nth term. The letter d is used to represent the common difference.

EXAMPLE 2 ■ Find a formula for the nth term of an arithmetic sequence.

Solution Start with the first term and keep adding the common difference.

$$\text{first term} \quad a_1$$
$$\text{second term} \quad a_2 = a_1 + d$$
$$\text{third term} \quad a_3 = a_2 + d = a_1 + d + d = a_1 + 2d$$
$$\text{fourth term} \quad a_4 = a_3 + d = a_1 + 2d + d = a_1 + 3d$$
$$\text{fifth term} \quad a_5 = a_4 + d = a_1 + 3d + d = a_1 + 4d$$

It appears that each term may be found by starting with a_1 and adding a specified number of d's. To determine how many d's to add, look more closely at the pattern:

$$a_1$$
$$a_2 = a_1 + d$$
$$a_3 = a_1 + 2d \qquad \textit{2 is one less than 3}$$
$$a_4 = a_1 + 3d \qquad \textit{3 is one less than 4}$$
$$a_5 = a_1 + 4d \qquad \textit{4 is one less than 5}$$

In the last three rows, the coefficient of d is one less than the number of the term. This pattern also holds for the first two rows if we write

$$a_1 = a_1 + 0d \qquad \textit{0 is one less than 1}$$
$$a_2 = a_1 + 1d \qquad \textit{1 is one less than 2}$$

We are now ready to write a general formula for the nth term, a_n.

$$n\text{th term } a_n = a_1 + (n - 1)d$$

Substituting 1, 2, 3, 4, and 5 in the formula will give the preceding results.

Formula for an Arithmetic Sequence

Let a_1 be the first term and d be the common difference for an arithmetic sequence. Then the nth term is given by the formula

$$a_n = a_1 + (n - 1)d$$

We may remember this formula by recalling that something must be added to a_1 to get a_n. A common mistake is to add $n * d$ rather than $(n - 1)d$. Example 3 shows a way to remember why it should be $n - 1$.

EXAMPLE 3   Your backyard is 120 feet wide. You want to build a fence and will need to place posts 10 feet apart. How many posts will you need?

Solution   The easy answer is wrong! You can't simply divide 120 by 10 and get 12 as your answer. Figure 12 illustrates why 12 does not work. From Figure 12 we can see that 13 fence posts are needed in order to create 12 spaces of 10 feet each between the posts.

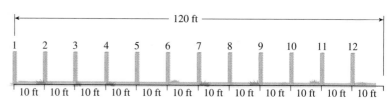

Figure 12   Twelve fence posts are not enough. Another post is needed at the end.

The Fence Post Principle

n fence posts create $n - 1$ spaces between the posts.

In Example 3, $n = 13$ and $n - 1 = 12$. In the formula for an arithmetic sequence, think of the terms of the sequence as fence posts and the spaces between the terms as common differences. According to the fence post principle, you will need $n - 1$ differences. Therefore, the formula is $a_n = a_1 + (n - 1)d$.

Applying the Arithmetic Sequence Formula

Example 4 shows how to apply the arithmetic sequence formula.

EXAMPLE 4   ■   Find the fourteenth term of the arithmetic sequence: $4, 7, 10, 13, \ldots$.

Solution   Because $7 - 4 = 3$, $10 - 7 = 3$, and $13 - 10 = 3$, there is a common difference of 3. We now know that $a_1 = 4$ and $d = 3$. We want the fourteenth term, so $n = 14$:

$$a_n = a_1 + (n - 1)d \qquad \textit{Arithmetic sequence formula}$$

$$a_{14} = 4 + (14 - 1) * 3 \qquad \textit{Substituting for } a_1, d, \textit{ and } n$$

$$a_{14} = 4 + (13) * 3 \qquad \textit{Applying the order of operations}$$

$$a_{14} = 4 + 39$$

$$a_{14} = 43$$

The fourteenth term of this sequence is 43.

■ ■ ■

EXAMPLE 5   The first term of an arithmetic sequence is 53. The ninth term is 93. Find the common difference.

Solution   We know that $a_1 = 53$, $n = 9$, and $a_9 = 93$. We again use the formula. This time we will have an equation to solve.

$$a_n = a_1 + (n - 1)d \qquad \textit{Arithmetic sequence formula}$$

$$93 = 53 + (9 - 1)d \qquad \textit{Substituting 53 for } a_1, \textit{9 for } n, \textit{ and 93 for } a_n$$

$$93 = 53 + 8d \qquad \textit{RS (Simplifying parentheses)}$$

$$40 = 8d \qquad \textit{A (Adding } ^-53 \textit{ on both sides)}$$

$$\frac{40}{8} = \frac{8d}{8} \qquad \textit{M (Dividing on both sides by 8)}$$

$$5 = d$$

The common difference is 5.

■ ■ ■

EXAMPLE 6   Suppose we have the sequence $1000, 991, 982, 973, \ldots$.

a. Does the number 100 appear in this sequence? If so, which term is it?

b. Does the number 13 appear in this sequence? If so, which term is it?

Solution   The common difference appears to be $991 - 1000 = {}^-9$. We check that the sequence is arithmetic by adding $^-9$ to 991 to get 982 and then again to 982 to get 973.

Thus we have $a_1 = 1000$ and $d = {}^-9$. For each example we know the value we want for a_n but we don't know if we can choose an n to get that value.

a. If 100 appears in the sequence, $a_n = 100$. We substitute into the formula:

$$a_n = a_1 + (n - 1)d \qquad \text{\textit{Arithmetic sequence formula}}$$

$$100 = 1000 + (n - 1) * {}^-9 \qquad \text{\textit{Substituting into the formula}}$$

$$100 = 1000 - 9n + 9 \qquad \text{\textit{RS (Applying the distributive property)}}$$

$$100 = 1009 - 9n \qquad \text{\textit{RS (Combining the constant terms)}}$$

$${}^-909 = {}^-9n \qquad \text{\textit{A (Adding $^-$1009 on both sides)}}$$

$$\frac{{}^-909}{{}^-9} = \frac{{}^-9n}{{}^-9} \qquad \text{\textit{M (Dividing both sides by $^-$9)}}$$

$$101 = n$$

When we solved for n, we got a whole number. We can conclude that 100 does appear in the sequence as the 101st term.

b. If 13 appears in the sequence, $a_n = 13$. We substitute into the formula:

$$a_n = a_1 + (n - 1)d \qquad \text{\textit{Arithmetic sequence formula}}$$

$$13 = 1000 + (n - 1) * {}^-9 \qquad \text{\textit{Substituting into the formula}}$$

$$13 = 1000 - 9n + 9 \qquad \text{\textit{RS (Applying the distributive property)}}$$

$$13 = 1009 - 9n \qquad \text{\textit{RS (Combining the constant terms)}}$$

$${}^-996 = {}^-9n \qquad \text{\textit{A (Adding $^-$1009 on both sides)}}$$

$$\frac{{}^-996}{{}^-9} = \frac{{}^-9n}{{}^-9} \qquad \text{\textit{M (Dividing by $^-$9 or multiplying by $-\frac{1}{9}$ on both sides)}}$$

$$110.667 \approx n$$

When we tried to solve for n, we got a fraction. We conclude that 13 is not a term in the sequence.

Exercises 3.4

---

1. Find the pattern for each sequence and then find the next three terms.

   a. $1, 2, 4, 8, \ldots$

b. $13, 23, 33, 43, \ldots$

c. $41, 39, 37, 35, \ldots$

d. $50, 51, 49, 52, 48, 53, \ldots$

2. Which sequences in Exercise 1 are arithmetic?

3. For each arithmetic sequence, determine a_1 and d.

   a. $17, 20, 23, 26, \ldots$

   b. $85, 80, 75, 70, \ldots$

   c. $15, 17.5, 20, 22.5, \ldots$

   d. $1, {}^-2, {}^-5, {}^-8, \ldots$

4. Find the nth term for each arithmetic sequence with the given information.

   a. $a_1 = 14, d = 4, n = 10$

   b. $a_1 = 30, d = {}^-3, n = 7$

   c. $a_1 = {}^-500, d = 19, n = 35$

5. How many fence posts are needed to make a fence 210 feet long with the posts 15 feet apart?

6. The first term of an arithmetic sequence is 11. The 18th term is 130. Find the common difference.

7. Does the number 1000 appear in the sequence 25, 38, 51, 64, $\ldots$? If so, which term is it?

8. The 100th term of an arithmetic sequence is 0 and the common difference is $^-8$. Find the first term.

CHAPTER 3 ■ KEY CONCEPTS ■

Basic Principle of Equation Solving If we are given an equation, we can add the same term on both sides or multiply by the same number on both sides and still have a valid equation. (Page 89)

Equivalent Expressions Equal quantities written in different form: for example, $x + x$ and $2x$ are the same for any x, so they are equivalent, and we may write $x + x = 2x$. (Page 98)

Simplified Form An expression is in simplified form if it has no parentheses and no terms can be combined. (Page 98)

Procedure for Simplifying an Expression (Page 99).

1. Use the special properties of 1 and $^-1$ if necessary.

2. Remove all parentheses using the distributive property.

3. Group like terms using the commutative property.

4. Combine like terms.

Procedure for Solving Linear Equations (Page 101).

1. If necessary, simplify the expression on the left side.

2. If necessary, simplify the expression on the right side.

3. If necessary, add the same terms on both sides until you have a variable term on one side and a constant term on the other side.

4. If necessary, multiply on both sides by the reciprocal of the coefficient of the variable in order to get the variable alone.

Seven Steps for Problem Solving These steps provide a logical way to set up and work through word problems. (Page 105)

Step 1 *Understand* the problem. The best way to do this is to read the statement of the problem *carefully* before you begin to solve it.

Step 2 *Visualize* the problem. The right way to carry out this step depends on what type of problem you are trying to solve. For some problems, especially those involving geometry and distance-rate-time problems, you will probably want to draw a picture of some sort. It might not be possible to draw a picture that will help you, but you can still try to *visualize* the problem by thinking of it as happening right in front of you.

Step 3 *Assign* variable(s). If you are going to use algebra to help you solve a problem, you will need to have variables to work with. You should assign a variable to the quantity for which you are solving (which will usually be easy to spot as a question in the original problem) and possibly to other quantities that are unknown at the start of the problem. A picture might help you work out what the variables should be.

Step 4 *Write equation(s)*. Use any information from the first two steps to write one or more equations involving the variables you assigned in step 3.

Step 5 *Solve* equation(s). Use the techniques we have discussed so far to solve any equations you wrote in step 4.

Step 6 *Answer* the question. Go back to the original problem and answer the question. It is important to remember that just writing $x = 3$, for example, will probably not answer the question asked in the original problem.

Step 7 *Check* your answer. Does your answer make sense? Go back to the original problem and make sure your answer works.

Exploration

Recall the equation for photosynthesis from the chapter opener, $H_2O + CO_2 = O_2 + C_6H_{12}O_6$. Balance the equation by following these steps:

a. Find out how many molecules of H_2O will be needed to provide the hydrogen (H) for one molecule of $C_6H_{12}O_6$.

b. Find out how many molecules of CO_2 will be needed to provide the carbon (C) for one molecule of $C_6H_{12}O_6$.

c. Find out how many extra oxygen atoms you will have. These extra atoms will make how many molecules of O_2?

d. Now fill in the blanks with the numbers of each molecule you will need:

$$\underline{} H_2O + \underline{} CO_2 = \underline{} O_2 + 1C_6H_{12}O_6.$$

e. Check to see that the equation balances:

Element	Atoms on Left Side	Atoms on Right Side
Carbon (C)	——	——
Hydrogen (H)	——	——
Oxygen (O)	——	——

f. How is checking a balanced chemical equation similar to checking an algebraic equation? How are the procedures different?

CHAPTER 3 ▪ REVIEW EXERCISES

Section 3.1 Solving Linear Equations in One Variable

1. Solve each equation for x.

a. $3x + 8 = 11$

b. $7 + x = 3 - 4x$

c. $5x + 7 = {}^-23$

d. $1.2 - x = .7 - .5x$

e. $6 = 2x + 9$

f. $7x - 8 = 5x + 13$

g. $\frac{1}{2}x + 6 = \frac{7}{2}x - 21$

h. $\frac{2}{3}x - 1 = 6 + \frac{1}{3}x$

2. Show that $x = 9$ is a solution to $2x - 3 = x + 6$ by substituting into both sides of the equation.

3. Suppose you leave home traveling at a rate of 50 miles per hour.

  a. Find the distances in the following table.

Time (hours)	Distance (miles)
1	50
2	?
3	?
⋮	⋮
t	?

  b. In the last row, we don't know the amount of time, so we let t represent the number of hours of travel. Explain why the expression $50t$ represents the distance (in miles) that is traveled.

  c. Suppose you travel 120 miles. What does the solution to the equation $120 = 50t$ represent?

  d. Solve the equation from part (c).

4. A formula for temperature in Kelvins in terms of Celsius temperature is $K = C + 273°$. Water boils at a temperature of 373 Kelvins. What is the equivalent Celsius temperature?

  a. In this example $K = 373$. Substitute this value for K and write the equation.

  b. Solve the equation for C to find the Celsius temperature.

5. Recall, from Example 1 of Section 2.2, the formula $T = 3S + 1$ for finding the number of toothpicks T required to make S squares in a row. How many squares are in a row made of 28 toothpicks? Substitute this value for T and solve the equation to find the number of squares.

6. Suppose you are considering joining a music club. At one club, membership fees are \$4 plus \$1 for each CD. At the other club, membership fees are \$2.50 plus \$1.50 for each CD. Find the number of CDs for which these two clubs cost the same.

  a. Let d represent the number of CDs purchased. An expression for the cost of the first club is $4 + 1d$. Write an expression for the cost of the other club.

  b. Write an equation showing that the two expressions are equal because we want their costs to be equal.

  c. Solve the equation to find the number of CDs.

Section 3.2 Simplifying Expressions to Solve Linear Equations

7. Simplify each expression.

  a. $3x + 2 - x - 5$

  b. $2(x + 1) + 3x - 4$

  c. $x - (6 - 4x) + 2x$

  d. $3(2x - 4) + x^2 - 12$

  e. $3y - x^2 - y + 4x^2$

  f. $\frac{1}{3} + x + \frac{1}{6} + 2x$

  g. $\frac{1}{2}x - \frac{1}{3}x$

  h. $\frac{3}{4}(2x + 8) - \frac{1}{2}x$

8. Explain how the properties of $^-1$ can be used to simplify $3x - (3 - x) + 3$.

9. Solve each equation for x. Next to each step, write **A** if you added (or subtracted) the same quantity on both sides of the equation, **M** if you multiplied (or divided) both sides of the equation by the same quantity, **LS** if you simplified the expression on the left side of the equation, and **RS** if you simplified the expression on the right side of the equation.

  a. $2x + 8 + x = 32$

  b. $5(x - 2) + 9 = 7(x + 3)$

10. Solve each equation for x.

  a. $x + 8 + x + 8 = 26$

  b. $4x - 3 + 6x = 5 + 3x - 1$

  c. $x + (x + 30) + (2x + 10) = 180$

  d. $4(x - 5) + x = 10 + 6x - 70$

  e. $1 - (x + 5) = 3(x - 2) + 4x$

  f. $\frac{1}{4}(8x + 2) = 6\left(\frac{1}{4}x - \frac{2}{3}\right)$

  g. $2 + 3(4x + 6) = x + 7 - (2x - 8)$

  h. $\frac{2}{3}(x - 9) + \frac{1}{3}x = 7x - 15$

11. Recall that a formula for the perimeter of a rectangle is $P = 2W + 2L$. Suppose a rectangle has a perimeter of 20 inches and a width of 4 inches. Substitute these values into the formula and solve the formula for L in order to find the length of this rectangle.

12. A formula for finding the area of the rectangle in the figure is $A = 4(x + 3)$. Find x when the area is 15 cm².

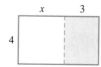

13. At 2:00 P.M., two trains leave the station in Hartford, one traveling north toward Springfield at a speed of 45 miles per hour and the other traveling south toward New Haven at 55 miles per hour. At what time will the two trains be 36 miles apart?

   a. Let t represent the time in hours that the trains travel. Do you expect t to be greater than 1 or less than 1? Explain.

   b. The southbound train travels a distance of $55t$ miles. Write an expression for the distance traveled by the northbound train.

   c. Write an equation showing that the sum of the distances traveled by the two trains is 36 miles.

   d. Solve the equation and find out (to the nearest minute) when the trains will be 36 miles apart.

In Exercises 14–16, use the fact that the sum of the measures of the three angles in any triangle is 180°.

14. In a triangle, angle B measures 20° more than angle A, and angle C measures 70° more than angle A.

   a. Let x represent the measure of angle A. What is the measure of angle B? What is the measure of angle C?

   b. Write an equation showing that the sum of the measures of these angles is 180°.

   c. Solve the equation for x.

   d. What are the measures of each angle?

15. In another triangle, one angle measures 90° and the other two angles have equal measures.

   a. Let x represent the measure of one of the unknown angles. Write an equation using the fact that the sum of the three angles is 180°.

   b. Solve the equation for x.

   c. What is the measure of the two unknown angles?

16. The measures of all three angles of an equilateral triangle are equal.

   a. Draw and label a diagram.

   b. Write and solve an equation to find the measures of the angles.

Section 3.3 The Problem-Solving Process

17. A pilot in Gridville (see Section 2.3) flies from $(2, 3)$ to $(^-5, 1)$ and then to $(1, ^-2)$. Find the total distance this pilot has flown.

   a. Understand the problem by writing what the problem is asking for.

   b. Visualize the problem by drawing a picture.

   c. Assign variables for the unknown(s).

   d. Write equations using the variables.

   e. Solve or simplify the equations.

   f. Answer the question.

   g. Check that your answer makes sense.

18. The in-bound lines on a tennis court form a rectangle. The length is 6 feet more than twice the width. The perimeter is 228 feet. Use the seven steps for problem solving to find the dimensions of the tennis court.

19. Sue has $40 to spend on her phone service each month. She pays a flat fee of $11.30 per month plus 6 cents for each minute she uses the phone. How much time can she spend on the phone each month?

20. Suppose Marion Jones gives her opponent a .3-second head start in a 200-m race. Jones' speed is 8.8 m/s and her opponent's is 8.6 m/s.

   a. How long does it take Jones to catch her opponent?

   b. At what distance does Jones catch her opponent?

   c. Who wins the race?

Section 3.4 Arithmetic Sequences (Optional)

1. Find the next three terms in each sequence and determine which sequences are arithmetic.

   a. 6, 10, 14, 18, . . .

   b. 5, 15, 45, 135, . . .

   c. 2, 0, 7, 0, 12, . . .

   d. 19, 17, 15, 13, . . .

2. Find the missing piece of information for each arithmetic sequence.

   a. $a_1 = 1$ and $d = 7$, find a_{10}

   b. $a_1 = ^-3$ and $a_9 = 5$, find d

   c. $d = 11$ and $a_{14} = 151$, find a_1

CHAPTER 3 ▪ TEST

1. Solve for x if $7x + 5 = 2x - 5$.

2. Solve for x if

$$6 - \left(\tfrac{4}{5}x + 2\right) = 9 + \tfrac{2}{5}x - 3$$

3. Show that $x = \tfrac{3}{2}$ is a solution to the equation $6x - 1 = 2x + 5$.

4. Write and solve an equation to find the value of x that makes the expressions $2x + 9 - 5x$ and $4(x - 3)$ equal.

5. A formula for Fahrenheit temperature in terms of Celsius temperature is

$$F = \tfrac{9}{5}C + 32$$

Find the Celsius temperature when the Fahrenheit temperature is $90°$.

6. An SUV holds 20 gallons of gasoline and gets 13 miles per gallon.

  a. Write an expression for the number of gallons in the SUV's gas tank if the SUV has traveled x miles.

  b. How much gas is left in the tank after 5 miles?

  c. How far can the SUV travel on a full tank of gas?

7. At 12:25 A.M. the Carpathia steamed toward the Titanic at a rate of 15.5 miles per hour. Suppose the Titanic was also drifting toward the Carpathia at a rate of 1.5 miles per hour. If the boats started 58 miles apart, at what time did they meet? (See the figure.)

  a. Identify the variable.

  b. Write an equation.

  c. Solve the equation and answer the question.

8. In triangle ABC, the measure of angle B is twice the measure of angle A. The measure of angle C is equal to the measure of angle B.

  a. Identify a variable and use it to write an equation.

  b. Solve the equation by any suitable method.

  c. Find the measure of each angle.

9. Doug is faster than Lance, so he decides to give Lance a 15-minute head start in a foot race. Doug runs 9 miles per hour and Lance runs 7.8 miles per hour.

  a. How long after he begins running does Doug catch Lance?

  b. Does your answer seem reasonable? Explain.

10. The perimeter of an isosceles triangle (two equal legs) is 20 cm. The remaining side is 4 cm more than three times the length of a leg. What is the length of each side of the triangle?

15.5 m/hr   1.5 m/hr

58 miles

Figure for Exercise 7

Systems of Linear Equations

4.1 ■ Slope and Rate of Change

4.2 ■ Forms of Linear Equations

4.3 ■ Graphical Solution of Systems of Equations

4.4 ■ Algebraic Solution of Systems of Equations

4.5 ■ Relationships Between Lines (Optional)

For Safety's Sake

Beginning in 1998 airbags became standard equipment on all new cars sold in the United States. As the table shows, the number of lives saved by airbags steadily increased throughout the 1990s (*Source:* National Highway Traffic Safety Administration).

Year	Number of lives saved
1993	169
1994	276
1995	470
1996	686
1997	842
1998	1042
1999	1263
2000	1584

Transportation officials use data like these to predict future trends. In this chapter you learn how to use an equation to predict lives saved by airbags in the year 2012. (See Exploration on p. 169.)

4.1   Slope and Rate of Change

AFTER STUDYING THIS SECTION YOU WILL BE ABLE TO

- Find the slope of a line given two points.
- Find the slope of a line from its equation.
- Interpret slope as a rate of change and the *y*-intercept as an initial value.

Linear Equations in Two Variables

In the first example of Chapter 3 John had to take his car to a mechanic to replace the timing chain. He was charged $200 for the repair and wanted to find out how long the mechanic worked. Now let us look at the same situation from the mechanic's point of view.

EXAMPLE 1   John's mechanic is replacing the timing chain on his car. The part costs $95 and she charges $60 per hour for labor. Find an equation to show how the total cost of the repair depends upon the amount of time it takes to replace the chain. Use your equation to make a table and a graph that represent this situation.

Solution   We use the formula

$$\text{total cost} = \text{variable cost} + \text{fixed cost}$$

first introduced in Section 2.4.

The fixed cost is the cost of the part or **$95**. The variable cost depends upon how many hours the job takes and is **60*t***, where *t* is the time measured in hours.

Substituting into the formula we have

$$\text{total cost} = 60t + 95$$

Substituting the values 1, 2, 3, and 4 for *t* gives us a table.

Time (hours)	Total Cost ($)
1	155
2	215
3	275
4	335

The table gives the mechanic a fairly good idea of how cost depends upon time. We can graph the four pairs of values, as shown in Figure 1. Notice that each tick mark on the vertical axis represents $50. We chose this scale so that all four data points could be displayed.

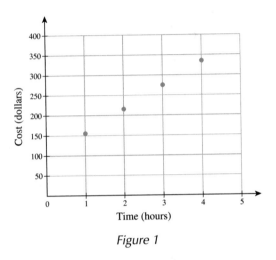

Figure 1

From Figure 1 we can see that the four points appear to lie on a straight line. We can confirm that it is a straight line by using a calculator. To do that, we need to name our variables x and y.

The equation

$$\text{total cost} = 60t + 95$$

becomes

$$y = 60x + 95$$

We enter the equation in the Y= menu. A friendly setting for the window is Xmin = 0, Xmax = 9.4, Xscl = 1, Ymin = 0, Ymax = 500, Yscl = 50.

The graph as it appears on the calculator screen is shown in Figure 2. If you use ⎥TRACE⎥ on your calculator, you will find all four points on this line, because we are using a friendly window. The final equation we found in Example 1 is called a *linear equation*.

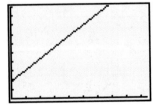

Figure 2 Y1 = 60X + 95(0 ≤ X ≤ 9.4, 0 ≤ Y ≤ 500)

Definition   Linear Equation in Two Variables

A **linear equation in two variables** is any equation with simple terms involving two different variables and possibly a constant term. If we let x stand for one variable and y for the other, then a linear equation in two variables can almost always be put in the form $y = $ coefficient $* x + $ constant. An equation in this form is also called a **linear function**.

The following are important facts about linear functions.

Facts about Linear Functions $y = $ coefficient $* x + $ constant

Fact 1   The constant term on the right-hand side is an **initial value**. In Example 1 the initial value is the cost for the timing belt, $95.

Fact 2   The coefficient of the variable on the right is a **rate**. In the example the rate is what she charges for labor, $60 per hour.

Fact 3   The variable on the left is the **dependent**, or **output, variable**. The letter y is usually used for this variable. In the example y is the total cost. It depends upon how many hours the mechanic works.

Fact 4   We compute the value of the dependent variable using the value of the **independent**, or **input, variable** on the right. The letter x is usually used for this variable. In the example x is the number of hours the mechanic works. We put a value for the input variable, x, into the equation and out comes a value for the output variable, y.

There is another extremely important fact about linear equations in two variables. You have already observed this in Figures 1 and 2.

Graphs of Linear Functions

The graph associated with any *linear equation in two variables* (*linear function*) is a straight line.

We can learn some important information about an equation from its graph.

EXAMPLE 2   Trace the graph in Figure 2 all the way to the left so that $x = 0$.

a. What do you notice about y?

b. What does this value represent?

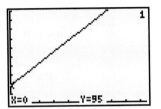

Figure 3 Trace to the point where X = 0.

Solution **a.** When you trace to the point where $x = 0$, you will find that $y = 95$, as shown in Figure 3. You can also find this value by substituting $x = 0$ into the equation $y = 60x + 95$.
b. $95 is the cost of the timing belt. It is also the **initial value**.

From Example 2 we see that the initial value of a linear function shows up as the y-coordinate of the point where the line crosses the y-axis. This point is called the **y-intercept**.
Here is another example of a linear equation in two variables.

EXAMPLE 3 Suppose we start a stopwatch when a sprinter is running at a constant rate of 30 feet/second and is 140 feet from the finish line. Find an equation that shows how his distance from the finish line depends upon the time shown on the watch. Draw a graph, make a table, and use them to find the y-intercept.

Solution We use the formula distance = rate * time, but we need to be careful. First, the initial value is 140, because we start 140 feet from the finish line. Second, the distance *decreases* as time increases. An appropriate equation is

$$\text{distance} = 140 - 30 * \text{time}$$

The graph is given in Figure 4.

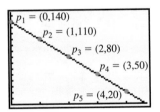

Figure 4 Graph of Y1 = 140 − 30X. We used a friendly window with Xmin = 0, Xmax = 4.7, Ymin = 0, and Ymax = 155.

We can enter Y1 = 140 − 30X in our calculator and make a table. Go to the TblSet menu and make sure that ΔTbl = 1. Let's set TblStart = 0, because negative input values certainly don't make any sense for this problem. Now when you press ⟨2nd⟩ TABLE, you should see a table like in Figure 5.

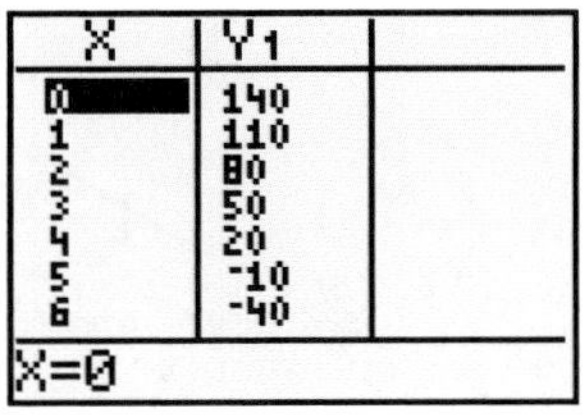

X	Y1
0	140
1	110
2	80
3	50
4	20
⋮	⋮

Figure 5

Now we can find the *y*-intercept by looking in the table for the value of *y* when $x = 0$. Clearly it is 140 feet, the distance the sprinter is from the finish line when we start the watch. This should not surprise us because the starting distance is the *initial value*. We may find the same result by tracing along the graph.

■ ■ ■

The Slope of a Line

Compare the graphs in Figures 2 and 4. Reading from left to right, each graph starts at a point on the *y*-axis, called the *y*-intercept. As you move to the right the line in Example 1 rises, but the line in Example 3 falls. This suggests that we may be able to describe each line in terms of the *run* and *rise* introduced in Section 2.3. Run and rise are used to compute a value called the *slope of a line*.

Definition   Slope of a Line

$$\text{slope} = \frac{\text{change in output}}{\text{change in input}} = \frac{\text{rise}}{\text{run}}$$

To compute the **slope of a line**, pick two points (x_1, y_1) and (x_2, y_2) on the line. Then **rise** $= y_2 - y_1$ and **run** $= x_2 - x_1$, so

$$\text{slope} = \frac{\text{rise}}{\text{run}} = \frac{y_2 - y_1}{x_2 - x_1}.$$

EXAMPLE 4   Show how to use the definition for slope to compute the slopes of the lines in each example.

a. Example 1

b. Example 3

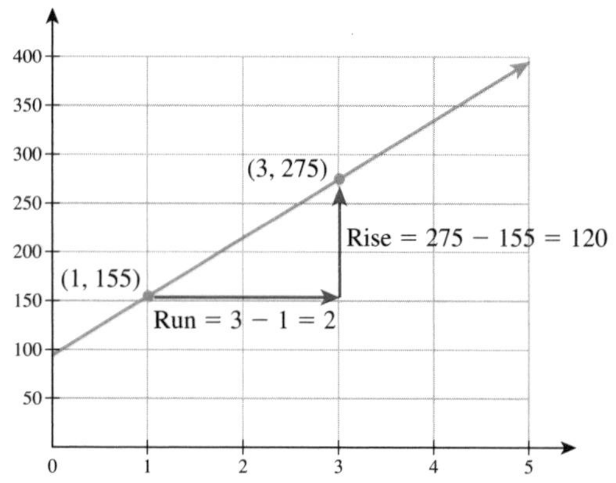

Figure 6

Solution

a. Use the table of values in Example 1 to pick two points on the line, as shown in Figure 6. From these points compute **run** = **2** and **rise** = **120**. Slope is then found to be the ratio

$$\frac{\text{rise}}{\text{run}} = \frac{120}{2} = 60$$

b. Use the table of values in Figure 5 to pick two points on the line shown in Figure 4. We'll use several different pairs to show we get the same result each time.

First, let's use $p_1 = (0, 140)$ and $p_2 = (1, 110)$. Substitute to get

$$\text{slope} = \frac{\text{rise}}{\text{run}} = \frac{y_2 - y_1}{x_2 - x_1} = \frac{110 - 140}{1 - 0} = {}^-30$$

Now let's use $p_1 = (0, 140)$ and $p_3 = (2, 80)$:

$$\text{slope} = \frac{\text{rise}}{\text{run}} = \frac{y_2 - y_1}{x_2 - x_1} = \frac{80 - 140}{2 - 0} = \frac{{}^-60}{2} = {}^-30$$

So far, so good. Now let's make the second point to the *left* of the first point. We'll use $p_5 = (4, 20)$ and $p_2 = (1, 110)$:

$$\text{slope} = \frac{\text{rise}}{\text{run}} = \frac{y_2 - y_1}{x_2 - x_1} = \frac{110 - 20}{1 - 4} = \frac{90}{{}^-3} = {}^-30$$

It still works! In fact, this formula for slope will work no matter what two points we choose on the line and in either order we subtract.

Example 4 illustrates an important concept.

Slopes of Lines

Straight lines have constant slope.

We may make another observation. The slope we found in Example 4(a) is 60. This is the same as the coefficient of x in the equation $y = 60x + 95$. It is the *rate* the mechanic charges for labor, $60 per hour.

In part (b) the slope is $^-30$. This is the same as the coefficient of x in the equation $y = 140 - 30x$. Note that we can write the equation as $y = ^-30x + 140$. The slope is also a rate, $^-30$ feet/second. It is a negative rate, because the distance to the finish line is decreasing as time increases.

Meaning of Slope

The slope of a line represents the **rate of change** of the output variable with respect to the input variable. In an application the rate may be expressed as units of y *per* units of x.

When interpreting slope in an application problem, keep the rate-of-change concept in mind. Think of the units for slope as something per something else. In the preceding examples we had dollars *per* hour and feet *per* second. Finally, we noticed that in both cases, the slope is the *coefficient* of x.

Finding the Slope

For the line given by the equation $y = \text{coefficient} * x + \text{constant}$, the coefficient of x is the slope of the line.

EXAMPLE 5 Graph these equations using your calculator and describe how changing the slope affects the steepness of a line. Notice that all these lines have the same y-intercept, $(0, 1)$.

$$y = 2x + 1$$
$$y = 1x + 1$$
$$y = \tfrac{1}{2}x + 1$$
$$y = 0x + 1$$
$$y = ^-\tfrac{1}{2}x + 1$$

$$y = {}^-1x + 1$$
$$y = {}^-2x + 1$$

Solution Figure 7 shows all seven equations graphed in the ZoomDecimal Window ($^-4.7 \leq x \leq 4.7, ^-3.1 \leq y \leq 3.1$). You may want to look at only one of them at a time.

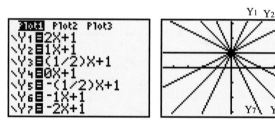

Figure 7 All seven equations are on the left, with the graphs on the right. Notice that we put parentheses around fractional coefficients of X.

We can make these observations:

1. The lines Y1, Y2, and Y3, which all have positive slope, rise as we move to the right.
2. The lines Y5, Y6, and Y7, which all have negative slope, fall as we move to the right.
3. The line Y4, which has zero slope, is horizontal.
4. The larger the *absolute value* of the slope (in other words the bigger the number, if you forget the minus sign), the steeper the rise or fall of the line.

■ ■ ■

We can summarize the previous example by noting the following facts.

How Do Graphs of Lines with Different Slopes Look?

Fact 1 Lines with positive slopes go to the right and up. The larger the positive value, the steeper the line.

Fact 2 A line with zero slope is horizontal.

Fact 3 Lines with negative slopes go to the right and down. The larger the negative slope in *absolute value*, the steeper the line.

EXAMPLE 6 Find the slope of the line passing through each pair of points.

a. $(^-4, 5), (^-1, ^-2)$
b. $(1, ^-2), (4, 3)$

c. $(^-3, 4), (5, 4)$

d. $(3, ^-2), (3, 1)$

Figure 8 shows the pairs of points and the lines passing through them.

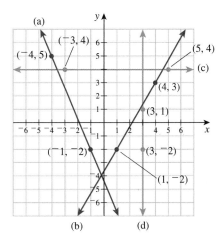

Figure 8

Solution

a. slope $= \dfrac{\text{rise}}{\text{run}}$

$= \dfrac{y_2 - y_1}{x_2 - x_1}$

$= \dfrac{^-2 - 5}{^-1 - {}^-4}$

$= \dfrac{^-2 + {}^-5}{^-1 + 4}$

$= \dfrac{^-7}{3}$

The line connecting $(^-4, 5)$ and $(^-1, {}^-2)$ has a negative slope. It goes to the right and down.

b. slope $= \dfrac{\text{rise}}{\text{run}}$

$= \dfrac{y_2 - y_1}{x_2 - x_1}$

$= \dfrac{3 - {}^-2}{4 - 1}$

$= \dfrac{3 + 2}{4 + {}^-1}$

$= \dfrac{5}{3}$

The line connecting $(1, {}^{-}2)$ and $(4, 3)$ has a positive slope. It goes to the right and up.

c. slope $= \dfrac{\text{rise}}{\text{run}}$

$= \dfrac{y_2 - y_1}{x_2 - x_1}$

$= \dfrac{4 - 4}{5 - {}^{-}3}$

$= \dfrac{0}{5 + 3}$

$= \dfrac{0}{8}$

$= 0$

The line connecting $({}^{-}3, 4)$ and $(5, 4)$ has zero slope. It goes from left to right without rising or falling. It is horizontal.

d. slope $= \dfrac{\text{rise}}{\text{run}}$

$= \dfrac{y_2 - y_1}{x_2 - x_1}$

$= \dfrac{1 - {}^{-}2}{3 - 3}$

$= \dfrac{1 + 2}{0}$

$= \dfrac{3}{0}$

We have a problem here because division by 0 is not allowed. We say that the slope is *undefined*. The line goes straight up and down. It is vertical.

EXAMPLE 7 Michael and Sarah start a business selling their shareware computer program over the Internet. Their web host charges them a flat fee of $150 per month and then charges them $.10 for every megabyte their customers download. The encoded file containing their program is 7.5 megabytes. They are hoping that because they got a good review on a popular website, their downloads will increase next month by 2000 units. How much will their cost go up if this happens?

Solution If we think of the number of programs downloaded as an input and the cost per month as the output, then the question they need to answer can be rephrased as, If the input goes up by 2000, by how much will the output go up? To answer this question we can use the slope of the linear equation relating input to output.

   Each program is 7.5 megabytes and each megabyte costs 10 cents, so they pay 75 cents, or $\frac{3}{4}$ of a dollar, per download. Because the slope of a line is the *rate of change* of the output with respect to the input (page 129), the slope of the line is .75.

We are given the change in input, or run, which is **2000**. We need to find the change in output, that is, the rise. Using the formula

$$\text{slope} = \frac{\text{rise}}{\text{run}}$$

we have

$$.75 = \frac{\text{rise}}{\textbf{2000}}.$$

Solving for rise gives 1500. Because the output is expressed in dollars, their cost will go up by $1500.

Notice that to solve this particular problem we did not need to use the flat fee nor did we need to know how many downloads they are currently selling each month.

■ ■

Exercises 4.1

1. For each situation, identify the variable cost, the fixed cost, and the rate of change.

   a. The charge for a telephone call from the United States to Japan is $1.25 plus 25 cents per minute.

   b. In 2012, first-class postage costs 25 cents plus 20 cents for every ounce a letter weighs.

   c. To rent a car from the Pinnacle Car Company, you must pay 25 cents for each mile driven plus an 8 dollar service fee.

2. Given the equations

   a. $y = 60x + 95$ b. $y = 2x + 4$
   c. $y = 3x$ d. $y = 800x + 1750$

   (1) What is the output for each equation when the input is zero?

   (2) Give another name for the constant term.

3. Suppose you are driving up a hill of steady incline. We describe the pitch, or steepness, of the hill algebraically as the slope. Let $y = .02x + 1000$ model this situation, where y is the elevation and x is the horizontal distance traveled, both measured in feet.

   a. Use this function to generate two ordered pairs called (x_1, y_1) and (x_2, y_2).

   b. Find the slope using the slope formula.

   c. Generate two more ordered pairs and calculate the slope again.

   d. Compare the slopes from parts (b) and (c). What does this imply about the rate of incline of the hill?

4. Find the slope of the line given by each equation.

   a. $y = 60x + 95$ b. $y = 2x + 4$
   c. $y = 3x$ d. $y = 800x + 1750$
   e. $y = {}^-5x + 1$ f. $y = \frac{4}{3}x - 7$

5. The figure shows a graph of four linear equations. Identify the slope of each line as a positive, zero, or negative slope.

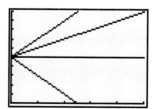

6. Given the three ordered pairs $A = (^-1, ^-3)$, $B = (0, ^-1)$, and $C = (1, 7)$:

   a. Graph the ordered pairs and connect the points.

   b. Does the graph appear to have a constant slope?

   c. Compute the slope between A and B and then between B and C.

   d. Do the slopes found in part (c) support your conclusion from part (b)?

7. In Section 2.3 you were introduced to Gridville, where the run and rise were used to find a new location.

   a. If you begin at $(0, 4)$ and know run $= 5$ and rise $= 3$ (so the slope $= \frac{3}{5}$), where will you end up?

   b. Begin at $(1, ^-3)$ and apply a slope of $\frac{^-3}{2}$ to find a new location.

   c. Any whole number such as 4 can be expressed as a fraction $\frac{4}{1}$. Starting at the point $(1, 5)$ and following a line with a slope of 4, find the next location.

   d. Start at $(^-1, 3)$ and use a slope of $\frac{1}{2}$ to find two new locations.

8. Show that a slope of $\frac{^-1}{2}$ is equivalent to the slope $\frac{1}{^-2}$ by using the following steps:

   a. Plot a starting point $(0, 3)$ on a graph.

   b. Use the slope of $\frac{\text{rise}}{\text{run}} = \frac{^-1}{2}$ to find a new point.

   c. Again, start at $(0, 3)$ and use the slope of $\frac{\text{rise}}{\text{run}} = \frac{1}{^-2}$ to find a new point.

   d. Are all three points on the same line? What does this imply about the slopes $\frac{^-1}{2}$ and $\frac{1}{^-2}$?

9. Find the slope of the line between each pair of points.

   a. $(^-4, 1)$ and $(2, ^-5)$ b. $(3, ^-5)$ and $(^-2, 6)$

   c. $(2, 4)$ and $(^-2, 1)$ d. $(0, ^-3)$ and $(5, ^-3)$

10. An investment of $1000 increases at the rate of $100 per year.

    a. What is the initial value?

    b. Use the rate of change to find the investment's worth after 1 year and 2 years.

    c. Does this investment's growth represent a linear relationship? Explain.

11. A different $1000 investment is appreciating according to the following table.

Elapsed Years	Value of Investment
0	$1000
1	$1100
2	$1210
3	$1331

a. What is the investment's initial value?

b. Is this investment's rate of change constant? Explain.

c. Does this investment's growth represent a linear relationship? Explain.

d. Which investment would you rather own, this one or the one in Exercise 10? Why?

12. The following table shows the dividend per share paid by the XYZ corporation.

Year	Years since 2000	Dividend per Share
2000	0	.25
2001	1	.25
2002	2	.25
2003	3	.25

Let x be the number of years since 2000 and y be the dividend per share.

a. Draw a graph.

b. Find the slope.

c. Interpret the slope.

13. The Super Light Soft-Drink Company claims its soda is less dense than water. An independent lab wishes to check the truth of the company's claim. They place a beaker weighing 50 g on a scale and weigh the beaker when it contains 10 mL, 20 mL, 30 mL, 40 mL and 50 mL. The results are presented graphically in the figure.

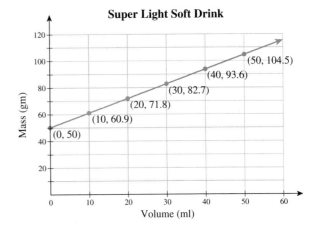

a. Calculate the density of Superlight by finding the slope of the line.

b. Compare Superlight's density with that of pure water (1.00). Did the company tell the truth?

14. Digitech computer software company can sell 400 disks a day at a price of $60. The company can, however, increase its sales by 28 disks a day for each $2 reduction in price.

   a. What is the rate of change?

   b. Interpret the rate of change.

   c. Use the rate of change to find additional entries for the table.

x (Price)	y (Number of Disks Sold)
60	400
58	428
56	456
⋮	⋮

15. The following table shows basal metabolic rates (BMR) for 22-year-old men and women of different weights and average height. BMR is the number of calories per day the body requires while at rest. [Harris-Benedict equation (http://www.weight-loss-i.com/calorie-needs-harris-benedict.htm)]

Weight	Female BMR	Male BMR
100	1283	1412
120	1371	1536
140	1459	1660
160	1547	1784
180	1635	1908
200	1723	2032

   a. Draw a graph using the BMR column for your gender.

   b. Find the slope.

   c. Interpret the slope.

Skills and Review 4.1

16. Point A is located at $(^-2, 1)$ and point B is located at $(3, ^-5)$. Find the distance traveled from point A to point B. Outline your work using the seven steps for problem solving.

17. Suppose you are making a choice between two cell-phone plans. Plan A charges $22.95 plus 7 cents for each minute of calling. Plan B charges $28.45 plus 3 cents for each minute of calling. After how many minutes would the two plans cost the same? Outline your work using the seven steps for problem solving.

18. Solve for x if $11 - x = 8(x + 4) - 3$.

19. Verify that $x = 5$ is a solution to the equation $^-4x + 23 = 2x - 7$.

20. Solve $5x - (6 - x) = 4 + 2x$ for x.

21. A formula for the circumference of a circle is $C = 2\pi r$. Find the radius of the circle if the circumference is $(\frac{11}{6})\pi$ cm.

22. The perimeter of an equilateral triangle is three times the length of a side. Let P represent the perimeter of the triangle and let s represent the length of a side of the triangle.

   a. Write a formula that shows how P depends upon s.

   b. Complete a table of values using your formula from part (a).

   c. Display your data from part (b) in a graph.

23. Simplify the expression $4c^2 - 5(d - 2) + 7c^2 + 6 - d$.

24. Evaluate $x + \frac{2}{3} - 4 + (^-3)^4$ for $x = 11$.

25. Convert 20 feet/minute into inches/second.

4.2 Forms of Linear Equations

AFTER STUDYING THIS SECTION YOU WILL BE ABLE TO

   ▪ Find an equation of a line given a slope and y-intercept, one point and the slope, or two points.

   ▪ Write the equation of a line in slope-intercept form.

   ▪ Use the x- and y-intercepts to sketch the graph of a linear equation.

Slope-Intercept Form

Any equation involving simple terms with two variables (say x and y) and possibly a constant term may be put in the form

$$y = \text{coefficient} * x + \text{constant}$$

using simple algebraic manipulations. In Section 4.1 we learned that the graph of this equation is a straight line. Linear equations in this form are so common that there is a special formula for them.

Definition   Slope-Intercept Form

A linear equation in two variables is in **slope-intercept form** if it is written

$$y = mx + b$$

where x and y can be replaced by any two variable names. The *slope* of the line is given by m, and the y-intercept is the point $(0, b)$.

The coefficient m and the constant b have important graphical meanings.

- b is the y-value at which the line crosses the y-axis, called the y-intercept. When we substitute $x = 0$ into the formula $y = mx + b$, we get

$$y = m * 0 + b = b$$

  We saw in Section 4.1 that b may also be considered the *initial value* of the output variable.

- m is the *slope* of the line, which you can think of as the *rate of change*. It tells us how much y changes if x increases by 1.

EXAMPLE 1   Michelle is going to start a business renting DVDs. She wants to make a bulk purchase of disks to start. A company offers to sell her disks for $22 each, with a fixed shipping charge of $400. Write a linear equation and draw a graph that Michelle can use to study this offer.

Solution   The input is the number of DVDs Michelle purchases, so we call that x. The output, y, is her cost. In this case, even if Michelle bought 0 DVDs (but had the empty carton shipped!), she would spend $400, so the line should cross the *y*-axis at the point (0, 400). Therefore, $b = 400$. Each extra DVD costs her $22, so the slope *m* is **22**.

We substitute for *m* and *b* in the formula $y = mx + b$. This gives Michelle the equation she wants:

$$y = 22x + 400$$

Figure 9 shows the graph of this equation. We check the slope by choosing two points on the line. The slope is

$$\frac{\text{rise}}{\text{run}} = \frac{4400}{200} = 22$$

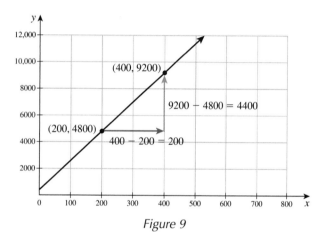

Figure 9

EXAMPLE 2

An airplane is flying at 30,000 feet and begins to descend to the airport at a constant rate of 250 feet/minute. What linear equation models the height of the airplane in terms of the number of minutes since it began descending?

Solution

Once again we are given a physical problem that lends itself to the *slope-intercept formula* very well. We know the initial value is 30,000 feet, and the rate of change (slope) is ⁻250 feet/minute. Notice that we made the slope a negative number because the airplane is losing altitude.

We let *y* represent the altitude (in feet) and *x* the time (in minutes) after the plane starts dropping. Again, we use the formula $y = mx + b$. We substitute $m = ^-250$ and $b = 30{,}000$ to obtain the equation

$$y = {}^-250x + 30{,}000$$

Let's check to see if this equation is a good model. If $x = 0$—in other words, if the plane is about to start descending—then

$$y = {}^-250 * 0 + 30{,}000 = 30{,}000$$

which is correct. To check the rate, let's see how high the plane is after **1** minute:

$$y = {}^-250 * \mathbf{1} + 30{,}000 = 29{,}750$$

The plane started at 30,000 feet and in 1 minute dropped to 29,750 feet, so it is descending 250 feet/minute, which is also correct. See Figure 10.

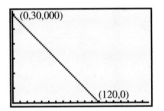

Figure 10 Graph of the altitude function Y1 = $^-$250X + 30,000. We have used the friendly window Xmin = 0, Xmax = 188, Ymin = 0, and Ymax = 31,000.

■ ■ ■

If we look carefully at Figure 10, we notice that the graph crosses not only the *y*-axis but the *x*-axis as well. The *y*-intercept is the initial altitude (the altitude when $x = 0$), but does the **x-intercept** have any special significance? If we look at the graph on our calculator, we can use $\boxed{\text{TRACE}}$ to find the coordinates of the *x*-intercept. We get the values given in Figure 10, (120, 0).

Does the point (120, 0) have some special meaning? This point indicates that 120 minutes after the plane has started to descend, the altitude *y* is 0. That means the plane is on the ground. This model for the altitude of the plane is good only for 120 minutes, because the plane won't get below the ground (we hope!).

We can solve for the *x*-intercept algebraically using the fact that it is the place where *y* must be 0. Setting *y* to **0** in the equation, we get

$$0 = {}^-250x + 30{,}000$$

$$250x = 30{,}000$$

$$\frac{250x}{250} = \frac{30{,}000}{250}$$

$$x = 120$$

which is just what the calculator graph gave us. In this case we were lucky that the graph gave us the *exact* value for the *x*-intercept. Sometimes tracing will give us only an approximation.

As in Example 2, we are often interested in both the *x*-intercept and the *y*-intercept. Here's how we find them.

Finding Intercepts

For any linear equation in two variables,

- We find the *y*-intercept by setting $x = 0$. The *y*-intercept is always (0, some number).
- We find the *x*-intercept by setting $y = 0$. The *x*-intercept is always (some number, 0).

Standard Form

Not all linear equations are written in slope-intercept form. In Example 3 we encounter a linear equation in **standard form**.

Definition   Standard Form of a Linear Equation

A linear equation in two variables is in **standard form** if it is written

$$Ax + By = C$$

A, *B*, and *C* may be any numbers as long as *A* and *B* are not both zero, and *x* and *y* can be replaced by any variable names.

Example 3 shows how to interpret the standard form of an equation.

EXAMPLE 3   Suppose there are two dams on a lake. In order to keep the lake level, the dams must release 1000 gallons of water per second. The first dam releases 8 gallons per second for each click its gates are opened, and the second dam releases 10 gallons per second for each click its gates are opened. The dam keeper needs an equation that will let him work out how much to open the second dam if he knows how far open the first dam is.

Solution   Let's let *x* be the number of clicks that the first dam is open and *y* be the number of clicks the second dam is open. We can compute how many gallons will be released in 1 second with the equation

$$\text{water flow} = 8x + 10y$$

We know that **water flow** has to be **1000**, so we can substitute:

$$1000 = 8x + 10y$$

Now we have an equation with two variables. We can get some idea what the graph of this equation looks like by finding both the *x*- and *y*-intercepts.

To find the x-intercept, we set $y = 0$ and substitute:

$$1000 = 8x + 10 * 0$$

$$1000 = 8x$$

$$\frac{1000}{8} = \frac{8x}{8}$$

$$125 = x$$

The x-intercept is $(125, 0)$.

To find the y-intercept, we set $x = 0$ and substitute:

$$1000 = 8 * 0 + 10y$$

$$1000 = 10y$$

$$\frac{1000}{10} = \frac{10y}{10}$$

$$100 = y$$

The y-intercept is $(0, 100)$.

We can now sketch the graph in the first quadrant using the two intercepts. See Figure 11. Because the line appears to have a negative slope, the dam keeper can see that as x increases, y decreases. This makes sense to him, because if he opens the first gate a little more, he can close the second gate a bit and still get the same amount of water flow. If the dam keeper wants to be able to determine quickly how to adjust the second dam based on how open the first dam is, standard form is not very useful. Having an equation in slope-intercept form expresses the variable for the second dam, y, as a function of the variable for the first dam, x. So he needs to solve for y *in terms of* x.

Start with the equation $1000 = 8x + 10y$. Don't worry about the fact that we don't know the value of $8x$. Treat it as if it were a known quantity, and subtract it from both sides of the equation to isolate y. This gives us

$$1000 - 8x = 10y$$

We now know that we can solve for y if we divide by 10 on both sides.

$$\frac{1000 - 8x}{10} = \frac{10y}{10}$$

Remember that dividing by 10 is like multiplying by $\frac{1}{10}$, so the distributive property applies.

$$\frac{1}{10} * 1000 - \frac{1}{10} * 8x = \frac{1}{10} * 10y$$

$$100 - .8x = y$$

This equation may be rearranged so that it is in slope-intercept form:

$$y = {}^-.8x + 100$$

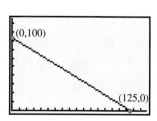

(0,100)

(125,0)

Figure 11

The dam keeper is satisfied. He may now take any value for x, substitute it into the equation, and find the corresponding value of y.

Although the dam keeper is happy with the equation $y = {}^-.8x + 100$, we might benefit by taking another look at it in connection with the graph in Figure 11. If we do that, we may observe the following.

- Using the formula $y = mx + b$, we know that $m = {}^-.8$. This gives us a negative slope, which is what we should expect from the line we see in Figure 11. Furthermore, if we go from the y-intercept to the x-intercept, we have **run** $= 125$ and **rise** $= {}^-100$. So

$$\text{slope} = \frac{\textbf{rise}}{\textbf{run}} = \frac{{}^-\textbf{100}}{\textbf{125}} = {}^-.8$$

   That's the same as m. So, we know we are on the right track.
- Using our formula $y = mx + b$, we know that $b = 100$. This gives us a y-intercept of $(0, 100)$, which is what is shown in Figure 11.
- Slope-intercept form is exactly what our calculator needs to draw a graph. We can enter the equation $y = {}^-.8x + 100$ in the Y = menu and find a suitable window (for example, $0 \le X \le 188, 0 \le Y \le 120$). We should get a graph that looks a lot like the one in Figure 11.

EXAMPLE 4 Jessica's father gives her a piggy bank when she turns 12 and tells her, "I put some money in the bank to get you started, but now you have to deposit some of your allowance into the bank each week to make it grow." Jessica deposits $5 into the bank each week. At the end of one year she breaks open the bank and discovers that she has $360. How much money did Jessica's father deposit initially?

Solution The information we are given is the rate at which the money is increasing ($5 per week) and the amount of money after 52 weeks (1 year). Because the rate never changes, we may use a linear equation to model the data. Let y be the amount in the savings account and x be the time in weeks since the account was opened. The rate is the slope, and the amount of money after 52 weeks gives us one point on the line.

Let's see what we can do with our favorite formula, $y = mx + b$.

We know the slope, m, is 5. And we know that when $x = 52, y = 360$. Let's substitute to get

$$y = mx + b$$

$$\textbf{360} = \textbf{5} * \textbf{52} + \textbf{b}$$

$$\textbf{360} = \textbf{260} + \textbf{b}$$

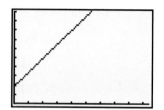

Figure 12 Jessica's father initially deposited $100 into the piggy bank. We have used the friendly window $0 \le X \le 94$, $0 \le Y \le 500$.

Now we have an equation with only one variable, b. We may solve for b by subtracting 260 on both sides to obtain

$$100 = b$$

Because the y-intercept is also the initial amount deposited, we can answer the question. Jessica's father deposited $100 initially.

■ ■ ■

We may also write an equation that shows how y depends upon x by substituting for both m and b in the formula $y = mx + b$.

$$y = mx + b$$

$$y = 5x + 100$$

A graph of this equation is shown in Figure 12.

EXAMPLE 5

PCBs were dumped into the Hudson river for many years. The United States Environmental Protection Agency extensively studied the concentration of these chemicals in various fish as part of the process of determining whether to force the General Electric company to dredge the river bottom. The approximate concentrations of PCBs in brown bullheads were as follows:

Year	Concentration (mg/kg)
1984	46
1985	42.5
1986	39

These points look as if they might lie on a straight line (Figure 13). Assuming they do, we should be able to find an equation that will allow us to determine the PCB concentration in past or future years and answer the following questions.

a. What was the concentration in 1980?

b. When will the concentration be 0?

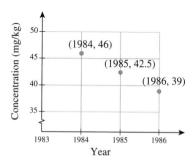

Figure 13 Data from the EPA (http://www.epa.gov/hudson).

Solution

This example is very different from our previous ones. We are *not* given an initial value, and we aren't even given a rate of change. All we have are the coordinates of some points on our line. Because the first question we want to answer is what is the concentration in 1980, we let 1980 be year 0. Our table of values is now as follows.

Years Since 1980, x	Concentration (mg/kg), y
4	46
5	42.5
6	39

In order to answer parts (a) and (b), we need to write an equation relating x and y. From the table we observe that an increase of 1 in x results in a decrease of 3.5 in y (we have approximated the actual concentrations; in most real-world situations you would *not* expect even three points to lie exactly on a line). In other words, when run $= 1$, rise $= {}^-3.5$. Therefore, we will choose a line with

$$\text{slope} = \frac{\text{rise}}{\text{run}} = {}^-3.5$$

a. We can use the slope-intercept formula for the equation of a line and substitute what we do know. We can use any of the first three pairs of values for x and y, and we know that the slope is $m = {}^-3.5$. Let's use the pair $(4, 46)$. We get

$$y = mx + b$$
$$46 = {}^-3.5 * 4 + b$$
$$46 = {}^-14 + b$$
$$60 = b \qquad \text{\textit{Adding} 14 \textit{on both sides of the equation}}$$

In slope-intercept form, b is the y-intercept, the value of y when $x = 0$. In this case $b = 60$ means the concentration of PCBs was 60 mg/kg in 1980, if our linear model is correct.

b. Now we have an equation in slope-intercept form:

$$y = {}^-3.5x + 60$$

We find the x-intercept of the graph, which corresponds to the point where the concentration is 0. We can enter the equation $y = {}^-3.5x + 60$ into our calculator and estimate the x-intercept, as shown in Figure 14. We can compute the approximate intercepts by using $\boxed{\text{TRACE}}$ in the friendly window Xmin $= 0$, Xmax $= 18.8$, Ymin $= 0$, and Ymax $= 62$; the x-intercept is about 17, so if our model is correct, the PCBs should have disappeared in $1980 + 17 = 1997$. We can also find the solution algebraically. We set $y = 0$ and solve for x.

$$0 = {}^-3.5x + 60$$
$${}^-60 = {}^-3.5x \qquad \text{\textit{Subtracting} 60 \textit{on both sides}}$$

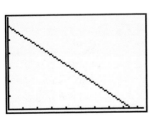

Figure 14

$$\frac{^-60}{^-3.5} = \frac{^-3.5x}{^-3.5}$$ *Dividing on both sides by $^-3.5$*

$$17.1 \approx x$$

It will take about 17 years for the PCBs to disappear completely.

If this model were accurate, the EPA would have a very tough time convincing anyone that dredging is necessary. In fact, any traces would be gone in only 17 years. In general, however, linear models are *not* well suited to situations like this. We can see this by looking at the actual PCB concentration in brown bullheads over a longer time period (Figure 15). The straight line works for a little while, but it quickly fails to model the actual data. The real concentration in fish drops slowly toward zero, whereas the linear equation implies that by the year 2000 the PCB concentration would be negative.

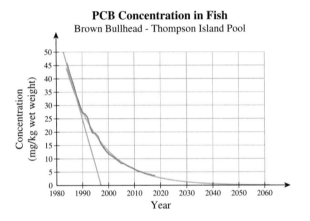

PCB Concentration in Fish
Brown Bullhead - Thompson Island Pool

Figure 15   Taken from http://www.epa.gov/hudson.

The following chart summarizes what we have learned about linear equations in this section.

How to Find an Equation of a Line

Given	Here's What to Do	Example
The slope, m, and the y-intercept, b	Substitute into the equation $y = mx + b$.	Example 1 (DVDs), Example 2 (airplane)
One point (x, y) and the slope, m	First substitute for x, y, and m in $y = mx + b$. Solve this equation for b. Then substitute m and b in $y = mx + b$.	Example 4 (piggy bank)
Two points, (x_1, y_1) and (x_2, y_2)	First find the slope $= \frac{\text{rise}}{\text{run}} = \frac{y_2-y_1}{x_2-x_1}$. Next substitute for x, y, and m in $y = mx + b$. Solve this equation for b. Then substitute m and b in $y = mx + b$.	Example 5 (PCBs)

How to Graph an Equation of a Line (Using a Calculator)

The equation is in slope-intercept form.	You may enter it directly into the Y= menu.	Examples 1, 2, 4, and 5
The equation is not in slope-intercept form.	First solve for y. Then enter the equation into the Y= menu.	Example 3 (dam keeper)

Exercises 4.2

1. Write each equation in the alternative form.

Slope-intercept Form	Standard Form
$y = 8x - 10$	?
?	$x + y = 7$
?	$6x - 2y = 7$

2. Find the slope and y-intercept for each of the equations.

   a. $y = .36x - .1$ **b.** $y = 4x + 9$

   c. $y = \frac{1}{3}x - 5$ **d.** $x + 4y = 7$

3. Consider the equation $y = {}^{-}3x + 5$.

   a. Is this equation in slope-intercept form or standard form?

   b. What is the slope, or rate of change?

   c. What is the y-intercept, or initial value?

   d. What is the x-intercept?

4. Given the graph shown:

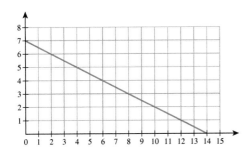

   a. Label the x- and y-intercepts on the graph.

   b. Use the x- and y-intercepts to find the slope.

   c. Use the slope and y-intercept to write an equation for the line.

5. Given the following table of values:

x	y
0	$^{-}4$
1	$^{-}2$
2	0

   a. What are the x- and y-intercepts?

   b. Use the intercepts to draw a graph by hand.

   c. Find the slope.

   d. Use the slope and y-intercept to write an equation.

6. Given the equation $4x + 5y = 20$:

   a. Find the x- and y-intercepts.

   b. Use the intercepts to draw a graph by hand.

7. Write an equation of the line with given slope and y-intercept.

   a. $m = \frac{3}{5}$, y-intercept $(0, 4)$

   b. $m = 2$, y-intercept $(0, {}^{-}1)$

   c. $m = 0$, y-intercept $(0, 7)$

   d. $m = \frac{-1}{2}$, y-intercept $(0, 0)$

8. Write an equation of the line with given slope and containing the given point.

   a. $m = 2, (5, 1)$ **b.** $m = \frac{-1}{3}, (6, 7)$

   c. $m = {}^{-}4, ({}^{-}3, 5)$ **d.** $m = 0, (1, 2)$

9. Write an equation of the line containing the given points.

   a. $(1, 3)$ and $(2, 2)$ **b.** $({}^{-}2, 1)$ and $(3, 6)$

   c. $(4, {}^{-}5)$ and $(0, {}^{-}3)$ **d.** $(3, 4)$ and $({}^{-}1, 4)$

10. At a local bank, the monthly service fee on a checking account depends on the number of checks written. The fees are $4.95 plus 10 cents for every check written.

a. What is the rate of change?

b. What is the initial value, or y-intercept?

c. Write an equation.

d. Draw a graph and label the information from parts (a) and (b).

11. A parachutist opens her chute at 3500 feet above the ground and falls at a rate of 22 feet/second after that. We wish to find a formula that models the parachutist's height in feet above the ground in terms of the time in seconds after she opens her chute. Let x be the time in seconds since she opened her chute and let y be her height in feet above the ground.

a. What is the value of y when $x = 0$?

b. If the value of x increases by 1, what will happen to the value of y?

c. Use the information in parts (a) and (b) to write a formula for the height, y, in terms of the time since the chute was opened, x.

12. Now we will model the situation from Exercise 11 with a table of values and a graph.

a. Make a table of values with inputs of 0, 40, 80, 120, and 160 seconds.

b. Draw a graph using a friendly window of $\text{Xmin} = 0$, $\text{Xmax} = 188$, $\text{Ymin} = 0$, $\text{Ymax} = 3600$.

c. Trace the graph to find an approximation for the x- and y-intercepts.

d. Find the exact x- and y-intercepts.

e. Interpret the x- and y-intercepts in relation to the real-world problem.

f. Find and interpret the slope.

13. Suppose you want to know the low temperature at a vacation spot. At 10 P.M. you hear the temperature is 75°F. Assume the temperature drops at a steady rate of 1.5°F each hour from the high at 2 P.M. until the low at 4 A.M. We can represent this problem with a table of values, an equation, and a graph.

a. Complete the table to find the low temperature.

Hour of Day	Elapsed Hours Since 2 P.M.	Temperature (°F)
10 P.M.	8	75
11 P.M.	9	73.5
12 A.M.	10	72
1 A.M.	?	?
2 A.M.	?	?
3 A.M.	?	?
4 A.M.	?	?

b. Use the rate of change and one of the ordered pairs from the table to write an equation for the temperature in terms of the hours since 2 P.M.

c. Find a friendly window to graph the equation. Trace the graph to approximate the low temperature. *Note:* The Y= menu requires that your equation be solved for y.

d. Because the low temperature occurs 14 hours after the high, let $x = 14$ hours and solve the equation from part (b) for y. This will give an exact low temperature.

14. Recall that the basal metabolic rate (BMR) determines the number of calories per day a person needs while at rest. The table shows BMR values for a 22-year-old male of average height. [Harris-Benedict equation (http://www.weight-loss-i.com/calorie-needs-harris-benedict.htm)]

Weight in Pounds	BMR
100	1412
120	1536
140	1660
160	1784
180	1908

a. Find the rate of change, or slope.

b. Write an equation for BMR in terms of weight.

c. Find the BMR for a 150-pound male.

15. Paul and Joan have a house-cleaning business. Paul can complete one job in 3 hours and Joan can complete one job in 2 hours. Let x represent the number of hours Paul works and y represent the number of hours Joan works.

a. Write an expression for the number of jobs Paul completes in terms of x.

b. Write an expression for the number of jobs Joan completes in terms of y.

c. Write an equation that shows how x and y are related if they complete a total of 6 jobs.

d. Write the equation in slope-intercept form.

e. Find a friendly window and make a graph.

f. Interpret the x- and y-intercepts.

g. Interpret the slope.

Skills and Review 4.2

16. Find m in the formula for the slope of a line,

$$m = \frac{y_2 - y_1}{x_2 - x_1},$$

when $x_1 = 5$, $x_2 = {}^-2$, $y_1 = {}^-1$, and $y_2 = 4$.

17. Shown here are the graph of a line and two points.

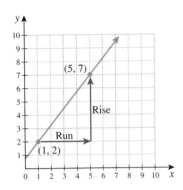

a. Find the run and rise.

b. Find the slope of the line.

c. The slope of a line is the steepness of the line connecting the two points, whereas the distance is the length of the line segment connecting the two points. Find the distance between the two points using the formula:

$$\text{distance} = \sqrt{\text{run}^2 + \text{rise}^2},$$

or

$$\sqrt{(x_2 - x_1)^2 + (y_2 - y_1)^2}.$$

18. Suppose two people start from the same place and travel in opposite directions. One person travels at 50 miles/hour. The other person travels at 60 miles/hour.

How long will it be before they are 385 miles apart? Outline your work using the seven steps for problem solving.

19. Solve for x if $1 - \frac{1}{3}(x + 9) = 4(5 - \frac{1}{4}x)$.

20. A formula for the area of a trapezoid is $A = (\frac{1}{2})(b_1 + b_2)h$.

  a. Find b_1 if $A = 13 \text{ cm}^2$, $b_2 = 7 \text{ cm}$, and $h = 2 \text{ cm}$.

  b. Evaluate the expression for the values of b_1, b_2, and h to check the accuracy of your work in part (a).

21. Find the length of the diagonal of the rectangle in the figure.

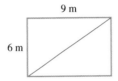

  a. Give an approximate answer.

  b. Give an exact answer.

22. Evaluate $-\sqrt{b^2 - 4ac}$ when $a = 3$, $b = {}^-4$, and $c = {}^-1$.

23. Use the distributive property (Section 2.1) to factor $(4 * 83) - (4 * 3)$. Simplify the result mentally using the order of operations.

24. Mentally evaluate

$$\frac{4^2 - 2^4}{3^{-1}}$$

Check your work on a calculator.

25. Mentally evaluate $-24 - {}^-8 - 6 + 22$.

4.3 **Graphical Solution of Systems of Equations**

AFTER STUDYING THIS SECTION YOU WILL BE ABLE TO

  ▪ Solve a system of linear equations in two variables by graphing.
  ▪ Identify an inconsistent system of linear equations in two variables.

Systems of Equations

You have now seen several examples of **linear equations in two variables**. We now examine what happens when we have two such equations. First, let's take a closer look at the relationship between an equation and the points that lie on its line.

Consider the graph in Figure 16. Each of the points labeled is on the line and must, therefore, make the equation that corresponds to the line $y = 3x + 5$ true. We can check two: p_1 is the point $(^-1, 2)$, so $x = {}^-1$ and $y = 2$. If we substitute these values for x and y, we get

$$2 \overset{?}{=} 3(^-1) + 5$$
$$2 = 2 \qquad \textit{OK!}$$

p_2 is the point $(1.5, 9.5)$, and we can check again:

$$9.5 \overset{?}{=} 3(1.5) + 5$$
$$9.5 = 4.5 + 5 \qquad \textit{OK!}$$

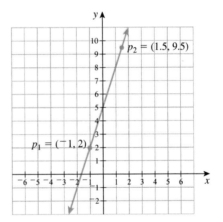

Figure 16 Any point on the line satisfies the equation $y = 3x + 5$.

The same thing will happen with *every* point on the line when we substitute its coordinates in the equation. Consequently, there are an *infinite* number of points that satisfy the given equation.

Definition   Solution of a Linear Equation in Two Variables

A **solution** of a linear equation in two variables is an ordered pair of numbers (x, y) that satisfies the equation.

Many real-life problems have lots of solutions. In Example 3 in Section 4.2, there are many pairs of values for x and y that satisfy the equation $y = {}^-.8x + 100$. These values give the dam keeper what he wants: a combination of clicks on the gates for the dams that will produce a flow of 1000 gallons each second. The only limitations are that x and y must be integers and neither of them can be negative. For instance, he can't open a dam 4.5 clicks or $^-3$ clicks. Some examples of pairs that do satisfy the equation are (0, 100), (25, 80), (50, 60), and (125, 0). There are other cases in real life, however, where there is only one solution. Often these cases involve *two* linear equations in two variables. We look for a pair of values (x, y) that satisfy *both* equations.

EXAMPLE 1   Suppose we are given the equations

$$4 = 3x - y$$
$$y = {}^-3x + 2$$

Can we find values of x and y that will satisfy *both* equations?

Solution   We will write the first equation in slope-intercept form so that we can graph it easily.

$$4 = 3x - y$$
$$4 + y = 3x$$
$$y = 3x - 4$$

Now we can graph both equations (see Figure 17). We know any point on the line with positive slope will make the equation $y = 3x - 4$ true, and any point on the other line will make $y = {}^-3x + 2$ true. The point that is on *both* lines makes both equations true.

From our graph, the solution is the point $(1, {}^-1)$.

■ ■

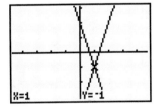

Figure 17   The point on both lines satisfies both equations. We use the zoom decimal window $^-4.7 \leq X \leq 4.7$, $^-3.1 \leq Y \leq 3.1$.

What makes Example 1 different from our previous examples is that we have *two* different linear equations. Instead of a variety of possible solutions, there is only one solution. It is found at the *intersection point* of the two lines.

Definition   System of Linear Equations in Two Variables

Two linear equations in two variables are called **a system of linear equations in two variables**. Any point that is a solution to both equations is a solution to the system of equations.

Because a solution to a system of linear equations is a point that is a solution to *both* equations, it occurs at a point on the lines of both equations in the system.

> ### Finding the Solution to a System of Linear Equations
>
> We can find the solution to a system of linear equations by finding the **intersection point** of the two lines corresponding to the equations in the system (if such a point exists). This can be done either graphically or algebraically.

EXAMPLE 2 Suppose that one long-distance phone company charges 3 cents per minute plus a monthly fee of $4, and another company charges 6 cents per minute with no monthly fee. How many minutes of phone calls could you make in a month to have the same charge from each company?

Solution We write equations for the cost of long distance calls per month for each company. If we let x be the number of minutes of calls, then the first company charges $y = 3x + 400$, because $4 is 400 cents. The second company charges $y = 6x$. We can enter these two equations in the calculator as Y1 and Y2. A graph of the two equations, in a first quadrant window, looks like the one in Figure 18.

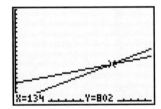

Figure 18 The two lines meet when X is about 134 minutes. We have used the friendly window $0 \le X \le 188, 0 \le Y \le 2000$.

The intersection point is the solution because at that point the minutes are the same and the cost is the same. We estimate the coordinates by tracing along one of the lines until we come as close as we can to the intersection point (Figure 18). The point seems to be about (134, 802).

We can get a more precise result using a calculator feature called *intersect*. This is how it works on a TI-84. First trace along one of the lines until the cursor is near the intersection point. Then press 2nd CALC. Scroll down to 5:intersect. Press ENTER three times, and the coordinates of the intersection point will appear on the screen: X ≈ 133.33333, Y ≈ 800 (Figure 19). We conclude that after about 133 minutes of phone calls, the cost of the two plans is the same.

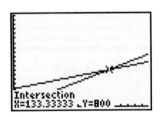

Figure 19 The two lines meet when X is about 133 minutes.

EXAMPLE 3

A hare is going to race a tortoise to prove that slow and steady *doesn't* always win. The hare will be a good sport and give the tortoise a head start of 10 miles. The hare can run at a speed of 18 miles/hour. The tortoise moves along at 2 miles/hour. How long will it take for the hare to catch the tortoise?

Solution

This is a distance-rate-time problem. If we let t represent the time (in hours) that they race, the hare travels a distance of $18t$ miles and the tortoise travels only $2t$ miles.

Figure 20 shows the distance covered by each runner and the tortoise's 10-mile head start. Let y represent the distance of each runner from where the hare started. For the hare, this is just how far he runs, so $y = 18t$. For the tortoise, we need to include the 10-mile head start, so $y = 2t + 10$.

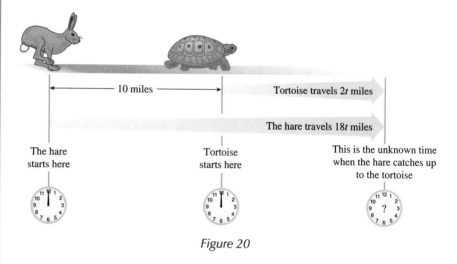

Figure 20

We may graph these equations to find the point of intersection. We'll have to use X in place of t for our calculator, so we have

$$Y1 = 18X$$

and

$$Y2 = 2X + 10$$

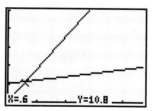

Figure 21   A graph with the hare's and the tortoise's distances versus time in the friendly window $0 \leq X \leq 4.7, 0 \leq Y \leq 50$.

From the graph in Figure 21 you can see that the line for the hare has a steeper slope and that he catches up to the tortoise in about .6 hour.

Inconsistent Systems

EXAMPLE 4

The hare is so proud of the fact that he caught up with the tortoise in less than one hour that he challenges a roadrunner to a race. He gives the roadrunner the same 10-mile head start as he gave the tortoise. Little does he realize that the roadrunner can also run at 18 miles/hour. Make a graph showing the result of this race.

Solution

By the same reasoning we used in Example 3, we have the equations

$$Y1 = 18X$$
$$Y2 = 18X + 10$$

When we graph this system of equations, we get two **parallel lines**, as shown in Figure 22.

It appears that these lines will never meet. The hare can't catch up with the roadrunner since they are both traveling at the same speed. Because there is no intersection point, the system of equations has no solution.

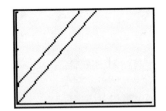

Figure 22 The hare and the roadrunner never meet.

Notice in Example 4 that the two lines have the same slope. This should not be surprising because you know that the slope of a line is the *rate of change* of the variables, and in this case the rate is the same, 18 miles per hour. This observation leads us to an important fact about parallel lines.

Slopes of Parallel Lines

Two different lines with the same slope are parallel.

We were unable to find a solution to the system of equations in Example 4. There is a name for such a system of equations.

Definition   **Inconsistent System**

A system of linear equations in two variables is **inconsistent** if the two equations have no common solution.

Exercises 4.3

1. The figure shows the graphs of two linear equations, with several ordered pairs on each line. What is the intersection of the two lines? Verify that the ordered pair at the intersection of the two lines is a solution to the system of equations: $y = {}^-x$ and $y = x + 2$.

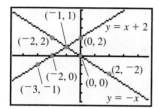

2. The sum of two numbers is 6. The difference of the same two numbers is 4.

   a. Let $x =$ one of the numbers and $y =$ the other number. Write a separate equation for each statement.

   b. From the set $\{1, 2, 3, 4, 5, 6\}$, find pairs of numbers that satisfy each statement.

   c. Pick the pair of numbers that satisfy both statements; this is the solution of the system of equations.

3. The sum of two numbers is 10. The difference of the same two numbers is 5.

   a. List three pairs of numbers that satisfy each statement.

   b. Plot the pairs of numbers that satisfy the first statement on a coordinate plane (Section 2.3) and connect the points.

   c. Plot the pairs of numbers that satisfy the second statement on the same coordinate plane and connect only the new points.

   d. Because one line represents all the pairs of numbers whose sum is 10 and the other line represents all the pairs of numbers whose difference is 5, what does the intersection of the two lines represent?

   e. Use the graph to find the coordinates of the intersection point.

4. If the graph of a system of equations forms parallel lines, how many solutions will the system have? What is the special name for this type of system of equations?

In Exercises 5–12, use a graphing method to find the approximate solution(s), if any, to the given systems of equations. Tell which systems of equations are inconsistent. *Note:* **Begin with a** ZOOM **8: ZInteger window and adjust if necessary.**

5. $y = {}^-x + 1$
   $y = x - 3$

6. ${}^-x + y = {}^-6$
   $2x + 5 = y$

   a. In what form are the original equations?

   b. What equations did you enter into the Y= screen?

   c. In what form are the equations for the Y= screen?

7. $x = y - 1$
   $2 = x - y$

   What do the slopes of these equations tell you about the solution(s)?

8. $x - 2y = 6$
   $y = 5$

9. $3y = 4x - 1$
   $y = 2x - \frac{1}{2}$

10. $x + y = 2$
    ${}^-y = {}^-2x + \frac{1}{4}$

11. $.7x - .1y = 0$
    $.2x + .6y = 4.4$

12. $x + y = \frac{13}{15}$
    $2x - 3y = \frac{11}{15}$

    Is the solution shown on the calculator exact? Explain.

13. The Pinnacle car company brags about its low rental car costs by offering the following cost comparisons against a competitor.

Miles Driven	Pinnacle's Cost	Competitor's Cost
0	$8.00	$20.00
10	10.50	20.50
20	13.00	21.00
30	15.50	21.50
40	18.00	22.00

a. Continue the cost comparison values for 50, 60, and 70 miles driven by noting the change in cost for each additional 10 miles driven. Recall that this is the rate of change discussed in Section 4.1.

b. At what number of miles do the two rental cars have the same cost?

c. On a graph of the data, what is this point called?

14. In the previous problem we found that each car's rental cost changed at a constant rate. Thus, each car's cost may be expressed as a linear equation. For Pinnacle, the cost equation is $C = .25d + 8$, and for their competitor, the equation is $C = .05d + 20$.

a. Approximate the solution of this system of equations by using the $\boxed{\text{TRACE}}$ or $\boxed{\text{2nd}}$ CALC 5:intersect feature on your graphing calculator.

b. How does this solution compare with your answer from Exercise 13(b)?

15. Suppose you are considering renting a car from one of two possible companies. Udrive's rental charges may be modeled by the equation $C = .10d + 35$, where d is the miles driven and C is the cost in dollars. Mile Rent-a-Car calculates its charges by the formula $C = .15d + 10$.

a. Graphically estimate the intersection of these two rental-cost equations.

b. Describe what the intersection in this problem means.

c. Which company would you rent a car from if you expected to drive at least 550 miles? Why?

Skills and Review 4.3

16. Write an equation of a line from the given information.

a. Slope of $-\frac{3}{4}$, y-intercept of $(0, 5)$

b. Slope of $\frac{1}{2}$, containing the point $(4, {}^-1)$

c. Containing the points $(5, 2)$ and $(0, {}^-1)$

17. Refer to the table of values for Pinnacle Rent-a-Car presented in Exercise 13.

a. Explain how you could find the y-intercept (initial value) for Pinnacle Rent-a-Car.

b. Show the calculation for finding the slope, or rate of change, for Pinnacle.

18. Write an equation of a line containing the points $(0, {}^-2)$ and $({}^-1, 4)$.

a. Write your equation in slope-intercept form.

b. Write your equation in standard form.

19. Find the slope and y-intercept for each line.

a. $y = {}^-3x + 2$

b. $3x - 2y = 6$

20. Consider the equation $2x + 3y = 18$.

a. Find the x-intercept.

b. Find the y-intercept.

c. By hand, draw a graph of the equation.

21. The traffic on a highway decreases constantly between the hours of 8 P.M. and midnight. Use the data in the table to find the rate of change in the number of vehicles per hour.

Time	Number of Vehicles
8	5000
9	4250
10	3500
11	2750
12	2000

22. Determine whether the line in each graph has a positive, negative, zero, or undefined slope.

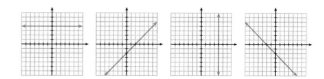

23. Find W in the formula for the perimeter of a rectangle, $P = 2L + 2W$, when $L = 4.5$ cm and $P = 15$ cm.

24. Recall from Section 2.4 that a function may be represented in four ways. Consider the problem situation where the number of words Ramona reads is a function of the time she is reading. Suppose she reads 300 words per minute. Express this function in each way.

a. As a table

b. As a graph

c. As a formula

25. Consider the expression $3x + 6 - (8x - 4)$.
    a. Simplify the expression.
    b. Evaluate the original expression for $x = {}^-3$.
    c. Evaluate your simplified expression for $x = {}^-3$.
    d. Do the evaluations agree? If not, go back and check your work.

4.4 Algebraic Solution of Systems of Equations

AFTER STUDYING THIS SECTION YOU WILL BE ABLE TO

- Solve a system of linear equations in two variables by the substitution method.
- Solve a system of linear equations in two variables by the elimination method.

Solving by Substitution

In the last section you used graphs to solve systems of linear equations. In this section you learn methods that do not require a graph. One method for solving a system of equations algebraically is called the **method of substitution**.

The Method of Substitution

Step 1   Put one of the equations in slope-intercept form, $y = mx + b$.

Step 2   Substitute the expression $mx + b$ for y in the other equation.

Step 3   Use algebraic manipulation to solve the new equation for x.

Step 4   Substitute this value of x back into the first equation to find the value of y.

Example 1 illustrates this method.

EXAMPLE 1   Show how the method of substitution may be used to solve the problem of the hare and the tortoise (Example 3, Section 4.3). A hare is going to race a tortoise to prove that slow and steady *doesn't* always win. He will be a good sport and give the tortoise a head start of 10 miles. The hare can run at a speed of 18 miles per hour. The tortoise moves along at 2 miles per hour. How long will it take for the hare to catch the tortoise?

Solution   As we did before, we let y represent the distance from where the hare started and x be the time in hours until the hare catches up. We have a system of two equations:

$$y = 18x$$

$$y = 2x + 10$$

The first step is to put one of the equations in slope-intercept form, which is not necessary because both equations are already in that form.

The second step is to substitute the expression $mx + b$ from one equation into y for the other equation. If we substitute $2x + 10$ from the second equation for y in the first equation, we have

$$2x + 10 = 18x$$

The third step is to solve this equation for x:

$$2x + 10 = 18x$$
$$10 = 16x$$
$$\frac{10}{16} = \frac{16x}{16}$$
$$.625 = x$$

Our solution is $x = .625$, which means that the hare overtakes the tortoise after .625 hours (which is $.625 * 60 = 37.5$ minutes). Note that this solution is more precise than the estimate we got from the graph in Example 3 in Section 4.3.

■ ■ ■

We could substitute $x = .625$ back into the equation $y = 2x + 10$ to determine how far the hare will have traveled when he catches the tortoise. We get $y = 2 * .625 + 10 = 11.25$, which means the hare will have gone 11.25 miles. The ordered pair $(.625, 11.25)$, or $x = .625$, $y = 11.25$ is the solution to the system of linear equations, but the problem asked only for how long the hare took, not how far he ran.

We can always use the method of substitution to solve a system of linear equations algebraically. It is easiest if at least one of our two equations is already solved for a particular variable, for instance, when it is in slope-intercept form.

EXAMPLE 2   Solve the following system of equations using the method of substitution.

$$y = 5x - 3$$

$$2x + y = 4$$

Solution   Because the equation $y = 5x - 3$ tells us the value of y in terms of x, we may substitute this into the equation $2x + y = 4$ and remove the y, leaving a linear equation in one variable.

$$2x + y = 4$$

$$2x + (5x - 3) = 4 \qquad \textit{Putting } 5x - 3 \textit{ in parentheses to indicate that the entire}$$
$$\textit{expression is substituted for } y$$

$$7x - 3 = 4 \qquad \textit{Removing parentheses (special property of 1) and}$$
$$\textit{combining like terms}$$

$$7x = 7$$

$$x = 1$$

Once we know the value of one variable, we can *substitute* again into the equation $y = 5x - 3$ to get the value of y:

$$y = 5x - 3$$
$$= 5 * 1 - 3$$
$$= 2$$

So, the solution is the ordered pair $(1, 2)$ because $x = 1$ and $y = 2$.

■ ■ ■

If neither equation is in slope-intercept form, then we must follow the first step in the list on page 155.

EXAMPLE 3   Solve the following system of equations using the method of substitution.

$$3x + y = 3$$
$$2x - 2y = 10$$

Solution   Neither equation is in slope-intercept form, so we must manipulate one equation until it is in that form and then do substitution. We can manipulate the equation $3x + y = 3$ like this:

$$3x + y = 3$$
$$y = {}^{-}3x + 3$$

Now, we can substitute for y in the equation $2x - 2y = 10$:

$$2x - 2y = 10$$
$$2x - 2({}^{-}3x + 3) = 10 \qquad \textit{Don't forget the parentheses}$$

Once we have reduced our system of equations in two variables to a single equation in one variable, we can solve using the steps we learned in Chapter 3:

$$2x - 2({}^{-}3x + 3) = 10 \qquad \textit{Original equation}$$

$$2x + 6x - 6 = 10 \qquad \textit{Using the distributive property to remove}$$
$$\textit{parentheses on left side}$$

$$8x - 6 = 10 \qquad \textit{Combining like terms on left side}$$

$$8x = 16 \qquad \textit{Adding 6 on both sides}$$

$$x = \frac{16}{8} \qquad \textit{Dividing on both sides by 8}$$

$$x = 2$$

Next, we substitute $x = 2$ into the equation $y = {}^-3x + 3$ to compute the value of y,

$$y = {}^-3x + 3$$

$$y = {}^-3 * 2 + 3$$

$$y = {}^-6 + 3$$

$$y = {}^-3$$

The solution to this system is $x = 2$ and $y = {}^-3$.

Solving by Elimination

Example 4 shows how to solve a system of equations when neither is in slope-intercept form.

EXAMPLE 4 Solve the following system of linear equations.

$$2x + 3y = 6$$

$$5x - 3y = 8$$

Solution We could solve it as we did the system in Example 3, but this would involve a series of steps: First, write one of the equations in slope-intercept form; next, substitute the resulting expression for one variable into the other equation; and then solve the new equation. There is an easier way.

We know that we may add the same quantity to both sides of an equation and still have a valid equation. The equation $5x - 3y = 8$ tells us that $5x - 3y$ and 8 are the *same quantity*. So we may add $5x - 3y$ to the left side of the equation $2x + 3y = 6$ and 8 to the right side of the equation $2x + 3y = 6$.

$$\begin{array}{r} 2x + 3y = 6 \\ + \ 5x - 3y = 8 \\ \hline 7x + 0 \ = 14 \end{array}$$

The sum of ^+3y and ^-3y is 0, so we get a simple linear equation in one variable, $7x = 14$. Then $x = \frac{14}{7} = 2$. We can substitute this value of x into either equation to find the value of y. We use the equation $2x + 3y = 6$:

$$2x + 3y = 6$$
$$2 * 2 + 3y = 6$$
$$4 + 3y = 6$$
$$3y = 2$$
$$y = \frac{2}{3}$$

The solution is $x = 2$ and $y = \frac{2}{3}$, or $(2, \frac{2}{3})$.

We call this method of solving a system of linear equations the **elimination method**, because we *eliminate* one of the variables. We were able to use the elimination method to easily solve the system of equations in Example 4 because $3x$ and ^-3x canceled out, *eliminating* the variable x. We can use the elimination method to solve other systems.

First we need to arrange the equations so that x-terms, y-terms, and constant terms line up with each other. This is easy if both equations are in standard form (see page 139).

Then, we need to make sure that the coefficient of one of the variables in the first equation is the *opposite* of the coefficient of the same variable in the second equation; when we add the corresponding sides of the two equations, that variable will then be eliminated.

Method of Elimination

Step 1 Put both equations in standard form, $Ax + By = C$.

Step 2 If necessary, multiply one or both equations by the same number on both sides so either the x-terms or the y-terms are opposites.

Step 3 Add the two equations to get an equation with only one variable. Solve for that variable.

Step 4 Substitute this value of x or y back into one of the original equations to find the value of the other variable.

EXAMPLE 5 Solve the system of equations:

$$2x + 4y = 32$$
$$3x + 4y = 28$$

Solution We need to find a way to eliminate one of the variables from the system. Because the coefficient of y in both equations is 4, if we multiply by $^-1$ on both sides of one equation, then the coefficients of y will be opposites; we can *add the equations* (left side to left side, and right side to right side) like this:

$$2x + 4y = 32$$
$$\underline{{}^-3x - 4y = {}^-28} \qquad \textit{Multiplying on both sides of the second equation by } {}^-1$$
$${}^-1x \qquad = 4 \qquad \textit{Adding the equations}$$
$$x \qquad = {}^-4 \qquad \textit{Multiplying by } {}^-1 \textit{ on both sides}$$

Now, we can substitute $x = {}^-4$ back into the equation $2x + 4y = 32$ to solve for y:

$$2x + 4y = 32$$
$$2 * {}^-4 + 4y = 32$$
$${}^-8 + 4y = 32$$
$$4y = 40$$
$$y = 10$$

The solution is $x = {}^-4$ and $y = 10$, or $({}^-4, 10)$.

■ ■ ■

Example 6 shows another example of using the elimination method.

EXAMPLE 6

You decide to enter the Iditarod sled dog race in Alaska. After extensive research into assembling a dog team, you decide to use two different types of dog. One type is a dog with very good endurance but who can only pull 55 pounds. The second type is a very strong dog who can pull 85 pounds, but has less endurance than the first type of dog. You will need 15 dogs for the team, and the team should be able to pull 975 pounds.

Solution

In order to figure out how many of each type of dog you will use, we may let x be the number of type 1 dogs and y the number of type 2 dogs. Because we need 15 dogs total,

$$x + y = 15$$

The other information in the problem is the number of pounds each type of dog can pull and the total number of pounds you need the team to pull. Because each type 1 dog can pull 55 pounds, x type 1 dogs can pull $55x$ pounds. Likewise, y type 2 dogs can pull $85y$ pounds. You need the team to pull 975 pounds, so

$$55x + 85y = 975$$

We now have a system of two equations in x and y. Both equations are in standard form, but neither the x- nor the y-coefficients are equal. Not to worry. We could multiply both sides of the first equation by 55 so that its x-term has the same coefficient as the x-term in the second equation. Better yet, if we multiply by ‾55, the x-terms will be *opposites*, and we will be all set to use the method of elimination. So our first equation becomes

$$^-55x - 55y = {}^-55 * 15$$
$$^-55x - 55y = {}^-825$$

We now have

$$\begin{array}{r} ^-55x - 55y = {}^-825 \\ 55x + 85y = 975 \\ \hline 30y = 150 \end{array}$$

The x-terms have been eliminated. We now solve for y:

$$\frac{30y}{30} = \frac{150}{30}$$
$$y = 5$$

Now that we have y, we can substitute into one of the equations and solve for x. In this case our best choice is $x + y = 15$, where we quickly find that $x = 10$.

You will need 10 type 1 dogs and 5 type 2 dogs for your Iditarod team.

■ ■ ■

In using the method of elimination, it is sometimes necessary to multiply *both* equations in order to eliminate one of the variables.

EXAMPLE 7 Solve the system of equations

$$4x + 3y = 29$$
$$3x - 2y = {}^-8$$

Solution In order to eliminate the y-terms we must make their coefficients opposites of each other. One way to do this is to find the least common multiple of 2 and 3, that is, 6. We can get $6y$ to appear in the first equation if we multiply by 2 on both sides. We can get ^-6y to appear in the second equation if we multiply by 3 on both sides.

We now have

$$\begin{array}{r} 4x + 3y = 29 \rightarrow 8x + 6y = 58 \\ 3x - 2y = {}^-8 \rightarrow 9x - 6y = {}^-24 \\ \hline 17x = 34 \\ x = 2 \end{array}$$

Once we have found $x = 2$, we substitute into one of the original equations to find y.

$$4 * 2 + 3y = 29$$
$$8 + 3y = 29$$
$$3y = 21$$
$$y = 7$$

Check by substituting $x = 2$ and $y = 7$ into the second equation:

$$3x - 2y = {}^-8$$
$$3 * 2 - 2 * 7 \stackrel{?}{=} {}^-8$$
$$6 - 14 \stackrel{?}{=} {}^-8$$
$${}^-8 = {}^-8 \quad OK!$$

Choosing a Method

You have learned three methods for solving systems of two linear equations in two variables. Often it will be up to you to choose which method to use. The chart in the following table gives you some guidance.

Method	Form of Equations	Advantages	Disadvantages
Graphing	Both equations must be in the form $y = mx + b$.	It quickly gives an estimate without much algebraic manipulation.	It may not give exact answers.
Substitution (an algebraic method)	At least one equation should be solved for one variable in terms of the other, as in $y = mx + b$.	It gives an equation in one variable very quickly.	It may become messy if the answers are fractions.
Elimination (an algebraic method)	Both equations should be in the form $Ax + By = C$.	If both equations are in standard form to begin with, the solution may be found in fewer steps than with substitution.	You need to think carefully about how to eliminate one variable.

Exercises 4.4

1. Which of the following are complete solutions to the given system of equations? *Note:* there may be more than one answer.

   $$x - 5y = 16 \qquad 2x + y = {}^-1$$

   a. $x = 1$

   b. $(11, {}^-1)$

   c. $x = 1$ and $y = {}^-3$

   d. $(1, {}^-3)$

   e. $y = {}^-3$

2. Verify by hand that $(^-2, 5)$ is a solution to the following system.

$$\tfrac{1}{2}x + \tfrac{1}{5}y = 0$$

$$y = ^-3x - 1$$

3. Given is a system of equations and a partial solution to them:

$$3x + 2y = 3$$

$$4x + y = ^-1$$

$$y = ^-4x - 1 \qquad \textit{Solving the second equation for } y$$

$$3x + 2(^-4x - 1) = 3 \qquad \textit{Substituting } ^-4x - 1 \textit{ for } y \textit{ into the equation } 3x + 2y = 3$$

$$3x - 8x - 2 = 3 \qquad \textit{Distributing to clear parentheses}$$

$$^-5x = 5 \qquad \textit{Solving for } x$$

$$x = ^-1$$

a. Explain why this system is not yet completely solved.

b. Complete the solution to the system and show it as an ordered pair.

In Exercises 4–6, use substitution to solve each system of equations.

4. $y = 2x - 7$
$y = ^-x + 8$

5. $3y = x + \tfrac{6}{5}$
$4x + 15y = ^-12$

6. $x + 2y = 6$
$y = \tfrac{3}{2}$

7. A mistake was made using elimination to solve the given system of equations.

$$4x - 3y = 22 \rightarrow 4x - 3y = 22 \rightarrow 4x - 3y = 22$$
$$3x - y = 14 \rightarrow 3(3x - y) = 3(14) \rightarrow 9x - 3y = 42$$
$$\overline{}$$
$$13x = 64$$
$$x = \tfrac{64}{13}$$
$$3\left(\tfrac{64}{13}\right) - y = 14$$
$$\tfrac{192}{13} - y = 14$$
$$y = \tfrac{10}{13}$$

Incorrect solution: $\left(\tfrac{64}{13}, \tfrac{10}{13}\right)$

a. Locate the error.

b. Correct the error and continue the process of elimination to find the correct answer.

In Exercises 8–10, use elimination to solve each system of equations.

8. $x + y = ^-3$
$x - y = ^-5$

9. $2x + 5y = 24$
$x - 3y = 1$

10. $7x - 3y = 13$
$5x - 2y = 27$

In Exercises 11–12, suppose you are equally comfortable with substitution or elimination to solve a system of two equations.

11. a. Explain which method requires fewer steps to solve the system:

$$7x - 3y = 4$$
$$^-2x - 3y = 4$$

b. Use the method you chose to solve the system.

12. a. Explain which of the two algebraic methods requires fewer steps to solve the system:

$$y = 5x + 1$$
$$y = x - 5$$

b. Use the method you chose to solve the system.

In Exercises 13–15, solve each system of equations using either substitution or elimination.

13. $x + 2y = 4$
$^-x = y + 3$

Check by substituting your solution in both equations.

14. $16x + 12y = 15$
$12x - 10y = 16$

15. $\qquad y = 2x - 1$
$^-4x + 2y = ^-5$

Your algebra probably gave you a strange result. Use your grapher to determine what kind of solution this system has.

Skills and Review 4.4

16. Use a graph to approximate the solution(s) to the system of equations.

$$x + 5y = {}^-13$$

$$y = 3x - 9$$

17. Use a graphing method to approximate the solution to the system of equations:

$$y - 5.3 = .21x$$

$$.72x + y = 6.4$$

18. Write an equation of a line from the given information:
   a. Slope of $\frac{5}{2}$ and y-intercept of $(0, {}^-1)$
   b. Slope of 3 and contains the point $({}^-4, 5)$
   c. Contains the points $({}^-2, 4)$ and $(5, {}^-1)$

19. Determine the x- and y-intercepts of the linear equation $2x - 3y = 6$. Use the intercepts to sketch a graph by hand.

20. Describe the slope of each linear equation as positive, negative, zero, or undefined. Explain how you arrived at your conclusions.
   a. $y = {}^-3$ **b.** $y = 2x$ **c.** $y = {}^-x + 5$

21. Which road is steeper, a road with constant slope ${}^-5$ or a road with constant slope 3? Explain your answer.

22. Company A charges $40 plus $.10 for each mile to rent an economy car for the day. Company B charges $30 plus $.15 for each mile to rent the same type of car. Use a graphing method to approximate the number of miles at which the cars cost the same. Use the seven steps for problem solving.

23. Recall from Section 2.3 that the distance formula is

$$\text{distance} = \sqrt{\text{run}^2 + \text{rise}^2}$$

   a. Find the distance between the two points $({}^-4, 3)$ and $(2, {}^-1)$. Leave the radical so that your answer is exact.
   b. Estimate the square root from part (a) (see Section 1.3).

24. Evaluate:

$$\left(\frac{x - 5}{6 - y}\right)^2 \quad \text{when} \quad x = 7, y = {}^-1.$$

25. If necessary, review exponents so that you can find the value of each expression without a calculator.
   a. 2^1 **b.** 2^0 **c.** 2^{-1}
   d. $({}^-4)^1$ **e.** $1.5 * 10^{-1}$

4.5 Relationships Between Lines (Optional)

In Example 4 in Section 4.3, we saw that two lines with the same slope are parallel and never meet. Any system of linear equations that consists of two *different* lines with the same slope is an *inconsistent system* (page 152) and has no solution. Because the hare gives the roadrunner a head start and they move at the same speed, the hare *can't* catch the roadrunner. There is one type of system with lines with the same slope that is different, however; we investigate it in the next example.

EXAMPLE 1   Suppose the hare realizes that he can't ever catch the roadrunner with the race setup in Example 4, page 152. Instead, the hare proposes giving the roadrunner an 18-mile head start but allows himself to start 1 hour ahead of the roadrunner. What happens in this race?

Solution   We can use the same reasoning we did in Example 3 in Section 4.3 to work out formulas for the distance each racer is from the starting line. If we let x be the number of hours since the hare starts running, then the hare is $y = 18x$ miles from the starting line after x hours. Because the roadrunner doesn't start running for an hour, he will be running for only $x - 1$ hours, but he gets an 18-mile head start. Therefore, his distance from the starting line is $y = 18(x - 1) + 18$ miles. We have a system of equations

$$y = 18x$$
$$y = 18(x - 1) + 18 = 18x - 18 + 18 = 18x$$

Both equations are the *same*. If we try to plot this, we get Figure 23. What happened? After the hare has been running for 1 hour, he reaches the roadrunner. Then, the roadrunner starts running at the same speed as the hare, and they stay right next to each other. In this system, instead of having two lines with the same slope that will never meet, we have two copies of the *same line*. In this case we say the lines are **coincident** and the system of equations is **dependent**. There are an infinite number of points that satisfy both equations.

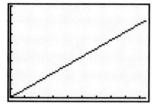

Figure 23

Another special example of pairs of lines are lines that are **perpendicular**—in other words, lines that meet at a right (90°) angle. Parallel lines are easy to identify, because they are lines with the same slope (which are not the same line—the lines in Example 1 are really the same and not parallel). There is an easy way to tell that lines are perpendicular by using the slope.

EXAMPLE 2   Find a relationship between the slopes of the legs of the right triangle in Figure 24, which meet at a 90° angle.

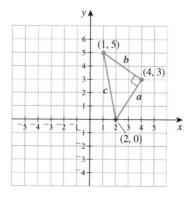

Figure 24

Solution   First, let's check to make sure this really is a right triangle. We will use the distance formula (page 71) to find the lengths of the sides, a, b, and c.

$$a = \sqrt{(4-2)^2 + (3-0)^2} = \sqrt{2^2 + 3^2} = \sqrt{13}$$

$$b = \sqrt{(4-1)^2 + (3-5)^2} = \sqrt{3^2 + (^-2)^2} = \sqrt{13}$$

$$c = \sqrt{(2-1)^2 + (0-5)^2} = \sqrt{1^2 + (^-5)^2} = \sqrt{26}$$

Now, let's see if these lengths work in the **Pythagorean theorem** (page 61).

$$a^2 + b^2 \stackrel{?}{=} c^2$$

$$(\sqrt{13})^2 + (\sqrt{13})^2 = 13 + 13 = 26 = (\sqrt{26})^2 \quad OK!$$

Recall that slope $= \frac{\text{rise}}{\text{run}}$, so for a we get slope $= \frac{3-0}{4-2} = \frac{3}{2}$. For b, slope $= \frac{3-5}{4-1} = \frac{^-2}{3}$. In this case, the two line segments are perpendicular, and the slopes are *negative reciprocals of each other*. The negative reciprocal of $\frac{3}{2}$ is

$$\frac{^-1}{\frac{3}{2}} = \frac{^-2}{3}$$

This relationship between the slopes of perpendicular lines is always true.

Slopes of Perpendicular Lines

Two lines with slopes m_1 and m_2 are *perpendicular* if their slopes are *negative reciprocals* of each other, in other words, if

$$m_1 = \frac{^-1}{m_2}$$

EXAMPLE 3 | Which pairs of lines are perpendicular?

a. $y = 3x - 5$ and $y = ^-3x + 2$
b. $y = 5x + 2$ and $y = ^-\frac{1}{5}x + 17$
c. Street 2 and Avenue $^-3$ in Gridville (Section 2.3)

Solution | a. The two slopes are $m_1 = 3$ and $m_2 = ^-3$. Taking the negative reciprocal,

$$\frac{^-1}{m_1} = \frac{^-1}{3} \neq m_2$$

so the lines are *not* perpendicular.

b. The two slopes are $m_1 = 5$ and $m_2 = -\frac{1}{5}$. Taking the negative reciprocal,

$$\frac{^-1}{m_1} = \frac{^-1}{5} = m_2$$

so the lines *are* perpendicular.

c. Street 2 is parallel to the x-axis, and the equation for it is $y = 2$, so it has slope $m_1 = 0$. Avenue $^-3$ has *undefined slope*, because every point on the avenue has the same x-coordinate. Hence the *run* is always 0, and we are not allowed to divide by 0. If we try to take the negative reciprocal of m_1, we get

$$\frac{^-1}{m_1} = \frac{^-1}{0} = \text{undefined}$$

which agrees with m_2, so the lines *are* perpendicular.

It is important to realize that checking whether lines are perpendicular is very difficult on a graphing calculator, because the *shape* of the window matters. Only *square* windows (where the pixel height of the window and the pixel width are the same) work well; other windows distort the picture (see Figure 25).

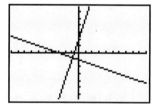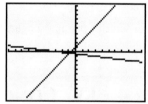

Figure 25 The lines $y = 3x + 2$ and $y = -\frac{1}{3}x - 1$, which are perpendicular, in a square window (left) and a window that is not square (right). Notice that in the square window, the lines do look perpendicular, but in the other window they don't.

Exercises 4.5

1. Show that the two lines in the figure are parallel by comparing their slopes.

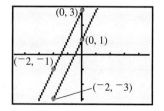

2. Show that the two lines in the figure are perpendicular by comparing their slopes.

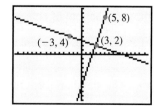

3. A line contains the points $(4, {}^-1)$ and $(6, 1)$. Another line contains the points $({}^-2, {}^-7)$ and $(2, {}^-3)$. Are the lines parallel, the same, perpendicular, or none of these? Explain your choice.

4. Classify each pair of linear equations as parallel, the same, perpendicular, or none of these.

   a. $y = 4x - 1,\ y = \frac{-1}{4}x + 5$

   b. $y = 2x,\ y = 6(\frac{1}{3}x)$

   c. $y = \frac{5}{3}x + 1,\ y = \frac{3}{5}x + 1$

   d. $y = x - 2,\ y = x - 4$

5. Classify each pair of linear equations as parallel, the same, perpendicular, or none of these. Recall that the slope is easiest to recognize when the linear equation is written in slope-intercept form, $y = mx + b$.

   a. $3x + 2y = {}^-1,\ 3x - y = 4$

   b. $4y = x - 12,\ y - 3 = \frac{1}{4}x$

   c. $2x + y = 1,\ 2x - 4y = {}^-5$

   d. $y = \frac{3}{5}x + 2,\ 3x = 5y - 10$

6. Complete the ordered pair in the figure to make the two lines perpendicular.

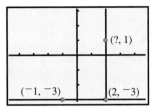

7. Will the two lines in the figure ever intersect? Explain your reasoning.

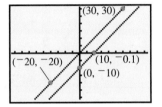

8. Suppose Miguel and Sofia run at the same speed of 10 feet per second. Miguel decides to give Sofia a 3-second head start in a race. The distance y in feet that Miguel runs is given by the equation $y = 10x$. The distance Sofia runs is given by the equation $y = 10(x + 3)$, where x represents Miguel's elapsed running time in seconds.

   a. Will Miguel ever catch Sofia? Explain.

   b. How do the linear equations support your answer?

CHAPTER 4 ▪ KEY CONCEPTS ▪

Linear Equation in Two Variables   A linear equation in two variables is any equation with simple terms involving two different variables and possibly a constant term. If we let x stand for one variable and y for the other, then a linear equation in two variables can almost always be put in the form $y = \text{coefficient} * x + \text{constant}$. An equation in this form is also called a **linear function**. (Page 125)

Initial Value, or y-intercept   The y-intercept is the point where the graph of a linear equation in two variables crosses the y-axis. This point is the value of y when $x = 0$, and hence it is also called the **initial value**. (Page 125)

Slope   The slope of a line is computed using the formula

$$\text{slope} = \frac{\text{rise}}{\text{run}} = \frac{\text{change in output}}{\text{change in input}}$$

It can be thought of as the rate of change of y in relation to x. Straight lines have constant slope. (Page 127)

Slope-intercept Form   The slope-intercept form of an equation is one way of writing a linear equation in two variables. We write $y = mx + b$, where m is the slope of the line, and b is the initial value (y-intercept). (Page 136)

Standard Form   The standard form of a linear equation in two variables is $Ax + By = C$, where A, B, and C are constants. (Page 139)

System of Linear Equations   Two linear equations in two variables make a system of equations. The solution to the system, if it exists, is the intersection point of the two lines. This point is a point that satisfies *both* equations in the system. (Page 149)

Inconsistent System   An inconsistent system of equations is a system of linear equations that has *no* solutions. (Page 152)

Methods for Solving Systems   The three methods for solving a system of linear equations are graphing, substitution, and elimination. The chart on page 162 can be used to help choose a method. (Page 162)

Exploration

The table in the chapter opener shows the number of lives saved by airbags for the years 1993 to 2000. Let x represent the number of years since 1993. (For 1993, $x = 0$, for 1994, $x = 1$, etc.) Let y represent the number of lives saved by airbags. The linear function $y = 199x + 95$ is considered by statisticians to be a good model for this set of data.

a. Graph the function $y = 199x + 95$ in an appropriate window.

b. What is the slope of the line?

c. On average, approximately how many additional lives were saved by airbags each year?

d. Use the function to predict how many lives will be saved by airbags in the year 2012.

e. Use the function to predict how many lives were saved by airbags in the year 1990. What is wrong with this prediction?

CHAPTER 4 ▪ REVIEW EXERCISES

Section 4.1 Slope and Rate of Change

1. Find the

$$\text{slope} = \frac{\text{rise}}{\text{run}} = \frac{y_2 - y_1}{x_2 - x_1}$$

of the line that contains each pair of points.

a. $(1, 2)$ and $(2, 6)$

b. $(^-5, ^-6)$ and $(^-8, 2)$

c. $(^-2, 3)$ and $(1, 0)$

d. $(4, ^-1)$ and $(7, ^-1)$

e. $(^-3, 2)$ and $(^-7, 4)$

2. Suppose there is no snow on the ground and it begins to snow at the rate of 2 inches per hour.

a. How much snow is on the ground at the beginning of the storm? This is the initial value.

b. What is the rate of change in inches of snow per hour?

c. Use the rate of change to find how much snow has fallen in 1 hour, 2 hours, and 3 hours. Present these findings in a table with time (in hours) as the input and the amount of snow (in inches) as the output.

d. Plot the table values on a coordinate plane. The points form a line. What is the slope of the line and how does it compare to the rate of change?

3. Vitomax can sell 5000 supplements a day at a price of $20. They can, however, increase their sales by 100 a day for each $3 reduction in price.

   a. What is the rate of change in supplements sold with respect to the price?

   b. Explain how the rate of change is used to find the second ordered pair in the table below.

   c. Use the rate of change to find a third ordered pair.

   d. What is the slope of the line connecting these points?

Input (Price in Dollars)	Output (Number of Supplements Sold)
20	5000
17	5100
?	?

4. What is the slope of the line containing the ordered pairs in the following table?

Input, x	Output, y
0	5
2	8
4	11
6	14

5. Match each equation with its graph in the figure.

   a. $y = 3x + 5$ b. $y = x$

   c. $y = {}^-x + 2$ d. $y = {}^-4$

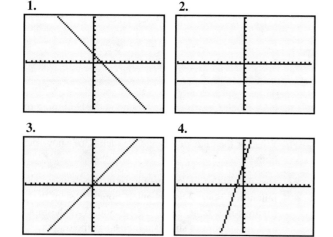

1.   2.

3.   4.

6. A line contains the point $(0, 3)$ and has a slope of $\frac{3}{2}$. By hand, sketch a graph of this line.

Section 4.2 Forms of Linear Equations

7. Suppose there are 5 inches of snow on the ground when it begins snowing at the rate of 2 inches per hour.

   a. What is the initial value?

   b. What is the rate of change in inches of snow per hour?

   c. We now have the slope and y-intercept. Use the slope-intercept formula to write an equation for the amount of accumulated snow in terms of the number of hours of snowfall.

8. Suppose each day you drink 300 mL from a container that initially holds 1800 mL of liquid. Let x represent the number of days you drink from the container and let y represent the amount of liquid (in mL) left in the container after x days.

   a. Write an equation for y in terms of x.

   b. Compare ordered pairs that satisfy your equation with those in the following table. They should be the same.

x (Days)	y (mL)
0	1800
1	1500
2	1200
3	900
4	600
5	300
6	0

9. Write an equation of the line with given slope and y-intercept.

   a. $m = 6$, y-intercept $(0, 2)$

   b. $m = \frac{1}{3}$, y-intercept $(0, 4)$

   c. $m = 2$, y-intercept $(0, 1)$

   d. $m = {}^-5$, y-intercept $(0, \frac{1}{2})$

   e. $m = 1$, y-intercept $(0, {}^-3)$

   f. $m = {}^-1$, y-intercept $(0, 5)$

10. Determine the slope and y-intercept for each equation. Some equations will need to be solved for y.

    a. $y = 4x + 3$ b. $y + 2 = {}^-(x - 1)$

    c. $y - 1 = 3(x - 2)$ d. $x - y = 3$

    e. $2x + 3y = 12$ f. $y = {}^-x + 2$

11. Solve the equation $3x - 4y = 12$ for y in terms of x.

12. Write an equation of the line with given slope and containing the given point.

    a. $m = 5, (^-2, 1)$ **b.** $m = 1, (^-4, 5)$

    c. $m = ^-3, (1, 4)$ **d.** $m = \frac{1}{2}, (2, ^-3)$

13. Write an equation of the line containing each pair of points.

    a. $(1, 4)$ and $(2, 6)$ **b.** $(4, ^-1)$ and $(5, 3)$

    c. $(2, 6)$ and $(6, ^-8)$ **d.** $(0, 4)$ and $(^-9, 7)$

14. Two musicians are writing songs for an album. One musician writes 3 songs for each month she works and the other writes 4 songs for each month he works. Their album contains 12 songs.

    a. The first musician's work rate in songs per month is $\frac{3}{1}$. What is the second musician's work rate?

    b. Let x represent the number of months that the first musician writes songs for the album and let y represent the number of months that the second musician writes songs for the album. Then, an expression for the number of songs from the first musician is $3x$. Give an expression for the second musician's number of songs.

    c. Write an equation showing that the total number of songs is 12.

    d. Suppose the first musician writes songs for 1 month. For how many months must the other musician write songs in order to complete the album?

    e. Mentally, find the intercepts using your equation from part (c) and interpret their meaning.

    f. Use the intercepts to sketch a graph by hand.

15. Mentally, find the x- and y-intercepts for each equation. Sketch the graph for part (a) only.

    a. $x + y = 5$

    b. $x - 2y = 4$

    c. $3x + 2y = 6$

    d. $\frac{1}{2}x - 5y = 10$

    e. $2x - \frac{1}{3}y = 4$

    f. $4x + 5y = 9$

Section 4.3 Graphical Solution of Systems of Equations

16. The graph of the system of equations $y = 2x + 1$ and $y = ^-1x + 4$ is shown in the figure.

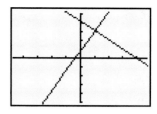

    a. Mark the solution of the system on the graph.

    b. What is this point on the graph called?

    c. Estimate the solution of the system using the graph. Each tick represents one unit.

For Exercises 17–21, use a graphing method to find the solution of each system of equations. Note any systems that do not have a solution.

17. $y = 3x + 1$
    $y = 2x + 2$

18. $\quad y = x - 1$
    $2x + y = ^-7$

19. $4x - 2y = 7$
           $y = 2x + 3$

20. $3x + \frac{1}{7}y = 2$
    $\frac{1}{2}x - y = 8$

21. $\quad y = ^-x + 5$
    $2x - y = 6$

22. The sum of two numbers is 78.2. The difference of the numbers is 29.3. Use a graph to find the two numbers.

23. Suppose you are comparing the cost of advertising in two local newspapers. The first charges $7 and an additional $.65 for each line of advertising. The second charges $8.30 plus $.52 for each line. For how many lines of advertisement will the cost for these two newspaper ads be the same? Use a graph.

Section 4.4 Algebraic Solution of Systems of Equations

24. Use substitution to find an exact solution to the system of equations in Exercise 21.

For Exercises 25–26, use substitution to solve each system of equations.

25. $\quad y = 5x + 1$
    $x + y = ^-11$

26. $y = 3x$
    $y = 7x - 2$

For Exercises 27–29, use elimination to solve each system of equations.

27. $3x + 4y = 7$
    $2x - 4y = 18$

28. $x - 5y = 10$
    $2x + 6y = 4$

29. $3x + 7y = 11$
    $4x - 5y = {}^-14$

For Exercises 30 and 31, use either elimination or substitution to solve the system of equations.

30. $\quad y = 9x - 6$
    $x + 2y = {}^-12$

31. $2x + 4y = {}^-5$
    $5x - 8y = {}^-26$

In Exercise 32, use the fact that the sum of the measures of two supplementary angles is 180°.

32. Two angles are supplementary. The larger angle measures 30° less than twice the measure of the smaller angle. Complete (a) through (c) to find the measure of each angle.

    a. Let x represent the measure of the smaller angle and y represent the measure of the larger angle. Write an equation involving the sum of the measures of these angles.

    b. Write an equation for the measure of the larger angle in terms of the measure of the smaller angle.

    c. The equations from parts (a) and (b) form a system of equations. Use algebra to solve this system.

33. A mouse runs past a cat. Then, $2\frac{1}{4}$ seconds later, the cat chases the mouse. The mouse runs 2 m/s and the cat runs 5 m/s. If both animals run in a straight line, how long will it take the cat to catch the mouse?

Section 4.5 Parallel and Perpendicular Lines

34. Classify each pair of linear equations as parallel, the same, perpendicular, or none of these.

    a. $y = 5x - 2$ and $y = 5x + 1$

    b. $y = \frac{1}{4}x$ and $y = {}^-4x + 7$

    c. $4x + 2y = 6$ and $y = {}^-2x + 3$

    d. ${}^-3x + y = 1$ and $x - 5y = 9$

35. A line contains the points $(0, {}^-3)$ and $(2, 9)$. Another line contains the points $(3, .5)$ and $(12, {}^-1)$. Are the lines parallel, the same, perpendicular, or none of these?

CHAPTER 4 ▪ TEST

1. Find the slope of the line that contains the points $({}^-6, 1)$ and $({}^-10, 2)$.

2. By hand, sketch the graph of a line with given slope passing through the origin.

    a. $m = 0$ b. $m = \frac{4}{3}$

    c. $m = 1$ d. $m = 2$

3. A type of tree grows 5 inches every 2 years.

    a. What is the rate of change in inches with respect to the number of years?

    b. An initial measurement of the tree is 250 inches. Use the rate of change to find two more ordered pairs in the following table.

Time (years)	Height (inches)
0	250
?	?
?	?

4. For Exercise 3, write a linear equation that models the height of the tree in terms of the number of years since its initial measurement.

5. Solve the equation $2x + 3y = 6$ for y in terms of x.

    a. What is the slope of this equation?

    b. What is the y-intercept?

6. Write an equation of a line with slope $\frac{{}^-3}{4}$ and y-intercept $(0, 2)$.

7. Write an equation of a line with slope 5 containing the point $(1, {}^-2)$.

8. Mentally, find the x- and y-intercepts of the equation $4x - 5y = 20$. Use the intercepts to sketch a graph by hand.

9. Renting a truck from company A costs $19.95 and an additional $.08 for each mile driven. Renting from company B costs $22.95 plus $.05 for each mile. Use a graph to find the number of miles at which these two rental trucks cost the same.

10. Use a graph to find the approximate solution to the system of linear equations.

$$y = 3x - \frac{15}{7}$$
$$6x + 7y = 3$$

11. Use algebra to find an exact solution to Exercise 10.

12. Find an exact solution to the system of equations.

$$2x + 7y = {}^-5$$
$$3x + y = {}^-17$$

13. Two angles are supplementary. One-third of the larger angle is 10° less than the smaller angle. Find the measure of both angles.

14. Describe the graph of a system of equations that has no solutions.

More Applications of Linear Equations

5.1 ■ Proportions

5.2 ■ Percent and Percent Change

5.3 ■ Mixtures and Investments

5.4 ■ Systems of Three Equations (Optional)

Coffee, Anyone?

The student center at a major university has just been renovated. There is now additional space to lease to commercial enterprises. A distributor of gourmet coffee is considering opening a franchise at the student center. However, the executives of this company want to know whether this is a good location for their business.

The coffee distributor hires a marketing firm to conduct a survey. The firm selects a random sample of students from the university and asks students in this sample whether or not they would patronize a gourmet coffee shop if one were opened on the campus. The results of this poll are used by the company to make its decision. In this chapter you learn how to apply proportions and percents to analyze information obtained from samples. (See Exploration on p. 206.)

5.1 Proportions

AFTER STUDYING THIS SECTION YOU WILL BE ABLE TO

- Solve proportion equations.
- Set up proportions.
- Apply proportions to problems.

When two rates or ratios are equal to each other, the equation that expresses this relationship is called a **proportion**. In this section you learn how to solve proportions and how to set up problems that involve proportions.

One application of proportion is found in **similar figures**. Think of a photocopier with a setting that allows you to enlarge or reduce a picture. When such a setting is used, the photocopy is *similar* to the original picture. This means that the two figures have the same shape and that all the distances in the original figure have been changed by the same ratio. In Figure 1, the original house has been enlarged by a ratio of 3 to 2. We can work out the proportion between the houses by measuring any two corresponding parts of the house. For instance, if on the original picture the base of the house measures 5 inches, then on the photocopy it measures 7.5 inches.

Figure 1   The photocopy is $\frac{3}{2} = 1.5$ times as large as the original.

Example 1 deals with similar triangles. Two triangles are similar if their angles have the same measures and corresponding sides are proportional. Similar figures are just *scaled* versions of each other, like the houses in Figure 1.

EXAMPLE 1   At a certain time of the day, a 3-foot stick casts a 5-foot shadow. Find the height of a tree that casts a 30-foot shadow.

Solution   Figure 2 shows how the stick, the tree, the shadows, and the rays of the sun form two triangles. Because the rays of the sun are parallel and both the stick and the tree form 90° angles with the ground, it can be shown, using theorems from geometry, that the two triangles are similar. Because corresponding sides of similar triangles have the same ratio, we can set up a proportion:

$$\frac{\textbf{height of stick}}{\textbf{length of stick shadow}} = \frac{\text{height of tree}}{\text{length of tree shadow}}$$

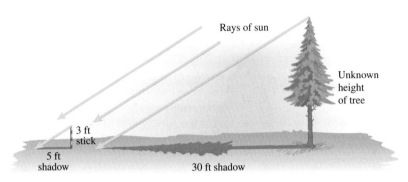

Figure 2

Let h represent the unknown height of the tree. Substituting the known quantities and h, we have

$$\frac{3}{5} = \frac{h}{30}$$

One way to solve this equation is to multiply both sides by 30. Then

$$30 * \frac{3}{5} = \frac{h}{30} * 30$$
$$18 = h$$

The tree is 18 feet tall.

■ ■ ■

Direct Variation

In Example 1 we saw that the ratio of any vertical object to its shadow is the same at any particular time of day. The ratio itself depends upon how high the sun is in the sky. If we let x represent the length of the shadow and y represent the height of the vertical object, we can write an equation with the variables x and y. In Example 1, the ratio is $\frac{3}{5}$, or .6, so the equation becomes

$$\frac{y}{x} = .6$$

This ratio, .6, is called the *variation constant*.

Definition   Direct Variation Equation

Two quantities, represented by the variables x and y, are said to be **directly proportional** if their ratio is constant:

$$\frac{y}{x} = k \qquad \text{or} \qquad y = kx$$

The **variation constant** k is the slope of the line passing through the origin that shows the relationship between x and y. When x and y are directly proportional, we can also say that y **varies directly as** x.

EXAMPLE 2   Roger bought 6 gallons of regular unleaded gasoline for $27.00. How much will it cost him to fill his car's 20-gallon tank?

Solution   The quantities are the amount of gasoline purchased and the total cost. They are directly proportional because their ratio is the price of regular unleaded gasoline in dollars per gallon. Let x represent the amount of gasoline purchased and y represent the cost. Then

$$\frac{y}{x} = k$$

We know that when $x = 6$ gallons, $y = \$27$. Substituting into the equation gives $k = \frac{27}{6} = 4.50$ dollars/gallon. In this case the variation constant is a rate involving two quantities, dollars and gallons.

Roger observes this as he pumps the gas because the values of y, x, and k are displayed on the pump (Figure 3). Note that gasoline stations typically display the unit price ending in $\frac{9}{10}$ cent. Thus the price for 1 gallon appears as $4.499, when to the nearest cent it is actually $4.50.

Once Roger knows k, he can answer the question. The **20**-gallon tank gives the value for x. Substituting into the equation we have

$$\frac{y}{20} = 4.50$$

Multiplying by 20 on both sides gives the solution $y = 90$. It will cost Roger $90 to fill the tank.

■ ■ ■

Figure 3

The Cross-Multiplication Property

Example 2 illustrates one method to solve proportions—that is, to begin by finding the value of the variation constant k. Another common method for solving proportions relies on the following property.

Cross-Multiplication Property

$$\text{If } \frac{a}{b} = \frac{c}{d}, \quad \text{then } ad = bc$$

We find the cross-multiplication property of proportions by multiplying by the quantity bd on both sides of the original equation.

EXAMPLE 3 | Show how to use the cross-multiplication property to solve the problem in Example 2.

Solution | Let $c =$ the cost of filling the tank. Then, because the cost and amount of gasoline are directly proportional, we have

$$\frac{27}{6} = \frac{c}{20}$$

$$27 * 20 = 6c \qquad \textit{Using the cross-multiplication property}$$

$$540 = 5c$$

$$\frac{540}{6} = \frac{6c}{6} \qquad \textit{Dividing by 6 (or multiplying by } \tfrac{1}{6} \textit{ on both sides)}$$

$$90 = c \qquad \textit{Simplifying both sides}$$

It will cost Roger $90 to fill the tank.

■ ■ ■

The next example shows how to use the cross-multiplication property as part of the seven-step process in solving a work-rate problem.

EXAMPLE 4 | Rashid and Joshua decide to make some extra summer money painting cars. Rashid has done this before, so he is faster than Joshua. Rashid can paint an entire car in 3 hours, and Joshua takes 4. How long will it take Rashid and Joshua working together to paint a car?

Solution | Step 1 To *understand* this problem, review Example 2 in Section 1.2, which explains how work rates are computed. The most important thing to remember is that because Joshua and Rashid are working together, they should complete the job faster than *either* of them could do it alone.

Step 2 Drawing a picture can help you *visualize* the problem. Rashid paints a whole car in 3 hours, so if we represent a whole car by a box, then we need to split the box into thirds, each of which Rashid paints in an hour. Similarly, we split Joshua's box into fourths, each of which he paints in 1 hour (see Figure 4). So, adding the part of the car that

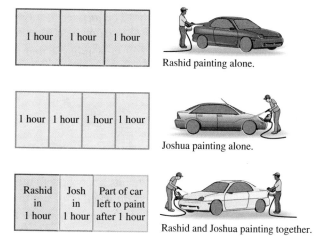

1 hour	1 hour	1 hour

Rashid painting alone.

1 hour	1 hour	1 hour	1 hour

Joshua painting alone.

Rashid in 1 hour	Josh in 1 hour	Part of car left to paint after 1 hour

Rashid and Joshua painting together.

Figure 4   Each *large* rectangle represents one car to be painted.

Rashid paints in 1 hour to the part that Joshua paints in 1 hour, we can see that there is still almost half of a car left to paint after one hour.

Step 3   We *assign* the variable t to represent the time it will take them to paint together.

Step 4   To *write an equation*, use the work-rate formula from Section 1.2.

$$\text{rate} = \frac{\text{work}}{\text{time}}$$

$$\text{Rashid's rate} = \frac{1 \text{ car}}{3 \text{ hours}}$$

$$\text{Joshua's rate} = \frac{1 \text{ car}}{4 \text{ hours}}$$

You can add Rashid and Joshua's rates (like putting the boxes together in Figure 4) to get their combined rate:

$$\frac{1}{3} + \frac{1}{4} = \frac{7}{12} \text{ cars per hour}$$

which lets you write

$$\frac{7}{12} = \frac{1 \text{ car}}{t}$$

Step 5   Use the cross-multiplication property to *solve* for t.

$$7t = 12 * 1$$
$$\frac{7t}{7} = \frac{12}{7}$$
$$t = \frac{12}{7}$$

Step 6   The *answer* to the question is that it will take them $\frac{12}{7} \approx 1.7$ hours to paint a car together.

Step 7   We can *check* that this makes sense because it is less than the time for either one alone but not too small, and it looks about right based on the last box in Figure 4.

Setting Up Proportions

Many students know how to use the cross-multiplication property effectively but are uncertain whether or not they have a correct proportion to begin with. Here is a technique that may prove to be helpful. If we have a situation involving a proportion, we should be able to label both ratios with an element they have in common. In addition, we should be able to do the same with the top row (the numerators) and the bottom row (the denominators). The next example illustrates this technique.

EXAMPLE 5   If a recipe that serves 8 people requires 3 cups of flour, then find how many cups of flour are needed to serve 20 people.

Solution   Let f represent the amount of flour needed to serve 20 people. Then there are several proportions that can be used to solve this problem (see Figure 5). Upon cross multiplying, each of these proportions leads to the equation $8f = 60$, and dividing both sides by 8 gives $f = 7.5$. For 20 people, 7.5 cups of flour are needed.

		Recipe	Amount needed			Recipe	Amount needed			People	Cups of flour
People		$\dfrac{8}{3}$	$= \dfrac{20}{f}$	Cups of flour		$\dfrac{3}{8}$	$= \dfrac{f}{20}$	Recipe		$\dfrac{8}{20}$	$= \dfrac{3}{f}$
Cups of flour				People				Amount needed			

Figure 5   Label the proportion to make sure the fractions relate the correct things; you can either have a fraction for the recipe amounts and one for the amount you will need or a fraction for the people and one for the cups of flour.

The labeling technique will guide us to one of several correct proportions. If we don't think carefully about labels, however, we might write an incorrect proportion such as

$$\frac{8}{20} = \frac{f}{3}$$

This is incorrect because recipe amount is in the numerator on the left and the denominator on the right.

Sampling

Proportions are found when a **sample** is used to draw a conclusion about an entire population. For instance, a polling organization might ask a random sample of about 1500 voters for whom they plan to vote in the next presidential election. From the information obtained in the sample, they predict the outcome of an election in which millions of people will vote.

Biologists use sampling to estimate the population of wildlife in a given environment. The technique is called "capture-recapture." Here's how the method works to estimate the number of fish of a certain species that live in one lake.

Step 1   Capture some fish and mark them with tags; then release them in the lake (Figure 6).

Figure 6   A sample of fish is captured and tagged.

Step 2   Allow the tagged fish enough time to swim around so that they are mixed up with the rest of the population (Figure 7).

Figure 7   The tagged fish are released into the lake.

Step 3   Return to the lake. Capture another sample of fish and count the number with tags (Figure 8).

Figure 8 A representative sample should have about the same proportion of tagged fish as the entire population.

Step 4   Use the number found in this sample to estimate the population of fish in the lake.

$$\frac{\textbf{tagged fish in sample}}{\textbf{total fish in sample}} = \frac{\textbf{tagged fish in lake}}{\textbf{total fish in lake}}$$

In these pictures we have the proportion

$$\frac{2}{6} = \frac{5}{15}$$

In reality, the numbers usually don't match perfectly. This technique just gives an estimate of the true population.

EXAMPLE 6 Biologists are studying small-mouth bass. They take **23** bass from Douglas Lake, tag them, and return them to the lake. Two weeks later they return and take a sample of **19** bass and find that **3** of them are tagged. Estimate the population of bass in Douglas Lake.

Solution Use the proportion

$$\frac{\textbf{tagged fish in sample}}{\textbf{total fish in sample}} = \frac{\textbf{tagged fish in lake}}{\text{total fish in lake}}$$

Let p represent the population of fish in the lake. Then

$$\frac{3}{19} = \frac{23}{p}$$

$$3p = 437 \qquad \textit{Cross multiplying}$$

Because $3p = 437$, $p \approx 145.7$. Because we cannot have a fractional fish, we estimate the bass population of the lake to be 146.

Exercises 5.1

1. If a car goes 50 miles on 2 gallons of gas, it can go 150 miles on 6 gallons of gas. Set up a proportion and show that the cross-multiplication property holds.

2. Solve the proportion

$$\frac{x}{3} = \frac{5}{8}$$

3. Solve for x using the cross-multiplication property of proportions.

$$\frac{x+4}{8} = \frac{11}{3}$$

4. Suppose a 4-foot stick casts a 3-foot shadow. At the same time of day a flagpole casts a 36-foot shadow. How tall is the flagpole?

5. Note that triangle ABD is similar to triangle ECD in the figure. Set up and solve a proportion to find the length of AD.

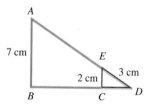

6. In Example 2 the equation $y = 1.5x$ gives the cost in dollars y of gasoline when x gallons are purchased.

   a. Draw a graph for this equation.

   b. What is the slope?

   c. What is the y-intercept?

   d. Is the slope or the y-intercept the same as the variation constant?

In Exercises 7–9 use the proportions A–D.

A. $\dfrac{6}{x} = \dfrac{7}{84}$

B. $\dfrac{6}{x} = \dfrac{84}{7}$

C. $\dfrac{x}{6} = \dfrac{7}{84}$

D. $\dfrac{x}{6} = \dfrac{84}{7}$

7. Which proportion has the same solution as proportion A?

8. Which proportion has the same solution as proportion B?

9. Write two other proportions with x, 6, 7, and 84 that have the same solution as proportion A.

10. Three bundles of asphalt roofing shingles cover 100 square feet. How many bundles do you need to cover 3000 square feet of roof?

11. Laura can pick up her toys in 5 minutes. Her mother can pick up the toys in 2 minutes. How long will it take Laura and her mother to pick up the toys together?

12. Running at a pace of one mile in 8 minutes, the average person burns 120 calories/mile. How many minutes would a person have to run to burn off a 600-calorie meal?

13. Latasha checks out a 145-page book from the library. She can read about 15 pages in 25 minutes. At this rate, how long will it take her to read the book?

14. An architect's drawing of a building has a scale of $\frac{1}{4}$ inch to 1 foot ($\frac{1}{4}$ inch on the drawing represents 1 foot of actual building length). If a wall measures 15 inches on the drawing, use a proportion to find the actual length of the wall.

15. Biologists capture 20 penguins and tag and release them. Later the biologists return and find that 4 are tagged in a sample of 17 penguins. Estimate the penguin population in the region.

Skills and Review 5.1

16. Solve for x and y by an algebraic method.
$$y = 2x - 8 \qquad 4x - y = 10$$

17. The sum of two supplementary angles is 180°. The larger angle is 10° more than 4 times the smaller. Find the measure of both angles.

18. A line has a slope of 1 and contains the point $(4, {}^-1)$.
  a. Find an equation of the line.
  b. Write your equation in standard form.

19. A line contains the points $(2, {}^-3)$ and $(5, 1)$.
  a. Find the slope.
  b. Find an equation of the line.

20. Two boats leave the same harbor heading in the same direction. The slower boat leaves at 10 A.M. and moves at a rate of 15 miles/hour. The faster boat leaves at noon and moves at a rate of 21 miles/hour. What time of day will the faster boat catch the slower boat?

21. Solve for x:
$$\frac{2x - 5}{3} = 5x$$

22. Solve for x: $x - 2(x + 3) + 7x + ({}^-4)^2 = 22$.

23. Recall that the area of a circle is πr^2. Find the exact area of a circle whose radius is 6 inches.

24. Evaluate $3 - 2 - 4 \div 2 + 5 * 2$.

25. Find the area of a parallelogram with base 11 mm and height 7 mm.

5.2 Percent and Percent Change

AFTER STUDYING THIS SECTION YOU WILL BE ABLE TO

- Solve problems involving percents of a whole.
- Solve problems involving percent increase and decrease.

Using Percent to Compare a Part to a Whole

Percent may be used to compare a part to the whole. In Figure 9 part of the bar is shaded. The shaded part represents $x\%$ of the whole bar. The ratio of the part to the whole gives the **percent**. In other words,

$$\frac{\text{part}}{\text{whole}} = \text{percent}$$

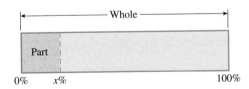

Figure 9

Multiplying both sides of this formula by the whole gives an equivalent formula:

$$\text{part} = \text{percent} * \text{whole}$$

The formula

$$\frac{\text{part}}{\text{whole}} = \text{percent}$$

may be used to find a percent when the whole and the part are known. The formula part = percent * whole may be used to find either the part or whole when the percent is known (the part can be found if you know the whole, and vice versa).

As the next three examples show, percents are used by nutritionists to help determine a balanced diet. For vitamins and minerals, the United States Department of Agriculture determines the recommended daily allowance (RDA), also called the recommended dietary intake or daily value (DV). References to RDA or DV are given on the labels of many food products and in nutritional guidebooks.

EXAMPLE 1 | The RDA for vitamin C is 60 mg. One-half of a pink grapefruit contains 47 mg of vitamin C. What percent of the RDA is provided by this serving?

Solution | Picture the situation with the diagram shown in Figure 10. The scale along the bottom of the bar shows percents. The scale on the top shows vitamin C in milligrams. More than half of the bar is shaded because **47** mg is more than half of **60** mg.

Figure 10

Both the part and the whole are known, so we may use the formula:

$$\text{percent} = \frac{\textbf{part}}{\textbf{whole}}$$

$$\text{percent} = \frac{\textbf{47 mg}}{\textbf{60 mg}} \approx .783 = 78.3\%$$

To change a decimal to percent, move the decimal point two places to the right and add a % sign, so we write $.783 = 78.3\%$.

This problem may also be solved with a proportion. A percent is a ratio with 100 in the denominator, so we can write

$$\frac{47}{60} = \frac{x}{100}$$

Use the cross-multiplication property to get

$$100 * 47 = 60x$$

Solving for x gives $x \approx 78.3$. That means that $x\% = 78.3\%$. The serving of grapefruit provides about 78% of the RDA for vitamin C.

EXAMPLE 2

One serving of a breakfast cereal provides 9% of the RDA for sodium. The RDA for sodium is 2500 mg. How much sodium is provided in one serving of the cereal?

Solution

Again, the scale along the bottom of Figure 11 shows percents and the scale along the top shows milligrams. The unknown is the milligrams of sodium in one serving of cereal, that is, the part. To estimate, think of 9% as slightly less than 10% and 10% of 2500 mg is 250 mg. So, we should have about 250 mg. To find a precise answer, use the formula part = percent * whole.

$$\text{part} = \textbf{percent} * \textbf{whole}$$
$$= .09 * 2500$$
$$= 225$$

Figure 11

If you prefer, you may use a proportion:

$$\frac{x}{2500} = \frac{9}{100}$$
$$100x = 9 * 2500$$
$$x = 225$$

One serving contains 225 mg of sodium.

EXAMPLE 3

One serving of orange juice contains 450 mg of potassium. The nutrition label says that this is 13% of the RDA. What is the RDA for potassium?

Solution

This time the unknown is the whole, as shown in Figure 12. To estimate the whole, think of 13% as a little more than 10%, so 10% of the whole is about 400 mg. The entire whole (100%) is ten times as much, or about 4000 mg.

Figure 12

To find a more precise answer, use the formula part = percent * whole.

$$\textbf{part} = \textbf{percent} * \text{whole}$$

$$450 = .13x$$

$$\frac{450}{.13} = x$$

$$3462 \approx x$$

Another method is to use a proportion:

$$\frac{\textbf{450}}{x} = \frac{\textbf{13}}{\textbf{100}}$$

$$450 * 100 = 13x$$

$$3462 \approx x$$

The RDA for potassium is about 3462 mg.

In this situation 3462 mg may be *too* precise. The RDA for potassium is probably **3500** mg. The food-distribution company could have used the formula $\frac{\text{part}}{\text{whole}}$ = percent to calculate the percent as

$$\frac{\textbf{450 mg}}{\textbf{3500 mg}} \approx .129 = 12.9\%$$

Rounding to the nearest percent, they would then report 13% on the nutrition label.

■ ■ ■

Solutions

A special type of whole-part situation occurs when one substance is dissolved in another to form a uniform mixture called a **solution**. For instance, table salt (sodium chloride) is dissolved in water to form a solution of salt water. The sodium chloride is the **solute**. The water is the **solvent** (Figure 13).

The strength of the solution is defined by the ratio of the mass of solute to the mass of solution, expressed as a percent. This ratio can be represented by a whole-part diagram like the one in Figure 14.

Figure 13

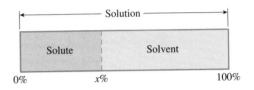

Figure 14

EXAMPLE 4 How much water and how much sodium chloride (NaCl) are needed to make 400 g of a 6% solution of sodium chloride?

Solution Because the whole (solution) is known to be 400 g and the percent is 6%, we need to find the part (solute). See Figure 15.

$$part = \textbf{percent} * \textbf{whole}$$

$$solute = \textbf{percent} * \textbf{solution}$$

$$x = \textbf{.06} * \textbf{400}$$

$$x = \textbf{24}$$

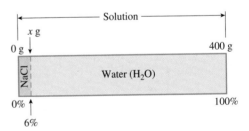

Figure 15

Thus we will need 24 g of solute, that is, sodium chloride (NaCl). To find how much water is needed, look at Figure 15:

$$\textbf{solution} = \textbf{solute} + solvent$$

$$\textbf{400} = \textbf{24} + solvent$$

$$376 = solvent$$

We will need to mix 376 g of water with 24 g of sodium chloride (NaCl) to produce 400 g of solution.

■ ■ ■

Definition

$$\text{Solute} = \text{percent} * \text{solution}$$
$$\text{Solution} = \text{solute} + \text{solvent}$$

Percent Change

Percent may also be applied to situations where something increases or decreases. For instance, the price of an item increases when a sales tax is added to it. Also, the price decreases when it is on sale. It is helpful in both situations to think of the original price as 100% and the change in price as a positive or negative quantity added to the original price. Recall the number line model for addition (Section 1.1):

$$\text{start} + \text{change} = \text{final}$$

See Figures 16 and 17.

Figure 16 Percent increase

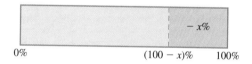

Figure 17 Percent decrease

EXAMPLE 5

The sales tax rate in Connecticut is 6.35%. Mary bought an air conditioner priced at $349.95. How much did she pay altogether?

Solution

Picture this situation as a percent increase (Figure 18). The total price is 106.35% of the original price: **$1.0635 * $349.75** = $372.17. Rounding to the nearest cent the total price is $372.17.

Another way to solve this problem is to calculate the tax (6.35% of $349.95 $\approx$ $22.22) and add the tax to the original price ($349.95 + $22.22 = $372.17).

■ ■ ■

Figure 18

Example 6 shows a percent decrease.

EXAMPLE 6 ■ A coat that normally costs $150 is on sale for $120. Find the percent discount.

Solution Picture this situation as a percent decrease. See Figure 19.

$$x\% = \frac{\text{sale price}}{\text{original price}} = \frac{\$120}{\$150} = .8$$

Figure 19

Thus the sale price is 80% of the original price. The discount is 20% of the original price.

Another way to solve this problem is to find the dollar amount of the discount ($150 − $120 = $30) and use it to calculate the percent discount directly:

$$\frac{\text{discount}}{\text{original price}} = \frac{30}{150} = .2$$

Again, the discount is 20% of the original price.

■ ■

Often, statisticians use percent increase or decrease.

EXAMPLE 7 According to the 2000 census, the population of Nevada was 1,998,000 to the nearest 1000. In 2010 the U.S. Census Bureau found the state's population to be 2,701,000. Find the percent increase over this 10-year period.

Solution

$$\frac{\text{new population}}{\text{original population}} = \frac{2701}{1998} \approx 1.352$$

```
                    ┌──────────── 2010 Population ────────────┐
                                1998              2701 (thousands)
   ┌──────────────────────────────┬──────────────────────┐
   │                              │                      │
   │       2000 Population        │      Increase        │
   │                              │                      │
   └──────────────────────────────┴──────────────────────┘
   0%                            100%                   ?%
```

Figure 20

The 2010 population is about 135% of the 2000 population. Nevada's population increased by about 35%. See Figure 20.

Caution: Notice that in order to compute percent change correctly, we must start with the *original* population. If we put the new (2010) population in the denominator we have the ratio $\frac{1998}{2701}$, which is approximately 74%. This gives 26% for the change in population, which is very different from the correct figure, 35%. Regardless of whether a quantity is increasing or decreasing, consider the *original* population as 100%.

Exercises 5.2

1. 8 is 25% of what number?

   a. Represent the question in a bar diagram.

   b. Estimate the number from your diagram.

   c. Find the exact number with a formula for the whole.

2. 3% of 1400 is what number?

3. 130 is what percent of 270?

For Exercises 4–11, draw a diagram for each situation and then solve the problem.

4. The laboratory grade for a chemistry course is based on 150 points. Jason wants to earn a grade of at least 80%. How many laboratory points must he earn?

5. In the 2010 election, Congressman Joe Courtney received 140,888 votes out of a total of 246,763 case in Connecticut's second Congressional District. What percent of the votes did Mr. Courtney receive? (Source: Connecticut Secretary of the State)

6. An ice cream label states that one serving contains 120 mg of cholesterol. That is 40% of the recommended daily allowance (RDA). What is the RDA for cholesterol? (http://www.nutribase.com)

7. How much water and how much sodium chloride are needed to make 250 g of a 9% solution of sodium chloride?

8. What is the strength of the solution made by dissolving 45 g of sodium chloride in 1455 g of water?

9. A dealer offers to sell you a used automobile for $6500. How much will you have to pay for the car when you include the 6% sales tax?

10. At a local gas station, the price of gasoline rose from $1.69 per gallon to $1.93 per gallon. Find the percent increase.

11. A clothing store has a sale in which all items are 40% off. How much would you have to pay for a pair of pants that originally sold for $29.95?

12. Jamie has trouble remembering formulas. For whole-part situations he remembers only the formula

$$\frac{\text{part}}{\text{whole}} = \text{percent}$$

If necessary, he solves this formula for the item he needs.

a. Solve this formula for the part.

b. Solve this formula for the whole.

13. Between 2000 and 2010, the populations of Arizona and California both increased. See the table. (http://www.quickfacts.census.gov)

State	2000 Population	2010 Population	Change
Arizona	5,130,632	6,392,017	1,261,385
California	33,871,648	37,253,956	3,382,308

a. Find the percent increase for Arizona.

b. Find the percent increase for California.

c. Explain why California had a larger change in population but a smaller percent increase.

14. Assume the tip on a meal is 15% of the cost of the meal. Let base meal be the cost before the tip and final meal be the cost of food with the tip (excluding tax).

a. Write a formula that can be used to find the final meal cost.

b. Assume a base meal costs $22.15. How much does the final meal cost?

15. Some small engines require a mix (solution) of oil and gasoline. Assume 3% of a solution is oil.

a. How much oil is required for 4 gallons of gasoline?

b. A gallon is 128 ounces. How many ounces of oil from part (a) are needed?

Skills and Review 5.2

16. Solve for x if $\frac{1}{3}x + 2 = \frac{5}{6}$.

17. Consider the proportion

$$\frac{3}{4} = \frac{10}{x}$$

a. Write two other proportions with 3, 4, 10, and x that have the same solution.

b. Use the cross-multiplication property to find the solution.

18. Solve for x and y by an algebraic method.

$$2x - 3y = 11$$
$$x + 4y = {}^-11$$

19. Use a graph to approximate the solution(s) to the system of equations.

$$y = {}^-\frac{1}{2}x + \frac{3}{2}$$
$$y = \frac{4}{3}x - 2$$

20. Find an equation of the line containing the points $({}^-1, {}^-5)$ and $(3, 4)$.

21. Matt is asked to find the slope of the line $y = 3x - 7$. He finds two ordered pairs that satisfy the equation and then he calculates the slope. Describe another method for finding the slope of the line.

22. Solve this problem using the seven steps for problem-solving described in Section 3.3: The length of a rectangle is 4 feet less than twice the width. The perimeter is 64 feet. Find the dimensions of the rectangle.

23. A video rental store charges $3.00 to rent a movie plus $1.00 each day. Complete this table:

Days Rented	Charge
1	?
2	?
?	7

24. Use the table values from Exercise 23 to find an equation that shows how the charge for a video tape depends upon the number of days it is rented.

25. Evaluate

$$5 + 2(6 - 4)^3$$

5.3   Mixtures and Investments

AFTER STUDYING THIS SECTION YOU WILL BE ABLE TO

- Solve problems involving mixtures.
- Solve problems involving investments.

As you will recall from Section 4.2, a linear equation in two variables, x and y, may be written in standard form as $Ax + By = C$. This form suggests that a certain amount of what x represents (Ax) is combined with a certain amount of what y represents (By) to produce a known quantity C. There are many applications that lead to equations of this form. In this section we learn how to solve a variety of problems that may be solved using a system of two equations in two variables, with one or both of the equations in standard form. Many of these equations involve applications of percents, which were introduced in Section 5.2.

EXAMPLE 1   At Kayla's Nut Shop, peanuts sell for $2 per pound and cashews sell for $5 per pound. A customer wants to buy a 10-pound mixture of peanuts and cashews and is willing to pay $28. How many pounds of each type of nut should Kayla use to make the mixture?

Solution   Before setting up this problem for an algebraic solution, let us observe Kayla as she goes through steps 1 and 2 of the problem-solving process, *understanding* and *visualization*.

Kayla thinks, "I need 10 pounds of nuts. If all 10 pounds are peanuts, the price for the mixture will be $20, which is too low. On the other hand, if they are all cashews, the price will be $50, too high. Suppose I make a half-and-half mixture—that would be 5 pounds of peanuts worth $10 combined with 5 pounds of cashews worth $25 for a total of $35. That's too much, so let me try again."

Kayla is using the age-old problem-solving strategy called guess-and-check. She may eventually arrive at a solution, but it will take some time. One reason we learn algebra is to be able to solve problems like this more efficiently. We can gain some insight into the problem by examining the data Kayla has supplied.

Let us *assign* the variable x to represent the amount of peanuts, in pounds, and y to be the amount of cashews, in pounds, thus reaching step 3 of the problem-solving process. Kayla has given us three pairs of values for a table.

x	y	
10	0	(price of mixture = $20)
0	10	(price of mixture = $50)
5	5	(price of mixture = $35)

If we graph these ordered pairs, they lie on a line with equation $x + y = 10$. We can call this equation the "weight equation." The weight equation line has (10, 0) as x-intercept and (0, 10) as y-intercept, as shown in Figure 21.

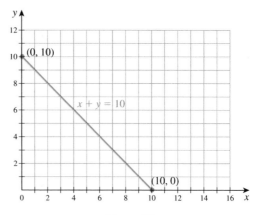

Figure 21

Kayla is not getting very far guessing and checking with this equation, so she tries another approach.

She reasons, "The customer wants to spend $28. If she spends it all on peanuts at $2 per pound she'll have 14 pounds of nuts—that's more than she wants. If she spends it all on cashews at $5 per pound, she'll have—let me see, $28 \div 5$—that comes out to 5.6 pounds. That's less than the 10 pounds that she wants. What if she spent $18 on peanuts and $10 on cashews?"

Kayla isn't finding a solution this way either, but she has given us another table.

x	y	
14	0	(All money spent on peanuts)
0	5.6	(All money spent on cashews)
9	2	($18 on peanuts and $10 on cashews)

The ordered pairs satisfy the equation money for peanuts + money for cashews = $28, or, in terms of x and y, $2x + 5y = 28$. We have now completed step 4 of the problem-solving process by *writing* two *equations*.

The graph in Figure 22 shows the original weight equation, $x + y = 10$, graphed with the money equation, $2x + 5y = 28$. It appears that the two lines intersect. We can now *solve* this system of equations (step 5):

$$x + y = 10 \qquad \textit{Weight equation}$$

$$2x + 5y = 28 \qquad \textit{Money equation}$$

We may solve each equation for y in terms of x and graph

$$Y1 = {}^-X + 10 \text{ (weight)} \qquad Y2 = {}^-.4X + 5.6 \text{ (money)}$$

Using a graphing calculator, we find an approximate solution, $x \approx 7.33$ and $y \approx 2.67$.

We can also solve by an algebraic method such as substitution or elimination. Solving by elimination,

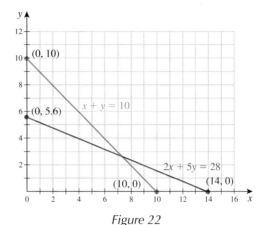

Figure 22

$$x + y = 10 \quad \rightarrow \quad {}^-2x - 2y = {}^-20$$
$$2x + 5y = 28 \quad \rightarrow \quad \underline{2x + 5y = 28}$$
$$3y = 8$$
$$y = \tfrac{8}{3} = 2\tfrac{2}{3}$$
$$x + 2\tfrac{2}{3} = 10$$
$$x = 7\tfrac{1}{3}$$

The *answer* to our question (step 6) is that Kayla should mix $7\frac{1}{3}$ pounds of peanuts with $2\frac{2}{3}$ pounds of cashews to produce the desired mixture. We can *check* this result (step 7) by showing that the total weight is 10 pounds and the total cost is $28.

■ ■ ■

Now let's apply the same technique to a situation involving chemical solutions.

EXAMPLE 2 ▌ A nurse needs 400 mL of a 35% solution of alcohol. She has one bottle which contains a 20% solution and another bottle which contains a 60% solution. How much of each solution should she mix together?

Solution ▌ Recall our discussion of solutions in Section 5.2. In Figure 23, the amount of alcohol (solute) in each container is represented by the shaded portion. We want to know how much of each solution to mix, so let $x =$ the volume (in mL) of 20% solution to be used and $y =$ the volume (in mL) of 60% solution. Our first equation is based on the relationship

volume of first solution + volume of second solution = volume of mixture,

$$x + y = 400$$

A second equation may be found by considering the amount of solute (in this case alcohol) in each container:

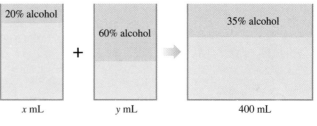

Figure 23

alcohol in first container + alcohol in second container = alcohol in mixture.

For each container we use the relationship part = percent * whole to find the quantities of alcohol:

$$.20x + .60y = .35 * 400$$

$$.20x + .60y = 140$$

We now have a system of two equations, which we can label the "solution equation" and the "alcohol equation":

$$x + y = 400 \qquad \textit{Solution equation}$$

$$.20x + .60y = 140 \qquad \textit{Alcohol equation}$$

This system can be solved by any method. Here we use substitution. Solve the first equation for y to get $y = 400 - x$ and substitute into the second equation:

$$.20x + .60(400 - x) = 140$$

$$.20x + 240 - .60x = 140$$

$$^-.40x + 240 = 140$$

$$^-.40x = ^-100$$

$$x = 250$$

$$y = 400 - 250 = 150$$

She will need 250 mL of the 20% solution and 150 mL of the 60% solution.

■ ■ ■

EXAMPLE 3 Marcel has $2000 to invest in an IRA. His financial advisor suggests grade A bonds, which pay yearly interest at the rate of 5%, and grade B bonds, which pay yearly interest at the rate of 9.5%. Of course, he would prefer the higher interest rate, but grade B bonds are a riskier investment. His advisor suggests that he diversify by putting a portion of his $2000 in each of the two types of bonds. Marcel decides to do that but wants to make sure that he earns a 7.5% yield overall. How much should he invest in each grade of bond to meet this goal?

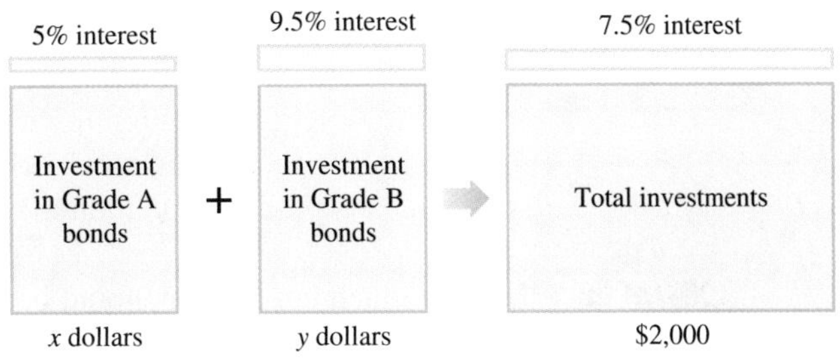

Figure 24

Solution Figure 24 shows a picture of this situation. Notice the similarity to the problem in Example 2, but also notice that in this case interest is not part of the original investment but rather is added onto it. Let x = amount of money (in dollars) invested in grade A bonds. Let y = amount of money (in dollars) invested in grade B bonds. Use the formula **interest = principal * rate * time**.

The interest for 1 year earned on grade A bonds is $x * (.05) * 1 = .05x$. The interest for 1 year earned on grade B bonds is $y * (.095) * 1 = .095y$. The interest for 1 year earned on the total investment is $2000 * (.075) * 1 = 150$.

We have two equations, an "investment equation" and an "interest equation."

$$x + y = 2000 \qquad \text{Investment equation}$$

$$.05x + .095y = 150 \qquad \text{Interest equation}$$

Again, we may use any suitable method to solve this system. We can use elimination if we multiply by $-.05$ on both sides of the first equation:

$$
\begin{array}{ll}
^-.05(x + y) = ^-.05(2000) & \rightarrow \quad ^-.05x - .05y = ^-100 \\
.05x + .095y = 150 & \rightarrow \quad .05x + .095y = 150 \\
\hline
& \qquad\qquad\quad .045y = 50 \\
& \qquad\qquad\qquad\quad y \approx \mathbf{1111.11} \\
& \qquad\quad x + \mathbf{1111.11} \approx 2000 \\
& \qquad\qquad\qquad\quad x \approx 888.89
\end{array}
$$

He should invest \$888.89 in grade A bonds and \$1111.11 in grade B bonds to meet his goal.

Note that in reality he probably won't be able to invest these amounts exactly, but this theoretical solution will help him come close to reaching his goal.

■ ■ ■

Although we used two variables to solve each of the previous problems, some students prefer to use only one variable. For instance, Example 3 could have been set up this way: Let x = amount of money (in dollars) invested in grade A bonds. Let $2000 - x$ = amount of money (in dollars) invested in grade B bonds. Then a single equation, $.05x + .095(2000 - x) = 150$ can be used to solve for x. You should convince yourself that this approach is very similar to solving the two equations in Example 3 with the substitution method.

Caution: All three examples included an equation of the form $x + y =$ something. The next two examples, however, demonstrate that this is not always the case. Avoid the temptation to view the previous examples as formulas that work whenever you have mixtures, solutions, or investments. Instead, think carefully about each problem situation to come up with appropriate equations.

EXAMPLE 4   How much pure water should be added to 200 mL of a 10% solution of sulfuric acid (H_2SO_4) to dilute its strength to 3%?

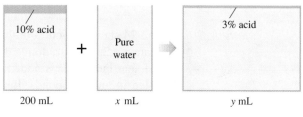

Figure 25

Solution   As usual, a picture is helpful (see Figure 25). Let $x =$ amount of pure water (in mL). Let $y =$ amount of mixture (in mL). We have two equations based on

volume of first solution + volume of second solution = volume of mixture

acid in first container + acid in second container = acid in mixture

$$200 + x = y \quad \textit{Solution equation}$$

$$20 + 0 = .03y \quad \textit{Acid equation}$$

Solving the second equation for y, we have $y \approx 666.7$ mL. Substituting for y in the first equation gives $x \approx 466.7$ mL.

About 467 mL of pure water are needed. *Note:* As a safety precaution, the 10% acid solution should be poured into the container containing the pure water, not the other way around. Always add acid to water, never water to acid!

■ ■ ■

Our final example is a distance-rate-time problem that involves an equation in standard form, $Ax + By = C$. In this case the terms Ax and By represent the distances traveled by the two boys and C represents the total distance.

EXAMPLE 5   Jason sets out from home at 9:00 A.M. and walks toward Nathan's house at the rate of 4 miles/hour. At 9:30 A.M. Nathan leaves his house, riding his bike in the direction of Jason's house at the rate of 10 miles/hour. The two houses are 16 miles apart. When will Jason and Nathan meet?

Solution   The situation is represented in Figure 26. There are several ways to approach this problem. One involves using two variables.

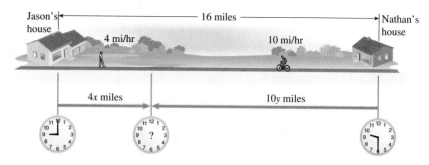

Figure 26

Let x represent the time in hours Jason travels. Let y represent the time in hours Nathan travels. Use the relationship distance = rate * time to find expressions for the distances both boys travel. Jason travels $4x$ miles and Nathan travels $10y$ miles. Because the total distance traveled is 16 miles, we have a *distance equation*:

$$4x + 10y = 16 \qquad \textit{Distance equation}$$

We also have a *time* equation, because Jason travels $\frac{1}{2}$ hour longer than Nathan does.

$$x = y + \tfrac{1}{2} \qquad \textit{Time equation}$$

Substituting x from the time equation into the distance equation gives us

$$4\left(y + \tfrac{1}{2}\right) + 10y = 16$$
$$4y + 2 + 10y = 16$$
$$14y + 2 = 16$$
$$14y = 14$$
$$y = 1$$
$$x = 1 + \tfrac{1}{2} = 1\tfrac{1}{2}$$

Nathan travels for 1 hour and Jason travels for $1\tfrac{1}{2}$ hours. They meet at 10:30 A.M.

Exercises 5.3

1. Often in linear combination problems, we can find a rough estimate for an answer before writing any equations. Consider Example 1, where a 10-pound mixture of nuts costs $28.

   a. Find the cost per pound of the mixture.

   b. Was the cost per pound of the mixture closer to the cost per pound of the peanuts or the cashews?

c. Of which nut, then, should there be more in the mixture? Explain your reasoning.

2. In Example 2 a nurse made 400 mL of a 35% solution of alcohol from a combination of 60% and 20% solutions of alcohol. Follow the steps for a quick check of the work from Example 2.

a. Is the 35% for the mixture closer to 60% or 20%?

b. What does this imply about the relative quantities of each solution?

c. How can this method be used to determine if the algebraic results are reasonable?

3. A chemist needs to make a mixture containing 30 mL of a 25% solution of hydrochloric acid (HCl). She has a 15% solution and a 40% solution of HCl.

a. Model this situation with a diagram such as Figure 23.

b. From your diagram write a volume equation, where volume of first solution + volume of second solution = volume of mixture.

c. Write a solute equation where HCl in first solution + HCl in second solution = HCl in mixture.

d. Without solving this system of equations, describe the steps necessary to find the amount of each solution on a graphing calculator.

4. Maria has $3000 to invest between two accounts and wants an overall yield of 7.5%. One account earns 5% and the other earns 9%. Suppose a student writes the following two equations to represent this situation.

$$x + y = 3000 \qquad \textit{Investment equation}$$

$$.05x + .09y = .075 \qquad \textit{Interest equation}$$

Find the error in the equations and correct it.

5. In Example 5, you were given the two equations

$$4x + 10y = 16$$

$$x = y + \tfrac{1}{2}$$

Describe what the terms represent in each equation.

6. An amusement park sells children's tickets for $4 and adult tickets for $7. One day the park sold 1000 tickets for a total of $6100. Complete the steps to find the number of children's and adult tickets sold that day.

a. *Assign* the variables as x = number of children's tickets sold, and y = number of adult tickets sold. Complete the table.

	Children	Adults	Together
Rate (ticket)	$4	$7	—
Number of tickets	x		
Cost ($)	$4x$		$6100

b. From the table *write* two *equations*, each containing x and y.

c. *Solve* the system of equations to find the number of each type of ticket sold that day.

7. A gourmet coffee company sells a 3-pound mix of chocolate raspberry beans and French vanilla coffee beans for $13. If the chocolate raspberry is $4 per pound and the French vanilla is $6 per pound, how many pounds of each coffee are in the mix? Complete the steps to answer the question.

a. *Assign* the variable(s).

b. Complete a table similar to Exercise 6.

c. *Write* the *equation(s)*. *Note:* It is possible to have one equation in one unknown.

d. *Solve* the equation(s) algebraically.

e. How many pounds of each coffee are in the mix?

8. A chemist has two bottles of hydrochloric acid (HCl). Bottle A contains a 36% solution and bottle B contains a 12% solution. She needs solutions of different concentrations. Match each of these solutions with a description of how she would make it. Do not set up equations or make any calculation; just choose the most reasonable answer.

36% HCl   12% HCl

a. 18% solution

b. 24% solution

1. Mix equal amounts from bottle A and bottle B.

2. Mix a large amount from bottle A with a small amount from B.

c. 30% solution   3. Mix a small amount from bottle A with a large amount from B.

d. 48% solution   4. You can't make this solution with bottles A and B.

9. A chemist mixes two solutions of alcohol to make 600 mL of a 31% solution of alcohol. If the first solution is 10% alcohol and the second is 40% alcohol, how much of each solution is in the mixture? Complete the steps to answer the question.

   a. Draw a picture.

   b. *Assign* the variables.

   c. *Write* a system of equation(s).

   d. *Solve* the equations graphically.

   e. *Answer* the question.

   f. *Check* your answer from part (e) to see if it seems reasonable.

10. Alana has $5000 to invest. She wants to maximize her income but portion her investments to reduce risk. She decides to invest in a CD paying 6% interest per year and a lower-grade bond paying 11% per year. How much should she put into each investment in order to earn 8% overall? Complete the steps to answer the question.

    a. Draw a picture.

    b. *Assign* the variables.

    c. *Write* the equation(s).

    d. *Solve* the equation(s) algebraically.

    e. *Answer* the question.

    f. *Check* your answer for reasonableness.

11. Thelma and Louise traveled by car from Wichita, Kansas, to Saint Louis, Missouri, a distance of 446 miles. Thelma drove for the first part of the journey, averaging 61 miles/hour. Louise got impatient and asked to take over. She drove the remainder of the trip, averaging 72 miles/hour. The total driving time was 6 hours 30 minutes. How long was each of the drivers behind the wheel?

    a. Draw a diagram.

    b. *Assign* one or two variables and use them to *write* an *equation* or a system of equations.

    c. *Solve* the equation(s) by any suitable method.

    d. *Answer* the question.

12. A 5-pound mixture of peanuts and almonds sells for $15. If the peanuts sell for $1.50 per pound and the almonds sell for $4 per pound, how many pounds of each type of nut are in the mix?

13. A theater company wants to keep its ticket prices low so they sell most of the 600 seats at $4 per ticket and sell some special seats at $12 per ticket. If the company makes $3040, how many of each kind of seat does it sell? Assume all the seats are sold, and solve this problem graphically.

14. A restaurant has 2 cups of an oil and vinegar salad dressing that is 88% oil. How much vinegar should be added to dilute the dressing to 55% oil?

15. A couple needs to borrow $5600 for a home improvement project. They borrow part of the money at 7.5% simple interest and the rest at 11.25% simple interest. How much do they borrow from each source, if the interest for one year is $476.25?

Skills and Review 5.3

16. Answer each question about percents.

    a. 140 is what percent of 250?

    b. 15% of 12 is what number?

    c. 35 is 60% of what number?

17. How much water and how much hydrochloric acid are needed to make 300 g of a 6% solution of hydrochloric acid?

18. In 2008 the U.S. budget deficit was $459 billion. In 2012 the budget deficit was $1,327 billion. (www. usgovrnmentdebt.us)

    a. How you can tell without doing any calculations that the percent change (from 2008 to 2012) was greater than 100%?

    b. Find the percent change in the budget deficit from 2008 to 2012.

19. Solve the proportion.

$$\frac{x}{3.2} = \frac{^-24}{7}$$

20. Julie bought 75 gallons of heating oil for $307.50. How much will 120 gallons of heating oil cost her?

    a. Set up a proportion.

    b. Solve the proportion using the cross-multiplication property.

21. Find the x- and y-intercepts of the equation,

$$9x - 4y = 36$$

22. Solve this problem using the seven steps for problem-solving. Two cars start at 2:00 P.M., one from San Diego and the other from Las Vegas, and they travel toward each other. The car from San Diego travels at 70 miles/hour and the car leaving Las Vegas travels at 75 miles/hour. The distance between San Diego and Las Vegas is 338 miles. At what time will the two cars meet?

23. Solve the equation for x.

$$4 - (x + 3) = 2(5x - 1)$$

24. Evaluate the expression

$$\frac{2(4x - 5) + 7}{6}$$

for $x = {}^-3$.

25. Find the missing side on the right triangle shown.

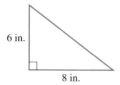

6 in.

8 in.

5.4 Systems of Three Equations (Optional)

In Sections 4.3 and 4.4 we solved systems of equations involving two variables: two variables and two equations. Many situations involve more than two unknowns, which can lead to systems of equations in *more than* two variables.

EXAMPLE 1 José and Valerie play a guessing game with coins. Valerie tells José that she has 15 coins in her pocket, some quarters, some dimes, and some nickels. The total value of the coins is $2.40, and she has 2 more quarters than dimes. José has to guess how many of each type of coin she has.

Solution We can use the seven problem-solving steps to help us with this problem. First, we read carefully and see that what José needs to find out is how many quarters, dimes, and nickels Valerie has in her pocket. To *visualize* the problem, it might help to get some coins and try out various combinations. Next, we need to assign variables. Because we are asked to find the numbers of quarters, dimes, and nickels, we need a variable for each. Let x be the number of quarters, y be the number of dimes, and z be the number of nickels.

We have not encountered a problem like this before; we have *three* variables to work with. We can carry out step 4, writing equations, by looking back at the problem.

$$x + y + z = 15 \qquad \textit{Valerie has 15 coins.}$$

$$.25x + .10y + .05z = 2.40 \qquad \textit{The total value is \$2.40.}$$

$$x = y + 2 \qquad \textit{She has 2 more quarters than dimes.}$$

We could try to solve this system of equations algebraically in the same way we solved systems of equations in Section 4.4, using substitution. Use the equation $x = y + 2$ to substitute for x in the equations $x + y + z = 15$ and $.25x + .10y +$

$.05z = 2.40$, which would give us two equations in two variables (y and z). Next, we could solve one of these new equations for y and substitute into the other equation, which would give an equation involving just z. We could solve this for z, and then substitute the value of z into the equation with y and z to find a value for y. Finally, we could substitute the values of y and z into any of the original equations to find the value of x.

Instead, we take advantage of our calculators, which can do the algebra for us in this case. First, we need to put the equations in *standard form*, with the variables on the left-hand side and any constant on the right-hand side.

$$x + y + z = 15$$

$$.25x + .10y + .05z = 2.40$$

$$x - y = 2$$

Now, we enter this system of equations into our calculator; first, choose 2nd MATRX, and then, EDIT. Choose one of the available names (say [A]) and press ENTER. The display will look like this:

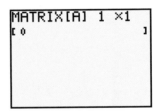

Push 3 ENTER 4 ENTER and the display becomes

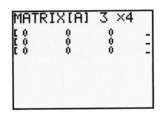

Next, we enter each coefficient to replace the zeros (... means there is another set of zeros off the screen). In this case, start with 1 ENTER, then 1 ENTER, then 1 ENTER, then 15 ENTER. This puts the first equation in. Then do .25 ENTER, .10 ENTER, and keep going until you have run out of equations. The display is now

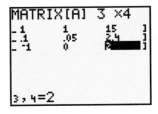

There is a zero on the third line because the coefficient of z in the last equation is zero.

To check your entry from the home screen, choose [2nd] MATRX, and then NAMES. Select [A] and press [ENTER]. You should see the following:

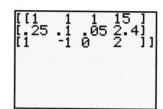

This is the **matrix** associated with our system of equations. The first column is all the coefficients of x, the second, of y, and the third, of z. The last column contains the numbers on the right-hand side of each equation.

Finally, choose [2nd] MATRX again, then MATH, scroll down to rref, and press [ENTER]. Enter the name [A] from the MATRX menu, close parentheses, and press [ENTER]. Now the display is [A]

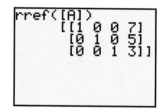

We care only about the numbers in the right column, **7**, **5**, and **3**. These are the solutions. The first number corresponds to the first variable, x, the number of quarters, and so on. The calculator says Valerie has 7 quarters, 5 dimes, and 3 nickels.

We can *check* this answer. $7 + 5 + 3 = 15$, so she has 15 coins, which is correct, and $.25(\mathbf{7}) + .1(\mathbf{5}) + .05(\mathbf{3}) = 1.75 + .5 + .15 = 2.40$, which is also right. Finally, **7** is 2 more than **5**, so Valerie has 2 more quarters than dimes.

■ ■ ■

This might seem like just as much work as doing the algebra, but with a little practice it goes quickly. You can also save time after the first problem by reusing A. When you choose EDIT the second time and pick A, all you need to do is change the numbers.

Exercises 5.4

1. José checks in his pocket and has Valerie guess what coins he has. He tells her he has 24 coins, some quarters, some dimes, and some pennies. The coins have a value of $3.84. He has twice as many dimes as pennies. How many of each coin does he have?

2. Solve the following system of three equations:

$$x + 2y + 3z = 4$$

$$5x - 5y + 7z = 8$$

$$10y + 11z = 12$$

a. Give the answers rounded to two decimal places.

b. If you use the full decimal as given by the calculator, is the answer exact? Explain.

3. A developer is building houses on a cul-de-sac. He builds three types of houses, small colonials, big colonials, and split-levels. Small colonials cost $135,000 to build and sell for $200,000. Big colonials cost $175,000 to build and sell for $250,000. Split-levels cost $150,000 to build and sell for $210,000. He will build 11 houses and plans on making a profit of $730,000. If he builds the same number of big colonials and split-levels, how many houses of each kind does he build?

CHAPTER 5 ▪ KEY CONCEPTS ▪

Direct Variation Equation   This equation involves two quantities, represented by the variables x and y, whose ratio is constant:

$$\frac{y}{x} = k \qquad \text{or} \qquad y = kx$$

The **variation constant** k is the slope of the line passing through the origin that shows the relationship between x and y. (Page 177)

Cross-Multiplication Property   If $\frac{a}{b} = \frac{c}{d}$, then $ad = bc$. (Page 178)

Setting Up Proportions   When setting up a **proportion** to solve a problem, check to make sure the fractions relate *corresponding* quantities. (Page 180)

Sampling   In sampling, a sample is taken from a large quantity and proportions relate the sample to the whole quantity. For example, suppose 10,000 people vote in a local election and a reporter asks 100 people for whom they voted. If 65 people say candidate A, then the reporter is probably safe in assuming that candidate A won the election. (Page 181)

Comparing a Part to a Whole   (Page 184)

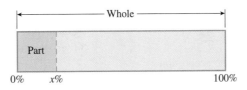

$$\frac{\text{part}}{\text{whole}} = \text{percent}$$

$$\text{part} = \text{percent} * \text{whole}$$

Solutions   (Page 187)

$$\text{solute} = \text{percent} * \text{solution}$$

$$\text{solution} = \text{solute} + \text{solvent}$$

Percent Change   Start + change = final. Consider the original quantity (start) to represent 100%. (Page 189)

Interest formula: interest = principal ∗ rate ∗ time

Mixtures and Investments   These problems often involve equations in standard form $Ax + By = C$. (Section 5.3)

Exploration

A sample of 500 students at a university are polled to see if they would patronize a proposed gourmet coffee shop. Of the students polled, 119 say yes. The total student population of the university is 18,500.

a. Set up and solve a proportion to estimate how many students would patronize the gourmet coffee shop.

b. What percent of the student population does the poll indicate would patronize the coffee shop?

c. All polls have a *margin of error*. The actual percentage in the population is likely to fall within a range determined by the sample percentage plus or minus the margin of error. For this poll the margin of error is 3.7%. Find the range of percents for this poll.

d. Given the margin of error, find the maximum and the minimum number of students (from the population) who are likely to patronize the coffee shop.

CHAPTER 5 ▪ REVIEW EXERCISES

Section 5.1 Proportions

1. Use the cross-multiplication property to solve each proportion.

a. $\dfrac{10}{4} = \dfrac{x}{18}$ **b.** $\dfrac{9}{x} = \dfrac{2}{3}$

c. $\dfrac{x}{5} = 3$ **d.** $\dfrac{5}{2} = \dfrac{8}{x+1}$

2. In Example 3 of Section 5.1, we found the proportion

$$\frac{9 \text{ dollars}}{6 \text{ gallons}} = \frac{c \text{ dollars}}{20 \text{ gallons}}$$

Write two other proportions that are also correct. *Note:* See Setting Up Proportions on page 180 for guidelines on how to write a proportion.

3. A formula for Celsius temperature in terms of Fahrenheit temperature is

$$C = \frac{F - 32}{1.8}$$

Notice that this equation is a proportion. Find the Fahrenheit temperature when the Celsius temperature is 20°.

4. The cost of heating oil is directly proportional to the number of gallons purchased. The Richards spent $682.50 on 175 gallons of heating oil. How much does 1 gallon cost? Use this unit price to find the cost of 150 gallons of heating oil.

Use proportions to solve Exercises 5–8.

5. At a certain time of day a 5-foot person casts a 4-foot shadow. How tall is a building that casts a 17-foot shadow?

6. At a local gas station, 15 gallons of regular gasoline cost $63. How many gallons of regular gasoline may be bought for $42?

7. Sid can perform a job in 2 hours. Joanne isn't nearly as skillful, so the same job takes her 6 hours. Suppose they work together on this job.

a. Without performing any calculations, how do you know that Sid and Joanne can finish this job in less than 2 hours?

b. Exactly how many hours does this job take if Sid and Joanne work together?

8. In a certain forest 42 deer are caught and tagged. A month later naturalists return to the same area and capture 22 deer, of which 9 have tags. Estimate the deer population in this forest.

Section 5.2 Percent and Percent Change

9. The formula for percent is $\frac{part}{whole}$ = percent.

a. Give a formula for the *part*.

b. Give a formula for the *whole*.

10. Use a bar diagram such as the one shown in Figure 9 (page 184) to represent the following question: 14 is what percent of 30?

11. Use your bar diagram from Exercise 10 to estimate the percent.

12. Use the formula from Exercise 9 to find the exact percent in Exercise 10.

13. 21 is what percent of 80?

a. Represent the question in a bar diagram.

b. Estimate the percent from your diagram.

c. Find the exact percent using the formula.

14. 15% of 72 is what number?

15. 12 is 6% of what number?

16. The RDA for calcium is 1000 mg. A cup of lactose-reduced milk contains 300 mg of calcium. What percent of the RDA for calcium is provided in a cup of this milk?

17. The RDA for saturated fat is 20 g. A serving of peanut butter is 15% of the RDA for saturated fat. How many grams of saturated fat are in one serving of peanut butter?

18. One serving of sun-dried raisins contains 2000 mg of fiber. That amount of fiber is 8% of the RDA for fiber. What is the RDA for fiber? (http://www.nutribase.com)

19. Give a definition for each term.

a. Solute

b. Solvent

c. Solution

20. What is the strength of a 200-g solution of sodium chloride that contains 18 g of sodium chloride?

21. Suppose the taxes and surcharges on a recent phone bill were 12.5% of the charges for phone calls. If the phone calls alone were $29.65, how much was paid altogether? Round your answer to the nearest penny.

22. An airline ticket on a major carrier was recently reduced from $420 to $305. To the nearest hundredth, what was the percent discount?

23. The population of a town increased 17% to 12,500 people. What was the original population?

Section 5.3 Mixture and Investments

24. At the Luscious Candy Shop, peanut butter fudge sells for $5 per pound and vanilla fudge sells for $7 per pound. A customer wants to buy a 2-pound mixture of the fudge and is willing to pay $13. How many pounds of each type of fudge can this customer purchase?

a. Assign any variables.

b. Write an equation or system of equations.

c. Solve the equation(s) for either variable so that they may be entered into the $\boxed{Y =}$ menu on your calculator.

d. Use a graph to approximate the number of pounds of each type of fudge.

25. A chemist requires 200 mL of a 22% solution of hydrochloric acid. The chemist has a 10% solution and a 30% solution. How much of each solution should the chemist mix together?

26. A checking account pays an annual interest rate of 2.3% and a savings account pays an annual interest rate of 5.4%. A total investment of $700 paid $34.30 in interest for the year. How much was deposited in each account?

5.4 Systems of Three Equations

27. Solve the following system of three equations and round your answers to two decimal places.

$$3y + z = 5$$
$$^-x + 2y + 4z = {}^-6$$
$$2x + 5y - 3z = 8$$

28. Giovanni has 31 coins in a jar containing pennies, nickels, and quarters. There are four times as many nickels as pennies. The coins have a value of $1.51. How many of each coin is in the jar?

CHAPTER 5 ■ TEST

1. Solve the proportion

$$\frac{10}{x} = \frac{3}{8}$$

2. When traveling abroad people often exchange currencies. Suppose 50 U.S. dollars buy 42.9 euros. How many U.S. dollars can be purchased with 200 euros?

3. Ladeen and Larry have a snow-plowing business. Using her truck alone, Ladeen can finish the plowing in 6 hours. Larry needs 8 hours with his truck. Using both trucks, how long will it take Ladeen and Larry to finish plowing?

4. In an artic region 15 polar bears are caught and tagged. A couple of months later, in the same region, 10 polar bears are caught, and 4 of them have tags. Estimate the polar bear population for this region.

For Exercises 5–7, use a bar diagram to support your answers.

5. 18 is what percent of 40?

6. 85% of 200 is what number?

7. 60 is 105% of what number?

8. A basketball player averages 20 points per game. One night she scores 16 points. What percent of her usual output was this?

9. Due to a shortage of memory chips a computer price was increased to $1800 from $1600. What was the percent increase on the price of this computer?

10. Which solution contains more acid, 150 mL of a 12% solution of sulfuric acid (H_2SO_4) or 130 mL of a 15% solution of H_2SO_4? Explain your answer.

11. A nut shop sells almonds for $7.75 per pound and peanuts for $3.25 per pound. In order to sell an overstock of peanuts, the shop owner decides to mix the peanuts with almonds. How many pounds of each kind of nut are in a 4-pound mixture that costs $19?

12. Fred has $5000 to invest between AAA bonds and a certificate of deposit (CD). The bonds pay a yearly rate of 7.5% interest and the CD pays a yearly rate of 5% interest. How much should Fred place in each investment in order to earn a 6.5% yield overall?

13. A juice company decides to charge more for its product by adding water to increase the volume. The current product contains 2 L and is 15% juice. How much water is added if the concentration is diluted to 8% juice?

Exponents and Factoring

- **6.1** ■ **The Laws of Exponents**
- **6.2** ■ **Products and Factors**
- **6.3** ■ **Factoring by Grouping**
- **6.4** ■ **Factoring Quadratic Trinomials**
- **6.5** ■ **Factoring the Sum and Difference of Two Cubes (Optional)**

Multiplying with Squares

In the late twentieth century the handheld calculator revolutionized many aspects of computation. Similarly, in fifteenth-century Europe the switch from Roman to Hindu-Arabic numerals made multiplication and division much easier.

Previously various algorithms were used to multiply with Roman numerals. One algorithm dating back to ancient Babylonia, involved looking up numbers in a table of squares. This method, outlined here, works if both numbers are odd or both are even. The introduction of Hindu-Arabic numerals made it possible for people to use the paper-and-pencil algorithms that your parents learned in school. One author has suggested that this change in number systems was a significant influence on the growth of commerce in the late middle ages, and thus changed the course of history.

Multiplying Using Squares

Step 1   Add the two numbers and divide by 2. Call the result x.

Step 2   Subtract the smaller number from the larger number and divide by 2. Call the result y.

Step 3   Find the squares of x and y in a table. Subtract y^2 from x^2. The result is the product of x and y. (See Exploration on p. 252.)

6.1 The Laws of Exponents

AFTER STUDYING THIS SECTION YOU WILL BE ABLE TO

▪ Explain the laws of exponents.

▪ Apply the laws of exponents to simplify expressions.

Discovering the Laws of Exponents

In this section you will learn some shortcuts that allow you to simplify expressions with exponents more easily. Let us begin by applying what we already know about exponents. Recall from Section 1.3 that repeated multiplication may be represented by positive integer exponents. We can use this definition to simplify expressions.

EXAMPLE 1 Simplify these expressions:

a. x^3x^4

b. $(y^3)^5$

c. $(xy)^6$

Solution

a. $x^3x^4 = (x * x * x)(x * x * x * x)$

$\qquad = x * x * x * x * x * x * x$ *Using the associative property of multiplication*

$\qquad = x^7$

b. $(y^3)^5 = (y * y * y)^5$

$\qquad = (y * y * y)(y * y * y)(y * y * y)(y * y * y)(y * y * y)$

$\qquad = y * y * y * y * y * y * y * y * y * y * y * y * y * y * y$

$\qquad = y^{15}$ *Using the associative property of multiplication*

c. $(xy)^6 = (xy)(xy)(xy)(xy)(xy)(xy)$

$\qquad = x * y * x * y * x * y * x * y * x * y * x * y$

$\qquad\qquad$ *Using the associative property of multiplication*

$\qquad = (x * x * x * x * x * x) * (y * y * y * y * y * y)$

$\qquad\qquad$ *Using the commutative property of multiplication*

$\qquad = x^6y^6$

Each of these results from Example 1 may be checked by assigning specific values to x and y. (If you do this, pick values other than 1 or 0, because 1 raised to any power is 1 and 0 raised to any positive power is 0.) For example, let $x = 3$ and let $y = 4$. Check each of the results.

EXAMPLE 1(a)

$$x^3 x^4 = x^7 \qquad \textit{Original equation}$$

$$3^3 3^4 \overset{?}{=} 3^7 \qquad \textit{Substituting 3 for x}$$

$$27 * 81 \overset{?}{=} 2187$$

$$2187 = 2187 \qquad \textit{OK!}$$

EXAMPLE 1(b)

$$(y^3)^5 = y^{15} \qquad \textit{Original equation}$$

$$(4^3)^5 \overset{?}{=} 4^{15} \qquad \textit{Substituting 4 for y}$$

$$64^5 \overset{?}{=} 1{,}073{,}741{,}824$$

$$1{,}073{,}741{,}824 = 1{,}073{,}741{,}824 \qquad \textit{OK!}$$

EXAMPLE 1(c)

$$(xy)^6 = x^6 y^6 \qquad \textit{Original equation}$$

$$(3 * 4)^6 \overset{?}{=} 3^6 * 4^6 \qquad \textit{Substituting 4 for y}$$

$$12^6 \overset{?}{=} 729 * 4096$$

$$2{,}985{,}984 = 2{,}985{,}984 \qquad \textit{OK!}$$

Example 1 illustrates that you can apply the definition of positive integer exponents to simplify expressions. But when you did that, you had to write a lot of x's and y's. Not only is that time consuming, but it is easy to make a mistake in counting. Therefore, it would be nice if we had shortcuts to aid in simplifying expressions with exponents.

Begin by making these observations. In Example 1(a), we found the product of x^3 and x^4. Notice that the exponent in the product is the sum of the two exponents ($7 = 3 + 4$). This leads us to the product law for exponents.

Product Law for Exponents

Let a be any number and let m and n be integers. Then

$$a^m a^n = a^{m+n}$$

In Example 1(b), we found the result when we raised one power (y^3) to another power. Notice that the exponent in the result is the product of the two exponents ($15 = 3 * 5$). This leads us to the power-of-a-power law for exponents.

Power-of-a-Power Law for Exponents

Let a be any number and let m and n be integers. Then

$$(a^m)^n = a^{mn}$$

In Example 1(c), we found the result when we raised the product of two numbers (x and y) to the same power. Notice that each of the two numbers is raised to that power and the results are then multiplied together. This leads us to the power-of-a-product law for exponents.

Power-of-a-Product Law for Exponents

Let a and b be any numbers and let m be an integer. Then

$$(ab)^m = a^m b^m$$

Applying the Laws of Exponents

Now that you have discovered these three laws of exponents, you can apply them.

EXAMPLE 2   Use the laws of exponents to simplify these expressions. State which law you are using and identify the values or expressions assigned to a, b, m, and n.

a. $(z^4)^7$
b. $2x^5 * 3x^4$
c. $(3y)^2$
d. $(xz^3)^4$

Solution   **a.** $(z^4)^7 = z^{4*7}$ *Using the power-of-a-power law with $a = z$, $m = 4$, and*
                             $n = 7$

$= z^{28}$

b. $2x^5 * 3x^4 = 2 * 3 * x^5 * x^4$ *Using the commutative property of*
                                    multiplication

$= 6x^{5+4}$ *Using the product law with $a = x$, $m = 5$,*
                         and $n = 4$

$= 6x^9$

Notice that we multiply the coefficients, 2 and 3, because they are factors. We *add* the 5 and the 4 because they are exponents for factors with the same base, x.

c. $(3y)^2 = 3^2 y^2$ *Using the power-of-a-product law with $a = 3$, $b = y$, and $m = 2$*

$\qquad\quad = 9y^2$

d. $(xz^3)^4 = x^4(z^3)^4$ *Using the power-of-a-product law with $a = x$, $b = z^3$, and $m = 4$*

$\qquad\qquad\; = x^4 z^{12}$ *Using the power-of-a-power law with $a = z$, $m = 3$, and $n = 4$*

EXAMPLE 3   The diameter of the sun is approximately $1.39 * 10^6$ km. Find the volume of the sun in cubic kilometers (km^3). Use this formula for the volume of a sphere: $\text{volume} = \frac{\pi}{6} * \text{diameter}^3$.

Solution $\text{volume} = \frac{\pi}{6} * \text{diameter}^3$

$\qquad\quad = \frac{\pi}{6} * (1.39 * 10^6 \text{ km})^3$ *Substituting into the formula*

$\qquad\quad = \frac{\pi}{6} * 1.39^3 * (10^6)^3 \text{ km}^3$ *Using the power-of-a-product law*

$\qquad\quad = \frac{\pi}{6} * 1.39^3 * 10^{6*3} \text{ km}^3$ *Using the power-of-a-power law*

$\qquad\quad = \frac{\pi}{6} * 1.39^3 * 10^{18} \text{ km}^3$

$\qquad\quad \approx 1.41 * 10^{18} \text{ km}^3$ *Using a calculator to find $\frac{\pi}{6} * 1.39^3$*

Note that the units (km) may be treated like a variable in applying the power laws, and that the answer is in cubic kilometers (km^3), an appropriate unit for volume.

We can check this answer by entering the entire expression in the calculator as $\frac{\pi}{6} * (1.39 * 10 \wedge 6) \wedge 3$. The display reads 1.40618682E18. Remember that E18 indicates *times* 10 *to the power* 18.

Negative Integer Exponents

The laws developed here apply to negative integer exponents as well as positive integer exponents. (In Chapter 9 you will learn that they apply to fractional exponents as well.) Recall the definition of negative exponents from Section 1.3.

Definition   Negative Integer Exponents

Let a be any number except 0 and let n be any positive integer. Then

$$a^{-n} = \frac{1}{a^n}.$$

This definition is used in the following example.

EXAMPLE 4 Use the laws of exponents to simplify these expressions. Express the final answer using only positive exponents.

a. $x^5 x^{-3}$

b. $x^{-5} x^3$

c. $(y^4)^{-2}$

d. $(x^2 y^{-1})^{-3}$

Solution

a. $x^5 x^{-3} = x^{5 + (-3)}$ *Using the product law*

$\qquad\quad = x^2$

b. $x^{-5} x^3 = x^{(-5) + 3}$ *Using the product law*

$\qquad\quad = x^{-2}$

$\qquad\quad = \dfrac{1}{x^2}$ *Using the definition of negative integer exponent*

c. $(y^4)^{-2} = y^{4*(-2)}$ *Using the power-of-a-power law*

$\qquad\quad = y^{-8}$

$\qquad\quad = \dfrac{1}{y^8}$ *Using the definition of negative integer exponent*

d. $(x^2 y^{-1})^{-3} = (x^2)^{-3} (y^{-1})^{-3}$ *Using the power-of-a-product law*

$\qquad\qquad\quad = x^{2*(-3)} * (y^{-1*(-3)})$ *Using the power-of-a-power law*

$\qquad\qquad\quad = x^{-6} y^3$

$\qquad\qquad\quad = \left(\dfrac{1}{x^6} \right) \left(\dfrac{y^3}{1} \right)$ *Using the definition of negative integer exponent*

$\qquad\qquad\quad = \dfrac{y^3}{x^6}$ *Multiplying fractions*

Here is an opportunity to apply negative exponents and the laws you have learned to a problem involving distance, rate, and time.

EXAMPLE 5 Light travels at a speed of $3 * 10^8$ m/s. One nanosecond (ns) is one billionth of a second, or 10^{-9} s. How far does light travel in 1 ns?

Solution We know the rate ($3 * 10^8$ m/s) and the time (10^{-9} s), so we can find the distance.

$$\text{distance} = \text{rate} * \text{time}$$

$$= 3 * 10^8 \text{ m/s} * 10^{-9} \text{ s}$$

$$= 3 * 10^{8 + (-9)} \text{ m}$$

$$= 3 * 10^{-1} \text{ m}$$

$$= 0.3 \text{ m}$$

Light travels .3 m, or about 1 foot, in 1 ns. That's a short distance in an extremely small amount of time.

■ ■ ■

Quotient Laws for Exponents

Example 1 showed the first three laws of exponents. These laws may be extended to include quotients as well as products. Let's see if we can discover the quotient laws by working Example 6.

EXAMPLE 6 ■ Use the definition of positive integer exponents to simplify these expressions:

a. $\dfrac{x^8}{x^5}$

b. $\dfrac{x^5}{x^8}$

c. $\left(\dfrac{x}{y}\right)^7$

Solution ■ a. $\dfrac{x^8}{x^5} = \dfrac{x * x * x * x * x * x * x * x}{x * x * x * x * x}$

$= \left(\dfrac{x}{x}\right)\left(\dfrac{x}{x}\right)\left(\dfrac{x}{x}\right)\left(\dfrac{x}{x}\right)\left(\dfrac{x}{x}\right)\left(\dfrac{x}{1}\right)\left(\dfrac{x}{1}\right)\left(\dfrac{x}{1}\right)$

$= \dfrac{x^3}{1}$

$= x^3$

b. $\dfrac{x^5}{x^8} = \dfrac{x * x * x * x * x}{x * x * x * x * x * x * x * x}$

$= \left(\dfrac{x}{x}\right)\left(\dfrac{x}{x}\right)\left(\dfrac{x}{x}\right)\left(\dfrac{x}{x}\right)\left(\dfrac{x}{x}\right)\left(\dfrac{1}{x}\right)\left(\dfrac{1}{x}\right)\left(\dfrac{1}{x}\right)$

$= \dfrac{1}{x^3}$

$= x^{-3}$

c. $\left(\dfrac{x}{y}\right)^7 = \left(\dfrac{x}{y}\right)\left(\dfrac{x}{y}\right)\left(\dfrac{x}{y}\right)\left(\dfrac{x}{y}\right)\left(\dfrac{x}{y}\right)\left(\dfrac{x}{y}\right)\left(\dfrac{x}{y}\right)$

$= \dfrac{x^7}{y^7}$

■ ■ ■

The results of Example 6 may be generalized.

> **Quotient Law for Exponents**
>
> Let a be any number except 0 and let m and n be integers. Then
>
> $$\frac{a^m}{a^n} = a^{m-n}$$

> **Power-of-a-Quotient Law for Exponents**
>
> Let a be any number, let b be any number except 0, and let m be an integer. Then
>
> $$\left(\frac{a}{b}\right)^m = \frac{a^m}{b^m}$$

Caution: There are three power laws for exponents: power-of-a-power, power-of-a-product, and power-of-a-quotient laws. There is, however, no "power-of-a-sum" law. Don't make the mistake of thinking that $(x + y)^m = x^m + y^m$.

EXAMPLE 7

Use all five laws of exponents to simplify these expressions. Express the final answer using only positive exponents.

a. $\dfrac{x^5 y^2}{x y^7}$

b. $\left(\dfrac{3x}{y^2}\right)^4$

c. $\left(\dfrac{x^2 y^3}{x y^4}\right)^{-1}$

Solution

a. $\dfrac{x^5 y^2}{x y^7} = \dfrac{x^5 y^2}{x^1 y^7}$ *Recognize that the x in the denominator may be written x^1*

$= \left(\dfrac{x^5}{x^1}\right)\left(\dfrac{y^2}{y^7}\right)$

$= x^{5-1} y^{2-7}$ *Applying the quotient law to both x- and y-factors*

$= x^4 y^{-5}$

$= \left(\dfrac{x^4}{1}\right)\left(\dfrac{1}{y^5}\right)$ *Using the definition of negative exponent to write y^{-5} as a fraction*

$$= \frac{x^4}{y^5}$$

b. $\left(\dfrac{3x}{y^2}\right)^4 = \dfrac{(3x)^4}{(y^2)^4}$ *Using the power-of-a-quotient law*

$$= \frac{3^4 x^4}{y^{2*4}}$$ *Using the power-of-a-product law in the numerator, power-of-a-power law in the denominator*

$$= \frac{81x^4}{y^8}$$

c. $\left(\dfrac{x^2 y^3}{xy^4}\right)^{-1} = \left(\dfrac{x^2 y^3}{x^1 y^4}\right)^{-1}$ *Think of x as x^1*

$$= (x^{2-1} y^{3-4})^{-1}$$ *Applying the quotient law to both x- and y-factors*

$$= (x^1 y^{-1})^{-1}$$

$$= x^{1(-1)} y^{(-1)(-1)}$$ *Applying the power-of-a-product law and the power-of-a-power law*

$$= x^{-1} y^1$$

$$= \left(\frac{1}{x}\right)\left(\frac{y}{1}\right)$$ *Rewriting x^{-1} as a fraction*

$$= \frac{y}{x}$$

Negative Exponents in Denominators

With some practice you should be able to apply these laws to any situation involving exponents. The most challenging problems may be those in which a negative exponent appears in the denominator. One more property of exponents comes in handy here.

Negative Exponent in the Denominator

Let a be any number except 0 and let n be a positive integer. Then

$$\frac{1}{a^{-n}} = a^n$$

This property can be demonstrated by considering the fact that $a^0 = 1$ and using the quotient law.

$$\frac{1}{a^{-n}} = \frac{a^0}{a^{-n}} = a^{0-(^-n)} = a^{0+n} = a^n$$

In effect, a factor with a negative exponent may be moved from the denominator to the numerator or from the numerator to the denominator if the sign of the exponent is changed.

EXAMPLE 8 Simplify

$$\left(\frac{x^2}{x^{-1}y^3}\right)^{-2}$$

Solution

$$\left(\frac{x^2}{x^{-1}y^3}\right)^{-2} = \left(\frac{x^{2-(^-1)}}{y^3}\right)^{-2} \qquad \textit{Using the quotient law to subtract the powers of } x$$

$$= \left(\frac{x^3}{y^3}\right)^{-2}$$

$$= \frac{(x^3)^{-2}}{(y^3)^{-2}} \qquad \textit{Using the power-of-a-quotient law}$$

$$= \frac{x^{-6}}{y^{-6}} \qquad \textit{Using the power-of-a-power law}$$

$$= \frac{y^6}{x^6} \qquad \textit{Moving factors with negative exponents from numerator to denominator and vice versa, changing the signs of the exponents}$$

Exercises 6.1

1. Simplify the expressions using repeated multiplication. See Example 1.

   a. x^2x^5 **b.** $(y^4)^3$ **c.** $(xy^2)^6$

2. Check your results from Exercise 1 by letting $x = 2$ and $y = 3$ and simplifying.

3. Use the product law for exponents, the power-of-a-power law for exponents, or the power-of-a-product law for exponents to simplify the expressions. State which fact you used and identify the values assigned to a, b, m, and n.

   a. $3a^4 * 4a^5$ **b.** $(b^3)^6$

   c. $(a^2b^4)^7$ **d.** $(4b)^3$

4. The earth is a sphere with an approximate diameter of $1.27 * 10^7$ m. Find the surface area of the earth using the formula surface area $= \pi * \text{diameter}^2$. Perform your work in scientific notation.

5. Use the laws of exponents to simplify each expression and the definition of negative exponents (page 213) to write the final answer with only positive exponents.

a. $k^{-2}k^6$ **b.** k^2k^{-6}

c. $(j^5)^{-3}$ **d.** $(j^{-5}k^2)^{-4}$

6. Check your answers to Exercise 5 by picking values for j and k and evaluating the expressions on your calculator.

7. Simplify the expressions and write with only positive exponents.

     a. $\dfrac{y^7}{y^3}$ **b.** $\dfrac{y^2}{y^8}$ **c.** $\left(\dfrac{y}{z}\right)^9$

8. A garden snail can move at a rate of $3.1 * 10^{-2}$ miles/hour. At this rate, how long would it take the snail to travel a distance of $1.55 * 10^3$ miles? Perform your work without using a calculator and write your answer in scientific notation. (World Almanac)

9. Correct the error in each line of the simplification of

$$\frac{(2x^3y^4)^3}{x^{-2}y^{12}}$$

$$\frac{(2x^3y^4)^3}{x^{-2}y^{12}} = \frac{6x^9y^{12}}{x^{-2}y^{12}}$$

$$= 6x^7y^0$$

$$= 6x^7(0)$$

$$= 0$$

10. Simplify the expressions and write the final answer using only positive exponents.

     a. $\dfrac{xy^6}{x^3y^2}$ **b.** $\left(\dfrac{4y}{z^3}\right)^2$

     c. $\left(\dfrac{a^{-3}b^2}{a^2b^5}\right)^3$

For Exercises 11–13, simplify the expressions and write the final answer using only positive exponents.

11. $\left(\dfrac{x^4y^{-3}}{x^5}\right)^{-1}$

12. $\dfrac{-6c^5d^{-2}}{(2c^{-3}d)^2}$

13. $\dfrac{4(x^7y^{-3})^0}{x^{-2}y}$

14. A formula for the volume of a sphere is $V = (\frac{4}{3})\pi r^3$, where r is the radius of the sphere. Find the exact volume of a sphere with a radius of $\frac{1}{2}$ m.

15. Find an integer value for n that will make the expression $\frac{x^3}{x^{-n}}$ equal to x.

Skills and Review 6.1

16. At a local candy shop, plain chocolate sells for $3 per pound and deluxe chocolate sells for $5 per pound. Suppose a 6-pound mixture of the two types of chocolate costs $27.

     a. What is the cost per pound of the mixture?

     b. Does your answer from part (a) suggest that there is more plain chocolate or deluxe chocolate in the mixture? Explain your reasoning.

17. We wish to find the exact amount of each type of chocolate in the previous exercise.

     a. Let x represent the number of pounds of plain chocolate and y the pounds of deluxe chocolate. Then a weight equation is $x + y = 6$ and a money equation is $3x + 5y = 27$. Explain what each term in the equations represents.

     b. Solve the system of equations in order to find the exact amount of each chocolate in the mixture.

18. A pair of sneakers is marked up from $60 to $80. Find the percent increase.

19. Solve the proportion

$$\frac{3}{10} = \frac{x}{12}.$$

20. Given the equation

$$y = \frac{x}{4} - 5.$$

     a. Find the slope.

     b. Find the y-intercept.

     c. Find the x-intercept.

21. Solve for x if $x - (7 - 3x) = 6x + 5$.

22. Verify the solution in Exercise 21.

23. Recall that a formula for the area of a triangle is

$$A = \frac{1}{2}bh.$$

Find the height of a triangle whose area is 20 cm² and base is 10 cm.

24. Write an algebraic expression to represent each statement.

  a. 5 more than a number

  b. 2 less than a number

  c. 12 minus a number

  d. The quotient of a number and 6

25. Evaluate $\sqrt{64} + 5 * 3^2$.

6.2 Products and Factors

AFTER STUDYING THIS SECTION YOU WILL BE ABLE TO

- Expand the product of a monomial and a binomial.
- Factor the product of a monomial and a binomial.
- Apply the zero-product property to solve equations of the form $ax^2 + bx = 0$.

Polynomials

Recall the distributive property, which states that for all numbers a, b, and c, $a * (b + c) = a * b + a * c$. This property is illustrated with an area model in Figure 1. In Section 2.1 we showed that the distributive property can be used in two ways:

1. We can expand $a(b + c)$ to get $ab + ac$.

2. We can factor $ab + ac$ to get $a(b + c)$.

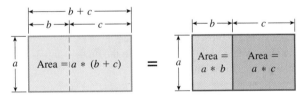

Figure 1 We can think of the rectangle as having one piece with area $a(b + c)$ or two pieces, one with area ab and one with area ac.

In this section, we extend our use of the distributive property by letting a, b, and c represent any algebraic expression involving the products of numbers and variables raised to positive integer powers. These expressions are called

monomials, indicating that they have one (mono-) term (-nomial). Here are some examples of monomials:

$$3x \qquad \text{a monomial in one variable, } x$$
$$x^4 y^2 \qquad \text{a monomial in two variables, } x \text{ and } y$$
$$^-2xyz \qquad \text{a monomial in three variables, } x, y, \text{ and } z$$
$$5 \qquad \text{a constant}$$

Monomials may be joined by addition and subtraction to form expressions with several terms called **polynomials**, indicating that they have many (poly) terms. Polynomials with two terms are called **binomials**, and polynomials with three terms are called **trinomials**.

For example, $3x + 2$ is a binomial with two terms, $3x$ and 2; $4x^2 - 7xy + y^2$ is a trinomial with three terms, $4x^2$, ^-7xy, and y^2. The middle term is considered to be negative because subtracting $7xy$ is the same as adding ^-7xy. We use these vocabulary words extensively in the next three sections of this book. Our work with polynomials relies on the laws of exponents, which we learned in the previous section.

Multiplying a Monomial by a Polynomial

Our first examples involve expanding. That is, we start with two factors, one monomial and one polynomial, and we multiply them together to find their product.

EXAMPLE 1 ■ Expand the product of $3x^2$ and $6x^3 + 5xy^2$.

Solution ■ An area model, as shown in Figure 2, can be used.

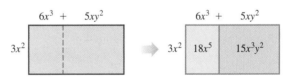

Figure 2   The area of the rectangle has two parts, $18x^5$ and $15x^3 y^2$.

a. Start with a diagram showing the factors with $3x^2$ on one side of the rectangle and $6x^3 + 5xy^2$ on the other. Draw a line to show that the large rectangle is divided into two smaller rectangles.

b. Find the area of each of the smaller rectangles, using the product law for exponents:

$$3x^2 * 6x^3 = 18x^5$$
$$3x^2 * 5xy^2 = 15x^3 y^2$$

c. Join the two terms to form the sum: $18x^5 + 15x^3 y^2$.

The whole problem may be written as follows:

$$3x^2(6x^3 + 5xy^2) = 3x^2 * 6x^3 + 3x^2 * 5xy^2$$
$$= 18x^5 + 15x^3y^2$$

Example 2 shows several other examples.

EXAMPLE 2 Expand these products:

a. $4xy(3x + 5y + 2z)$
b. $10x(7x - 6)$
c. $^-(x^2 - 3x - 4)$

Solution We show each example with an area model and with the steps written out symbolically.

a. This example shows the product of a monomial and a trinomial. See Figure 3.

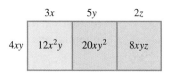

Figure 3

$$4xy(3x + 5y + 2z) = (4xy * 3x) + (4xy * 5y) + (4xy * 2z)$$
$$= 12x^2y + 20xy^2 + 8xyz$$

b. See Figure 4.

	7x	⁻6
10x	70x²	⁻60x

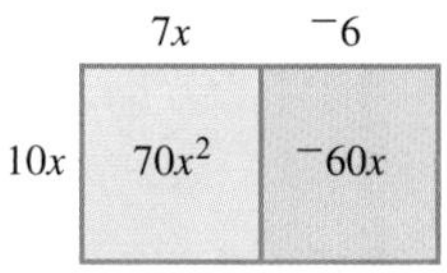

Figure 4

Note: Strictly speaking, there is no such thing as a negative length or a negative area. The area model, however, still works with negative quantities.

$$10x * (7x - 6) = (10x * 7x) + (10x * {}^-6)$$
$$= 70x^2 + {}^-60x$$
$$= 70x^2 - 60x$$

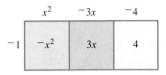

Figure 5

c. This example shows that the opposite of a polynomial may be thought of as a product of $^-1$ times the polynomial. (Recall the special properties of $^-1$, page 52.) See Figure 5.

$$^-(x^2 - 3x - 4) = {}^-\mathbf{1}(x^2 - 3x - 4)$$
$$= ({}^-\mathbf{1} * x^2) + ({}^-\mathbf{1} * {}^-3x) + ({}^-\mathbf{1} * {}^-4)$$
$$= {}^-x^2 + 3x + 4$$

Reversing the Process: Finding Factors

Recall from Section 2.1 that factoring is the reverse process of expanding. We are given a polynomial. We try to find two factors, one a monomial and the other a polynomial, which multiplied together give us the original polynomial. Again, an area model can help us visualize the process.

EXAMPLE 3 ■ Use an area model to find factors that give the product $6x^2 - 15x$.

Solution

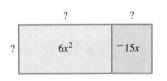

Figure 6 What can the height be?

Write $6x^2 - 15x$ as a sum, $6x^2 + {}^-15x$. Let the two terms, $6x^2$ and ^-15x, both represent areas of rectangles. Draw a diagram showing the two areas, as in Figure 6.

We need to find an expression for the height of the rectangle, one that will allow us to find values that will fit along the top. In other words, we must find a *common factor* for $6x^2$ and ^-15x.

We could try x. Then we have the situation shown in Figure 7.

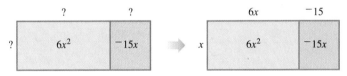

Figure 7 x is a common factor of $6x^2$ and ^-15x.

We think: x times what gives us $6x^2$? The answer is $6x$. We then think: x times what gives us ^-15x? The answer is $^-15$. We write $6x$ and $^-15$, as shown on the right in Figure 7. In symbols, we write

$$6x^2 - 15x = 6x^2 + {}^-15x$$
$$= x(? + ?)$$
$$= x(6x + {}^-15)$$
$$= x(6x - 15)$$

More simply, we can write $6x^2 - 15x = x(6x - 15)$.

Greatest Common Factor

In the solution to Example 3 we chose x as a common factor. We could have chosen 3 because it is a factor of both $6x^2$ and $^-15$. Better yet, we could choose $3x$ as a common factor. We then have the situation shown in Figure 8. In symbols, we can write $6x^2 - 15x = 3x(2x - 5)$. When factoring a polynomial as the product of a monomial and a binomial, it is customary to find the **greatest common factor (GCF)** of the terms in the polynomial. We know we have found the greatest common factor if, after factoring out, there is no common factor left in the terms of the polynomial. Prime numbers are used in a procedure to find the GCF of the terms of a polynomial.

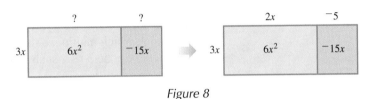

Figure 8

Definition   Prime Number

A prime number is a positive integer with exactly two factors, the number itself and 1.

For example, 7 is a prime number because it has exactly two factors, 7 and 1. On the other hand, 6 is not a prime number because it has four factors, 6, 3, 2, and 1. The following steps let you find the GCF of any two monomials.

Finding the Greatest Common Factor (GCF)

Step 1   List all the variables and all the prime factors of the numerical coefficients.

Step 2   When a variable or prime number does not appear, include that factor to the zeroth power. Remember that anything (except zero) raised to the zeroth power is 1.

Step 3   Take the smallest power of each variable factor and each prime factor to form the GCF.

Example 4 illustrates finding the GCF of two monomials.

EXAMPLE 4   Find the GCF of these monomials.

a. $x^7 y^2$ and xy^6
b. $14x^3 y$, $2x^6 y^4$, and $12y^5$
c. $84x$ and $140y$

Solution   **a.** The powers of x are x^7 and x^1. The smaller power is x^1. The powers of y are y^2 and y^6. The smaller power is y^2. Taking the smaller powers, the GCF is $x^1 y^2$, or xy^2.

b. The powers of x are x^3, x^6, and x^0. The smallest power is x^0. The powers of y are y^1, y^4, and y^5. The smallest power is y^1. We now know that the GCF contains y^1. We can leave out x because its smallest power is $x^0 = 1$.

You may be able to see by inspection that the GCF of 14, 2, and 12 is 2. So, the GCF of the three monomials is $2y$. The procedure in step 2 may also be used to get the same result:

Factor the coefficients into prime factors: $14 = 2 * 7$; $2 = 2$; and $12 = 2^2 * 3$.

- The powers of 2 are 2^1, 2^1, and 2^2. The smallest power is 2^1.
- The powers of 3 are 3^0, 3^0, and 3^1. The smallest power is 3^0.
- The powers of 7 are 7^1, 7^0, and 7^0. The smallest power is 7^0.

Taking all the smallest powers, the GCF is $2^1 * 3^0 * 7^0 * x^0 * y^1$, or $2y$.

c. The smallest powers of x and y are x^0 and y^0, so the GCF does not contain any variable factors. Because the numerical coefficients are relatively large, you may want to use **factor trees** (as shown in Figure 9) to find the prime factors.

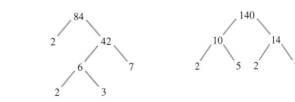

$84 = 2 * 2 * 3 * 7 = 2^2 * 3 * 7$ $140 = 2 * 5 * 2 * 7 = 2^2 * 5 * 7$

Figure 9

- The powers of 2 are 2^2 and 2^2. The smallest power is 2^2.
- The powers of 3 are 3^1 and 3^0. The smallest power is 3^0.
- The powers of 5 are 5^0 and 5^1. The smallest power is 5^0.
- The powers of 7 are 7^1 and 7^1. The smallest power is 7^1.

Taking all the smallest powers, the GCF is $2^2 * 7^1 = 28$.

In Example 5, we find the GCF of several terms.

EXAMPLE 5 ■ Factor completely: $8x^4y^2z - 6x^5yz^2 - 4x^3y^3$.

Solution

The first step is to find the GCF of the monomials. By inspection the greatest common factor for the numerical coefficients is 2. To find the GCF of the variable factors, proceed as in Example 4:

- The powers of x are x^4, x^5, and x^3. The smallest power is x^3.
- The powers of y are y^2, y^1, and y^3. The smallest power is y^1.
- The powers of z are z^1, z^2, and z^0. The smallest power is z^0.

The GCF is $2x^3y$.

You are now ready to factor the polynomial:

$$8x^4y^2z - 6x^5yz^2 - 4x^3y^3 = 2x^3y(? - ? - ?)$$

- To find the coefficient in the first term, think: 2 times what gives 8? Answer: 4.
- To find the power of x in the first term, think: x^3 times what gives x^4? Answer: x^1.
- To find the power of y in the first term, think: y times what gives y^2? Answer: y.

Don't forget to include z in the first term. So the first term inside parentheses is $4xyz$:

$$8x^4y^2z - 6x^5yz^2 - 4x^3y^3 = 2x^3y(4xyz - ? - ?)$$

Do the same for each of the other terms:

$$8x^4y^2z - 6x^5yz^2 - 4x^3y^3 = 2x^3y(4xyz - 3x^2z^2 - 2y^2)$$

That's it!

Check the answer by expanding: $2x^3y(4xyz - 3x^2z^2 - 2y^2) = 8x^4y^2z - 6x^5yz^2 - 4x^3y^3$. Get in the habit of always checking your answer to the factoring problem. If you do, you will usually catch any mistakes.

■ ■ ■

Factoring Out a Negative Number

Sometimes it is desirable to have a positive coefficient for the first term in the polynomial factor. If the first coefficient is negative, you may use a negative number for the GCF.

EXAMPLE 6 ■ Factor these expressions so that the first term of the polynomial factor has a positive coefficient.

a. $^-12x^2 + 33x$

b. $^-16y - 7z$

Solution   **a.** The GCF of $^-12x^2$ and $33x$ is $3x$. Take ^-3x as the common factor:

$$^-12x^2 + 33x = {}^-3x(? + ?)$$

- Think: ^-3x times what gives $^-12x^2$? Answer: $4x$ (negative times positive = negative).
- Think: ^-3x times what gives $33x$? Answer: $^-11$ (negative times negative = positive).

$$^-12x^2 + 33x = {}^-3x(4x + {}^-11) = {}^-3x(4x - 11)$$

Again, you should check the answer by expanding $^-3x(4x - 11)$.

b. $16y$ and $7z$ appear to have no common factor, so their GCF is 1. We can take $^-1$ as the common factor.

$$^-16y - 7z = {}^-1(? + ?)$$

- Think: $^-1$ times what gives ^-16y? Answer: $16y$ (negative times positive = negative).
- Think: $^-1$ times what gives ^-7z? Answer: $7z$ (negative times positive = negative).

$$^-16y - 7z = {}^-1(16y + 7z)$$

Common Binomial Factors

In all the cases we have seen so far, the common factor has been a *monomial.* In the next two sections we encounter situations in which there is a common *binomial* factor. The next example illustrates this.

EXAMPLE 7   **a.** Factor $7xz - 4z$.
b. Factor $7x(y + 5) - 4(y + 5)$.
c. Show how (a) and (b) are related to each other.

Solution   **a.** The GCF of the two terms is z. So $7xz - 4z = z(? + ?) = z(7x - 4)$.
b. A common factor is the expression in parentheses, which is $y + 5$. The greatest common factor is also $y + 5$ because x does not appear in the second term and 4 and 7 have no common factor other than 1.

$$7x(y + 5) - 4(y + 5) = (y + 5)(? + ?) = (y + 5)(7x - 4)$$

To check this result, you need to expand the product of two binomials. You will learn how to do that in the next section.

c. (a) and (b) are essentially the same problem if we let z replace the binomial $y + 5$ in (b). When factoring out a common binomial factor, you may want to think of representing the binomial $(y + 5)$ as another variable, such as z.

The Zero-Product Property

If the product of two numbers is zero, then at least one of them must be zero. This is called the zero-product property, and it can be used to solve certain types of equations.

The Zero-Product Property

Suppose $a * b = 0$. Then either $a = 0$ or $b = 0$.

You can convince yourself that the zero-product property is true if you think of factor pairs that give a product of zero: for example, $4 * 0 = 0$, $0 * 5 = 0$, $^-3 * 0 = 0$, and $0 * 0 = 0$. In all cases, either the first or the second factor is zero. In the last case both factors are zero. On the other hand, if neither factor is zero, you get either a positive product (if both factors are positive or both are negative) or a negative product (if one factor is positive and the other factor is negative).

The zero-product property may be used to solve some equations.

EXAMPLE 8 ■ Solve the equation $x^2 - 6x = 0$.

Solution

The expression on the left side of the equation has a common factor, x, and so it may be rewritten $x(x - 6) = 0$. Now we can apply the zero-product property. The factors are $a = x$ and $b = x - 6$. So, either $x = 0$ or $x - 6 = 0$. This means that the equation has two solutions, $x = 0$ and $x = 6$. Up until this point most equations you have seen have had just one solution. In the next chapter you will learn that this is an example of a quadratic equation. Some quadratic equations have two solutions.

You may check this result with a calculator. Enter $Y1 = X \wedge 2 - 6X$ and make a table of values with TblStart $= 0$ and ΔTbl $= 1$. You will find that both $x = 0$ and $x = 6$ give values of 0 for Y1.

Exercises 6.2

1. Use an area model, such as the one shown in Figure 4, to show that the expansion of $3(x + 5)$ equals $3x + 15$.

2. Find the product of $2a$ and $4a^2 + 7a^3b$.

Expand the products in Exercises 3–5.

3. $8z(5z - 3)$

4. $6a^2b(2a + 3b - 7c)$

5. $^-(^-x^2 + 9x - 5)$

6. Recall that a prime number is divisible only by one and itself.

    a. Find six prime numbers.

    b. Factor 90 into a product of prime factors.

    c. Rewrite your prime factors of 90, showing all duplicate factors as a single factor with an exponent.

    d. Write 75 as a product of its prime factors.

    e. Find the greatest common factor (GCF) of 75 and 90.

7. a. Use the figure to show the factorization of $10x - 6$.

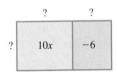

    b. Find the GCF of $54y$ and 72, then factor completely $54y + 72$.

    c. Find the GCF and factor completely: $14x^3 + 7xy - 42x^2$.

    d. Verify your factorization from part (c) by expanding using the distributive property.

8. Consider the monomials, x^2 and x^3.

    a. Use the steps on page 224 to find the greatest common factor (GCF) of the two monomials.

    b. Use the laws of exponents to show that x^3 is divisible by x^2.

9. Factor completely:

    a. $18x^5 + 6x^3$

    b. $21x^2y^3 - 15xy^4$

10. Find the GCF and factor completely, $3xy^4z^2 - 12x^3y^2z + 9x^5z^3$. Expand your result to check your answer.

11. The surface area of a right circular cylinder is $2\pi rh + 2\pi r^2$ (see the figure). Factor out the GCF to find an equivalent expression for the surface area.

Surface area = $2\pi rh + 2\pi r^2$

12. Factor out $^-1$ from each binomial.

    a. $^-x - 5$

    b. $^-3x + 8$

13. Consider the expression $(x + 3)4y + (x + 3)9$. This expression has two terms.

    a. What is the common binomial factor in the two terms?

    b. Factor out the common binomial (GCF).

14. a. Factor $xz - 5z$.

    b. For the expression $x(2x - 3) - 5(2x - 3)$, what could you replace $(2x - 3)$ with in order to make it identical to the binomial in part (a)?

    c. Factor $x(2x - 3) - 5(2x - 3)$.

15. Factor the expression on the left side of each equation and then use the zero-product property to solve each equation.

    a. $x^2 + 4x = 0$

    b. $x^2 - 11x = 0$

Skills and Review 6.2

16. Expand the product and write your final answer with only positive exponents.

$$2x^3y(5x^5 - x^4y^{-1} + 3z^{-2})$$

17. Use the rules of exponents to simplify. Write your answer with only positive exponents.

$$\left(\frac{6xy^4}{2x^5y^4}\right)^{-2}$$

18. Given the expression $\frac{5+x^4}{x^3}$.

   a. Is $5 + x$ or $\frac{5}{x^3} + x$ equivalent to the given expression?

   b. Evaluate the expressions when $x = {}^-2$.

   c. Does your evaluation support your answer from part (a)? Explain.

19. How much alcohol is in 2 L of a 25% solution of alcohol?

20. A chemist needs 2 L of a 25% solution of alcohol. She has a bottle that contains a 20% solution and another bottle that contains a 50% solution. She wants to know how much of each solution she should mix together.

   a. Write a solution equation.

   b. Write an alcohol equation.

   c. Solve the system of equations.

   d. Answer the question.

21. A 3-inch by 5-inch picture is enlarged so that the length of the enlargement is 6 inches more than its width. Find the width and length of the enlargement using either a proportion or some other method of your choice.

22. Solve the system of equations by an algebraic method.

$$5x - 2y = {}^-22$$
$$4x - 3y = {}^-19$$

23. Given an equation in standard form, $5x + 6y = 70$.

   a. Find the slope.

   b. Find the x- and y-intercepts.

24. Find the equation of the line passing through the points $({}^-1, 5)$ and $(2, {}^-4)$. See Section 4.2.

25. Find the distance between the points $({}^-6, 3)$ and $(6, 8)$.

6.3 Factoring by Grouping

AFTER STUDYING THIS SECTION YOU WILL BE ABLE TO

- Expand the product of two polynomials.
- Square a binomial.
- Use grouping to factor a polynomial with four terms.

Multiplying Polynomials

In the last section you saw how an area model represents the product of a monomial and a polynomial. The same method may be used to show multiplication by polynomials, each having two or more terms.

EXAMPLE 1 ■ Expand $(x + 3)(2x^2 + 4x + 5)$.

Solution Start with a diagram showing the factors $(x + 3)$ on one side of a rectangle and $(2x^2 + 4x + 5)$ on an adjacent side (Figure 10). Then find the area of each of the smaller rectangles (Figure 11).

The individual terms shown in Figure 11 can now be written as a polynomial with six terms:

$$(x + 3)(2x^2 + 4x + 5) = 2x^3 + 4x^2 + 5x + 6x^2 + 12x + 15$$

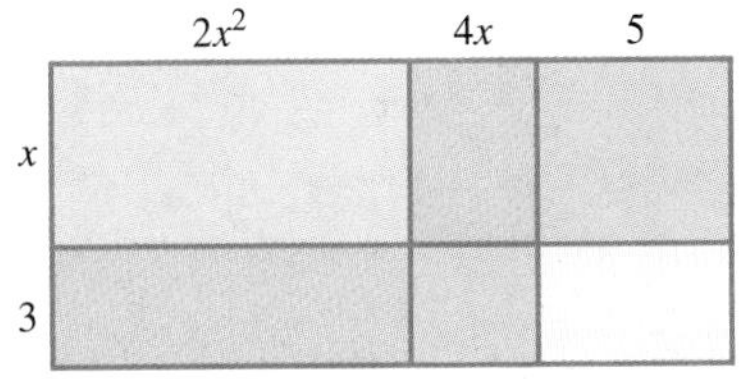

Figure 10 Each monomial in a factor goes with a row or column.

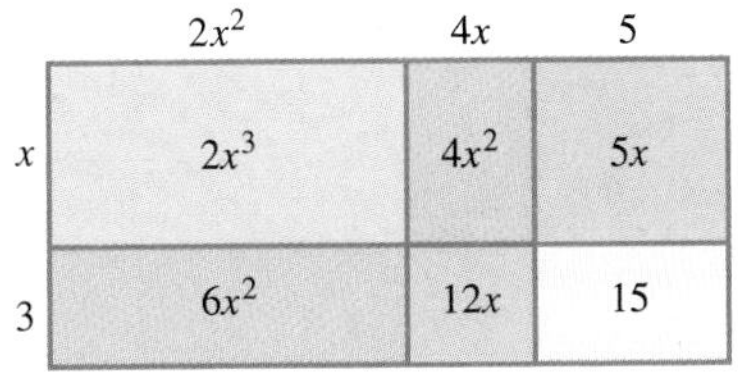

Figure 11

Combine like terms to get a polynomial with four terms:

$$(x + 3)(2x^2 + 4x + 5) = 2x^3 + 10x^2 + 17x + 15$$

You may always use an area model to expand the product of polynomials. With some practice, however, you may prefer not to draw a diagram but just to write out the results. When you do that, remember that you are really using the distributive property twice:

$$(x + 3)(2x^2 + 4x + 5) = x(2x^2 + 4x + 5) + 3(2x^2 + 4x + 5)$$
$$= 2x^3 + 4x^2 + 5x + 6x^2 + 12x + 15$$
$$= 2x^3 + 10x^2 + 17x + 15$$

■ ■ ■

Note: In Example 1, both factors, $x + 3$ and $2x^2 + 4x + 5$, and the expanded polynomial $2x^3 + 10x^2 + 17x + 15$ are written in **descending order**: that is, the highest power of x comes first, followed by the second highest power, and so on, with the constant term last. In the remainder of this book we will usually write polynomials in descending order, because this makes it easier to keep track of like terms.

EXAMPLE 2 ■ Expand $(x - 7)(3x + 4)$.

Solution ■ Think of $x - 7$ as $x + {}^-7$. Then draw an area model (Figure 12).

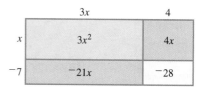

Figure 12

Combine terms to obtain

$$(x - 7)(3x + 4) = 3x^2 + 4x - 21x - 28$$
$$= 3x^2 - 17x - 28$$

Squaring a Binomial

A special application of polynomial multiplication occurs when a binomial is squared. Figure 13 shows an area model for $(a + b)^2$.

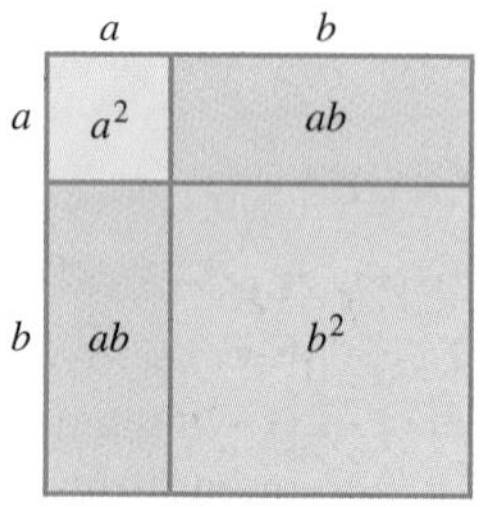

Figure 13

Square of a Binomial

$$(a + b)^2 = a^2 + 2ab + b^2$$

Think: The square of $a + b$ is the square of the first term (a^2) plus twice the product of the two terms ($2ab$) plus the square of the second term (b^2).

Caution: Don't forget the middle term: $(a + b)^2 \neq a^2 + b^2$! This formula for $(a + b)^2$ may be used in solving quadratic equations, as you will see in Chapter 7. It may also be used to prove the Pythagorean theorem (see Exercise 15).

EXAMPLE 3 Expand each binomial square.

a. $(x + n)^2$
b. $(2x + 3y)^2$
c. $(x - 5)^2$

Solution

a. $(x + n)^2 = x^2 + 2xn + n^2$ *Squaring the binomial with $a = x$ and $b = n$*

b. $(2x + 3y)^2 = (2x)^2 + 2 * 2x * 3y + (3y)^2$ *Squaring the binomial with $a = 2x$ and $b = 3y$*

$$= 4x^2 + 12xy + 9y^2$$ *Using the power-of-a-product law*

c. $(x - 5)^2 = (x + {}^-5)^2$ *Subtracting is the same as adding*
                                            the opposite

$$= x^2 + 2 * x * {}^-5 + ({}^-5)^2$$
$$= x^2 - 10x + 25$$

Factoring the Product of Polynomials

Now we come to a greater challenge. We can always expand the product of two polynomials by creating an area model. But can we always factor a polynomial into two or more polynomial factors with integer coefficients? The answer is no, not all polynomials may be factored. Such polynomials are called **prime**, just as a prime number is an integer whose only factors are itself and 1.

There are techniques, however, for factoring some polynomials. We discuss some of those techniques in this course. A key strategy for these factoring problems is called **grouping**, as Example 4 shows.

EXAMPLE 4   **a.** Use an area model to factor $5y - 6x - 15 + 2xy$.
                b. Use symbolic manipulation to factor $5y - 6x - 15 + 2xy$.

Solution   **a.** The only strategy we have learned so far is to look for a common factor. Unfortunately $5y$, ${}^-6x$, ${}^-15$, and $2xy$ have no factor other than 1 in common. Observe, however, that $5y$ and ${}^-15$ do have a common factor, 5. This suggests that $5y$ and ${}^-15$ may be grouped together. An area model may be used to show the grouping (Figure 14). The GCF for these two terms is 5, so we write 5 on the common side. We think: 5 times what is $5y$ and 5 times what is ${}^-15$? We write y and ${}^-3$, as shown in Figure 15 at the right.

Figure 14   Because $5y$ and ${}^-15$ have a common factor, we put them in the same row.

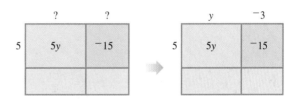

Figure 15

We now need to place ^-6x and $2xy$ in the area model. Two possibilities are shown in Figure 16. We ask whether or not y and $^-3$ are factors of the products with which they are aligned. We choose the placement shown in Figure 16 on the right.

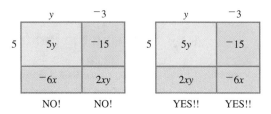

Figure 16

The final step is to find the remaining factor: $2x$ is the GCF of $2xy$ and ^-6x, as shown in Figure 17.

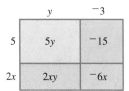

Figure 17

We can now write

$$5y - 6x - 15 + 2xy = (5 + 2x)(y - 3)$$

We have found two binomial factors for our original polynomial. The diagram in Figure 17 can be used to check our work by verifying that each of the four terms in the rectangles is equal to the product of the two terms on its sides.

b. You can factor by grouping without an area model if you prefer. You may have to rearrange the terms to accomplish this. Here is how you can use symbolic manipulation to factor $5y - 6x - 15 + 2xy$.

$5y - 6x - 15 + 2xy = 5y - 15 + 2xy - 6x$ *Using the commutative property to rearrange terms*

$\qquad = (5y - 15) + (2xy - 6x)$ *Forming groups of two terms*

$\qquad = 5(y - 3) + 2x(y - 3)$ *Finding the GCF for each group*

$\qquad = (y - 3)(5 + 2x)$ *Factoring out the common binomial factor, $y - 3$*

A Test for Factorability

Factoring by grouping will work for some polynomials but not all. The next example leads to a way of testing a polynomial with four terms to see whether or not it can be factored by the grouping method.

EXAMPLE 5
a. Use an area model to factor $ac + ad + bc + bd$.
b. Find the product of each pair of diagonally opposite terms in the area model.

Solution
a. The first two terms, ac and ad, have a common factor, a. Once they are grouped together, it is natural to group bc and bd, as shown in Figure 18. Therefore, $ac + ad + bc + bd = a(c + d) + b(c + d) = (a + b)(c + d)$.

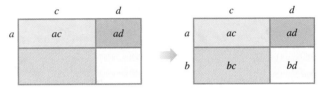

Figure 18 $ac + ad + bc + bd = (a + b)(c + d)$

b. Along each diagonal of the large rectangle in Figure 18, there are two pairs of terms. Going from northwest to southeast, we have ac and bd, with a product of $acbd$. Going from northeast to southwest, we have ad and bc, with a product of $adbc$. Because of the commutative property of multiplication, $acbd = adbc$, and we may conclude that the two diagonal products are equal. See Figure 19.

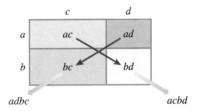

Figure 19 The products along the diagonals are equal.

The following test summarizes what we discovered in Example 5.

The Diagonal Test for Grouping

A polynomial with four terms may be factored by grouping if the product of one pair of terms is equal to the product of the other two terms. The

(continued)

polynomial may then be written in the form

$$ac + ad + bc + bd = (a + b)(c + d),$$

as in Figure 18.

EXAMPLE 6 ■ Factor $x^3 - 12x + 48 - 4x^2$.

Solution Use the diagonal test for grouping. Start with the first term, x^3, and see what other term it can be paired with:

$$x^3 * {}^-12x = {}^-12x^4 \neq 48 * {}^-4x^2 \qquad \textit{No}$$
$$x^3 * {}^-4x^2 = {}^-4x^5 \neq {}^-12x * 48 \qquad \textit{No}$$
$$x^3 * 48 = 48x^3 = {}^-12x * {}^-4x^2 \qquad \textit{Yes}$$

The last pair, x^3 and 48, works because its product is equal to ${}^-12x * {}^-4x^2$. Now use an area model to place each pair along a diagonal.

Figure 20 shows that there is more than one way to arrange the factors. In both cases x^3 and 48 appear along one diagonal and ${}^-4x^2$ and ${}^-12x$ along the other diagonal. The factorization is the same in both cases: $x^3 - 4x^2 - 12x + 48 = (x^2 - 12)(x - 4)$. If you prefer to use symbolic manipulation, rearrange the terms so that one pair, say, x^3 and 48, are the first and last terms and the other two terms are in the middle.

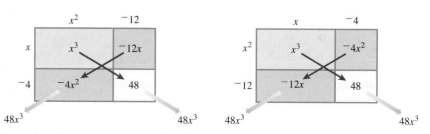

Figure 20 We get two pictures for the same factorization depending on where we place the terms.

$$x^3 - 4x^2 - 12x + 48 = x^2(x - 4) + {}^-12(x - 4) \qquad \textit{Factoring out common factors for the first pair and second pair of terms: notice that the second common factor is negative}$$

$$= (x - 4)(x^2 - 12) \qquad \textit{Factoring out the common binomial factor}$$

EXAMPLE 7   ■   Use the diagonal test to factor $x^4 - x^2 + x + 3$.

Solution   Try to pair the first term with another term:

$$x^4 * 3 = 3x^4 \neq {}^-x^2 * x \qquad No$$

$$x^4 * x = x^5 \neq {}^-x^2 * 3 \qquad No$$

$$x^4 * {}^-x^2 = {}^-x^6 \neq x * 3 \qquad No$$

Because none of these pairings works, the diagonal test fails and $x^4 - x^2 + x + 3$ cannot be factored. It is a prime polynomial.

■ ■ ■

The following procedure can be used to factor some polynomials with four terms.

Procedure for Factoring a Polynomial with Four Terms

Step 1   Apply the diagonal test for grouping. If the test works, go on to steps 2 and 3. If the test fails, then the polynomial cannot be factored.

Step 2   Arrange the terms so that the product of the first and last terms is equal to the product of the middle two terms.

Step 3   Use an area model or factor symbolically.

Exercises 6.3

1. a. Complete the area model in the figure to expand $(x + 6)(3x^2 + 1)$.

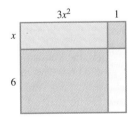

	$3x^2$	1
x		
6		

b. Without an area model, expand $(x + 6)(3x^2 + 1)$.

c. Check your answer by substituting a value for x into the original expression and into the expanded expression.

2. Use an area model to expand $(2x - 3)(x^2 - 5x + 4)$. On a calculator, enter the original expression as Y1 and the expanded expression as Y2. Check your answer by comparing your calculator's table values for the original expression to that for your expansion.

3. Expand $(x + 7)(4x - 9)$. On a calculator, enter the original expression as Y1 and the expanded expression as Y2. Use a window of $^-9.4 \le X \le 9.4$, $^-100 \le Y \le 100$, and check your expansion by comparing the graphs of Y1 and Y2.

4. Expand $(y + 3)(y^2 - 3y + 9)$.

5. The side of a square is $x + 4y$. Find its area.

6. In this section, you were shown a shortcut for squaring a binomial. Use this shortcut to perform the following operations.

    a. $(a - b)^2$ **b.** $(2x + y)^2$ **c.** $(3x - 7y)^2$

7. Expansion is the reverse of what process?

8. Use an area model to show that the polynomial $6 + 12y - x - 2xy$ is equivalent to its factored form, $(6 - x)(1 + 2y)$.

9. Use an area model to factor the polynomial $2y^2 + 7x + 2xy + 7y$.

10. Use symbolic manipulation to factor $xy - 5x - 4y + 20$. See Example 4(b) for an illustration.

Exercises 11 and 12 concern the four groupings of the polynomial $3x - xy + 6 - 2y$ in the figure.

a.

$3x$	^-2y
6	^-xy

b.

$3x$	^-xy
6	^-2y

c.

$3x$	6
^-xy	^-2y

d.

6	^-2y
$3x$	^-xy

11. Use the diagonal test for grouping to determine which one grouping arrangement does not lead to a factorization.

12. In Exercise 11, you determined that one grouping arrangement does not lead to a factorization. Factor the remaining groupings to show that each will produce the same factorization of $3x - xy + 6 - 2y$.

For Exercises 13 and 14, use the diagonal test for grouping to determine if the polynomial can be factored, and, if so, factor it.

13. $6x^3 - 2x^2 - 15x + 5$

14. $2a + 2b + 5x + 5y$

15. Prove the Pythagorean theorem by following the steps indicated below.

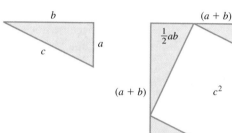

A square with side equal to $a + b$ is shown at the right of the figure. Four copies of a right triangle are arranged along the sides. The region in the middle of the large square is a smaller square whose side is of length c.

  a. Find the area of one of the right triangles.

  b. Find the total area of all four right triangles.

  c. Find the sum of the area of the four right triangles and the square in the middle whose side is of length c.

  d. Find the area of the large square using the expansion of $(a + b)^2$.

  e. Write an equation with the results from (c) and (d).

  f. Subtract the same quantity from both sides of the equation to arrive at $a^2 + b^2 = c^2$.

Skills and Review 6.3

16. Solve the equation $^-2x^2 + 14x = 0$.

17. Expand the product $6x(x^2 - 2x + 11)$.

18. Simplify and write without negative exponents: $a^4(3ab^2)^{-3}$.

19. Randy has $5000 to invest. He invests some of the money in an annuity earning 8.2% annual interest and the remainder in a CD that pays 5% annual interest. How much should Randy invest in each account if he wants to earn a 7% yield overall?

20. On August 13, 2012, the Nasdaq composite index for stocks opened at 2983.66. The index gained 1.884% that day. Find the closing index. (*Note:* The index is measured to the nearest hundredth). (http://dynamic.nasdaq.com)

21. A beverage company found that in a sample of 1500 people, 276 would use their new power drink. Predict the number of people who will use their power drink in a market of 1,400,000 people.

22. Simplify $4x^3 + x^2(x - 2) + 3x^2$.

23. Solve for x if

$$\frac{2}{3}x - \frac{1}{4} = \frac{5}{6}$$

24. Verify that $x = 12$ is a solution to the equation $^-2x + 6x + 7 = 5(x - 1)$.

25. Evaluate $\frac{^-b}{2a}$ for $a = \frac{1}{5}$ and $b = ^-\frac{3}{2}$.

6.4 Factoring Quadratic Trinomials

AFTER STUDYING THIS SECTION YOU WILL BE ABLE TO

- Factor quadratic trinomials.
- Factor the difference of two squares.
- Completely factor polynomials requiring several steps.
- Apply the zero-product property to solve equations of the form $ax^2 + bx + c = 0$, where $a \neq 0$.

In the previous section you learned how to factor some polynomials with four terms by the method of grouping. We can now extend this method to **quadratic trinomials**. These polynomials have three terms (hence the name *trinomial*), and the term with the highest power of the variable contains a square (hence the adjective *quadratic*). Factoring quadratic trinomials is a skill that is used in solving some equations, as we see at the end of this section.

Splitting the Middle Term

The fundamental strategy we use to factor quadratic trinomials is to create four terms out of three and use the grouping method you already know. The next example shows how we can do this by *splitting the middle term*.

EXAMPLE 1 ■ Factor $x^2 + 8x + 12$.

Solution ■ We can split the middle term, $8x$, into two terms, $6x$ and $2x$. Then we rewrite the trinomial as $x^2 + 6x + 2x + 12$. Now we have a polynomial with four terms. We apply the diagonal test for grouping and find that the product of the first and last terms ($x^2 * 12 = 12x^2$) is the same as the product of the two middle terms ($6x * 2x = 12x^2$). We factor by grouping, as shown in Figure 21. We can conclude that

$$x^2 + 8x + 12 = (x + 2)(x + 6)$$

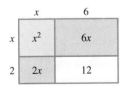

Figure 21

At this point you might reasonably ask how we knew to split $8x$ the way we did. Why didn't we say $8x = 3x + 5x$ or $8x = 4x + 4x$? That's a good question, and it must be answered if we are to succeed in factoring trinomials.

Let's look at the diagonal product $12x^2$ and ask ourselves how we can find two middle terms that will give $12x^2$ as a product. Obviously we are looking for two x terms, so our terms will have the form ____x and ____x. We can fill in the blanks with pairs of numbers that have a product of 12. There are three such pairs:

$$1 * 12 = 12$$
$$2 * 6 = 12$$
$$3 * 4 = 12$$

We can make these factors coefficients of x-terms and add them together to see which give us the desired middle term $8x$.

$$1x + 12x = 13x \qquad No$$
$$\mathbf{2x + 6x = 8x} \qquad \textit{Yes}$$
$$3x + 4x = 7x \qquad No$$

Procedure for Factoring a Quadratic Trinomial

Step 1   Write the terms of the quadratic trinomial in descending order.
Step 2   Find the diagonal product of the first and last terms.
Step 3   Find all factor pairs for the diagonal product.
Step 4   Search systematically for a pair whose sum is the middle term. Use this pair to split the middle term.
Step 5   Factor with an area model or symbolically by grouping.

EXAMPLE 2   Factor these trinomials:

a. $2x^2 + 9x + 10$
b. $x^2 - 13x + 36$
c. $3x^2 + 20x - 7$
d. $10x^2 - 3 - x$

Solution   **a.** $2x^2 + 9x + 10$ is already in descending order. The diagonal product is $2x^2 * 10 = 20x^2$. The middle term must be split so that $9x =$ ____$x +$ ____x. We need to find factor pairs for 20.

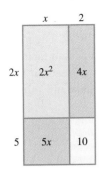

Figure 22

$$1 * 20 = 20 \qquad 1x + 20x = 21x \qquad No$$
$$2 * 10 = 20 \qquad 2x + 10x = 12x \qquad No$$
$$\mathbf{4 * 5 = 20} \qquad \mathbf{4x + 5x = 9x} \qquad \textit{Yes}$$

We split the middle term $9x$ into two terms, $4x$ and $5x$. See Figure 22. Symbolically, we have

$$2x^2 + 9x + 10 = 2x^2 + 4x + 5x + 10$$
$$= 2x(x + 2) + 5(x + 2) \qquad \textit{Factoring by grouping}$$
$$= (x + 2)(2x + 5)$$

b. $x^2 - 13x + 36$ is already in descending order. The diagonal product is $x^2 *$ $36 = 36x^2$. The middle term must be split so that $^-13x = \underline{\quad}x + \underline{\quad}x$. We need to find factor pairs for 36. Because the middle term is negative and 36 is positive, we look for two negative factors.

$$^-1 * {}^-36 = 36 \qquad {}^-1x + {}^-36x = {}^-37x \qquad No$$
$$^-2 * {}^-18 = 36 \qquad {}^-2x + {}^-18x = {}^-20x \qquad No$$
$$^-3 * {}^-12 = 36 \qquad {}^-3x + {}^-12x = {}^-15x \qquad No$$
$$\mathbf{{}^-4 * {}^-9 = 36} \qquad \mathbf{{}^-4x + {}^-9x = {}^-13x} \qquad \textit{Yes}$$
$$^-6 * {}^-6 = 36 \qquad {}^-6x + {}^-6x = {}^-12x \qquad No$$

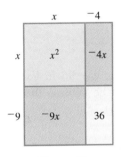

Figure 23

We split the middle term, ^-13x, into two terms, ^-4x and ^-9x. See Figure 23. Symbolically, we have

$$x^2 - 13x + 36 = x^2 - 4x - 9x + 36$$
$$= x(x - 4) - 9(x - 4) \qquad \textit{Factoring by grouping: } {}^-9 \textit{ is a}$$
$$\textit{negative common factor.}$$
$$= (x - 4)(x - 9)$$

c. $3x^2 + 20x - 7$ is already in descending order. The diagonal product is $3x^2 *$ $^-7 = {}^-21x^2$. The middle term must be split so that $20x = \underline{\quad}x + \underline{\quad}x$. We need to find factor pairs for $^-21$, so we will need one positive and one negative factor. Since the middle term is positive, the positive factor must have larger absolute value than the negative factor.

$$^-1 * 21 = {}^-21 \qquad {}^-1x + 21x = 20x \qquad \textit{Yes}$$
$$^-3 * 7 = {}^-21 \qquad {}^-3x + 7x = 4x \qquad No$$

We split the middle term, $20x$, into two terms, ^-1x and $21x$. See Figure 24. Symbolically, we have

$$3x^2 + 20x - 7 = 3x^2 - 1x + 21x - 7$$
$$= x(3x - 1) + 7(3x - 1) \qquad \textit{Factoring by grouping}$$
$$= (3x - 1)(x + 7)$$

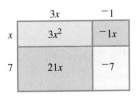

Figure 24

d. First rewrite $10x^2 - 3 - x$ so that the powers of x are in descending order: $10x^2 - x - 3$. The diagonal product is $10x^2 * {}^-3 = {}^-30x^2$. The middle term must be split so that ${}^-1x =$ _____$x +$ _____x. We need to find factor pairs for ${}^-30$, so we need one positive and one negative factor. Because the middle term is negative, the negative factor must have larger absolute value than the positive factor.

$$1 * {}^-30 = {}^-30 \qquad 1x + {}^-30x = {}^-29x \qquad \textit{No}$$
$$2 * {}^-15 = {}^-30 \qquad 2x + {}^-15x = {}^-13x \qquad \textit{No}$$
$$3 * {}^-10 = {}^-30 \qquad 3x + {}^-10x = {}^-7x \qquad \textit{No}$$
$$\mathbf{5 * {}^-6 = {}^-30} \qquad \mathbf{5x + {}^-6x = {}^-1x} \qquad \textit{Yes}$$

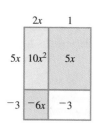

Figure 25

We split the middle term, ${}^-x$, into two terms, $5x$ and ${}^-6x$. See Figure 25. Symbolically,

$$10x^2 - x - 3 = 10x^2 + 5x - 6x - 3$$
$$= 5x(2x + 1) - 3(2x + 1) \qquad \textit{Factoring by grouping: } {}^-3 \textit{ is}$$
$$\textit{a negative common factor.}$$
$$= (2x + 1)(5x - 3)$$

■ ■ ■

Example 3 shows a trinominal that cannot be factored.

EXAMPLE 3 ■ Show that the trinomial $x^2 - 7x + 24$ cannot be factored.

Solution Suppose $x^2 - 7x + 24$ could be factored. Proceed as we did in Example 2. The diagonal product is $24x^2$. The middle term must be split so that ${}^-7x =$ _____$x +$ _____x. We need to find two negative factors for 24.

$${}^-1 * {}^-24 = 24 \qquad {}^-1x + {}^-24x = {}^-25x \qquad \textit{No}$$
$${}^-2 * {}^-12 = 24 \qquad {}^-2x + {}^-12x = {}^-14x \qquad \textit{No}$$
$${}^-3 * {}^-8 = 24 \qquad {}^-3x + {}^-8x = {}^-11x \qquad \textit{No}$$
$${}^-4 * {}^-6 = 24 \qquad {}^-4x + {}^-6x = {}^-10x \qquad \textit{No}$$

We tried every possible pair and found that none of them work, so $x^2 - 7x + 24$ cannot be factored with integers. It is considered a prime polynomial.

■ ■ ■

Other Applications of Splitting the Middle Term

Splitting the middle term can be used to factor some trinomials with more than one variable or with higher powers of x.

EXAMPLE 4   Factor these trinomials.

a. $x^2 - 11xy - 42y^2$

b. $2x^4 + 9x^2 + 7$

Solution   **a.** $x^2 - 11xy - 42y^2$ is written in descending order for powers of x. The diagonal product is $^-42x^2y^2$. The middle term must be split so that $^-11xy = \underline{\quad}xy + \underline{\quad}xy$. We need to find factor pairs of $^-42$, one positive and one negative. Because the middle term is negative, the negative factor must have larger absolute value than the positive factor.

$$1 * {}^-42 = {}^-42 \qquad 1xy + {}^-42xy = {}^-41xy \qquad No$$

$$2 * {}^-21 = {}^-42 \qquad 2xy + {}^-21xy = {}^-19xy \qquad No$$

$$\mathbf{3 * {}^-14 = {}^-42} \qquad \mathbf{3xy + {}^-14xy = {}^-11xy} \qquad \textbf{\textit{Yes}}$$

$$6 * {}^-7 = {}^-42 \qquad 6xy + {}^-7xy = {}^-1xy \qquad No$$

We split the middle term, ^-11xy, into two terms, $3xy$ and ^-14xy. See Figure 26. Symbolically,

$$x^2 - 11xy - 42y^2 = x^2 + 3xy - 14xy - 42y^2$$

$$= x(x + 3y) - 14y(x + 3y) \qquad \text{\textit{Factoring by grouping:}}$$
$$\text{\textit{^-14y is a negative}}$$
$$\text{\textit{common factor}}$$

$$= (x + 3y)(x - 14y)$$

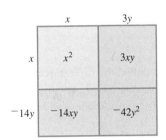

Figure 26

b. $2x^4 + 9x^2 + 7$ is written in descending order. The diagonal product is $14x^4$. The middle term must be split so that $9x^2 = \underline{\quad}x^2 + \underline{\quad}x^2$. We need to find two positive factors of 14.

$$1 * 14 = 14 \qquad 1x^2 + 14x^2 = 15x^2 \qquad No$$

$$\mathbf{2 * 7 = 14} \qquad \mathbf{2x^2 + 7x^2 = 9x^2} \qquad \textbf{\textit{Yes}}$$

We split the middle term, $9x^2$, into two terms, $2x^2$ and $7x^2$. See Figure 27. Symbolically,

$$2x^4 + 9x^2 + 7 = 2x^4 + 2x^2 + 7x^2 + 7$$

$$= 2x^2(x^2 + 1) + 7(x^2 + 1) \qquad \text{\textit{Factoring by grouping}}$$

$$= (x^2 + 1)(2x^2 + 7)$$

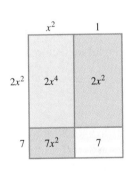

Figure 27

A Special Binomial

Example 5 considers a special binomial, the difference of two squares.

EXAMPLE 5   Factor $x^2 - 49$.

Solution $x^2 - 49$ is a binomial rather than a trinomial, but we can still split the middle term if we think of it as $0x$. The diagonal product is $^-49x^2$. The middle term must be split so that $0x = \underline{\quad}x + \underline{\quad}x$. We need to find factor pairs for $^-49$ and need one positive and one negative number because they must add to zero.

$$1 * {}^-49 = {}^-49 \qquad 1x + {}^-49x = {}^-48x \qquad No$$

$$7 * {}^-7 = {}^-49 \qquad 7x + {}^-7x = 0x \qquad Yes$$

We split the middle term, $0x$, into two terms, ^-7x and $7x$. See Figure 28. Symbolically,

$$x^2 - 49 = x^2 + 0x - 49$$
$$= x^2 - 7x + 7x - 49$$
$$= x(x - 7) + 7(x - 7)$$
$$= (x - 7)(x + 7)$$

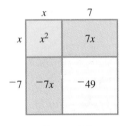

Figure 28

The binomial $x^2 - 49$ is an example of a pattern called the **difference of two squares**. Note that x^2 is the square of x and 49 is the square of 7. The difference of two squares may always be factored by splitting a zero middle term. In general we have $a^2 - b^2$ with a middle term of $0ab$.

The Difference of Two Squares

$a^2 - b^2$ can be factored as $(a - b)(a + b)$.

Caution: Note that the sum of two squares, $a^2 + b^2$, cannot be factored.

Factoring Completely

Some polynomials may be factored in several steps. Always look for a common monomial factor first. If there is one, then you may be able to factor one or more of the resulting factors by grouping, splitting a middle term, or using the difference of two squares. Keep going until the polynomial is completely factored.

EXAMPLE 6   Factor each polynomial.

a. $12x^2 - 18x + 6$
b. $2xy^2 - 50x$
c. $x^4y^2 - 4x^3y^2 - 2x^4y + 8x^3y$

Solution   **a.** $12x^2 - 18x + 6 = 6(2x^2 - 3x + 1)$ *The common factor is 6*
$$= 6(2x^2 - 2x - 1x + 1)$$ *Splitting the middle term*
$$= 6(2x(x - 1) + {}^-1(x - 1))$$ *Factoring by grouping*
$$= 6(x - 1)(2x - 1)$$

b. $2xy^2 - 50x = 2x(y^2 - 25)$ *The common factor is 2x*
$$= 2x(y - 5)(y + 5)$$ *Factoring as the difference of two squares*

c. $x^4y^2 - 4x^3y^2 - 2x^4y + 8x^3y = x^3y(xy - 4y - 2x + 8)$ *The common*
factor is x^3y
$$= x^3y((xy - 4y) + ({}^-2x + 8))$$ *Grouping*
$$= x^3y(y(x - 4) + {}^-2(x - 4))$$
$$= x^3y(x - 4)(y + {}^-2)$$
$$= x^3y(x - 4)(y - 2)$$

■ ■

Solving Equations by Factoring

Section 6.2 introduced the zero-product property. We can use this property to solve quadratic equations in which a quadratic trinomial is equal to zero. In the next chapter we learn more about quadratic equations and different methods for solving them. In the meantime, here are examples of quadratic equations that can be solved by factoring.

EXAMPLE 7   Solve these equations.

a. $x^2 - 7x - 18 = 0$
b. $2x^2 + 5 = 11x$

Solution   **a.** $x^2 - 7x - 18 = 0$
$$x^2 - 9x + 2x - 18 = 0$$ *Splitting the middle term on left side*
$$x(x - 9) + 2(x - 9) = 0$$ *Factoring by grouping*
$$(x - 9)(x + 2) = 0$$

Now apply the zero-product property: Either

$$x - 9 = 0 \quad \text{or} \quad x + 2 = 0$$
$$x = 9 \qquad\qquad x = {}^-2$$

Typically for equations like this there is more than one solution. Both of them should check in the original equation.

Check for $x = 9$	Check for $x = {}^-2$
$x^2 - 7x - 18 = 0$	$x^2 - 7x - 18 = 0$
$9^2 - 7*9 - 18 \overset{?}{=} 0$	$({}^-2)^2 - 7*({}^-2) - 18 \overset{?}{=} 0$
$81 - 63 - 18 = 0$ *OK!*	$4 + 14 - 18 = 0$ *OK!*

b.
$$2x^2 + 5 = 11x$$

$$2x^2 - 11x + 5 = 0 \qquad \textit{Making the right side zero by subtracting}$$
$$\textit{11x on both sides}$$

$$2x^2 - 1x - 10x + 5 = 0 \qquad \textit{Splitting the middle term}$$

$$x(2x - 1) - 5(2x - 1) = 0 \qquad \textit{Factoring by grouping}$$

$$(2x - 1)(x - 5) = 0$$

Now apply the zero-product property: Either

$$2x - 1 = 0 \qquad\qquad\qquad \text{or} \quad x - 5 = 0$$

$$2x = 1$$

$$x = \frac{1}{2} \qquad\qquad\qquad\qquad x = 5$$

Check for $x = \frac{1}{2}$ $\qquad\qquad$ Check for $x = 5$

$$2x^2 - 11x + 5 = 0 \qquad\qquad 2x^2 - 11x + 5 = 0$$

$$2 * \left(\frac{1}{2}\right)^2 - 11 * \left(\frac{1}{2}\right) + 5 \stackrel{?}{=} 0 \qquad\qquad 2 * 5^2 - 11 * 5 + 5 \stackrel{?}{=} 0$$

$$2 \left(\frac{1}{4}\right) - \frac{11}{2} + 5 \stackrel{?}{=} 0 \qquad\qquad 2 * 25 - 55 + 5 \stackrel{?}{=} 0$$

$$\frac{1}{2} - \frac{11}{2} + 5 \stackrel{?}{=} 0 \qquad\qquad 50 - 55 + 5 = 0 \quad \textit{OK!}$$

$$-\frac{10}{2} + 5 \stackrel{?}{=} 0$$

$$^-5 + 5 = 0 \quad \textit{OK!}$$

Exercises 6.4

1. Place the terms of each polynomial in descending order and determine which are quadratic trinomials.
   a. $x + x^2 - 6$ $\qquad\qquad$ **b.** $x^3 - x + 6$
   c. $x^2 + 3$ $\qquad\qquad\qquad$ **d.** $5 - x + 4x^2$

2. Follow these steps to factor the trinomial $x^2 + 18x + 32$.
   a. Find the diagonal product.
   b. List all the factor pairs for the diagonal product.
   c. Choose the factor pair that adds to equal the middle term.

d. Rewrite the trinomial with a split middle term.

e. Create an area model and factor your four-term polynomial from (d).

For Exercises 3–4, factor each trinomial.

3. $2x^2 + 7x + 3$

4. $4x^2 + 5x - 6$

5. George decided that $x^2 - 5x + 6$ wouldn't factor. His incorrect conclusion was based on this algebraic work:

$$x^2 - 5x + 6 = x^2 - 3x - 2x + 6 \qquad \textit{Spliting the middle term}$$

$$= (x^2 - 3x) - (2x + 6) \qquad \textit{Forming groups of two terms}$$

$$= x(x - 3) - 2(x + 3) \qquad \textit{Finding the GCF of each group}$$

George stopped here because he couldn't find a GCF.

a. Use the diagonal test for grouping to show that $x^2 - 3x - 2x + 6$ does factor.

b. Use an area model to factor the polynomial.

c. Find the error in George's symbolic work and correct it.

For Exercises 6–7, factor each trinomial.

6. $x^2 - 12x + 35$

7. $^-11x + 6x^2 - 10$

For Exercises 8 and 9, show that each trinomial can't be factored. Do this by trying to split the middle term.

8. $x^2 + 4x + 6$

9. $5x^2 - 3x + 8$

For Exercises 10 and 11, use Example 4 as a model to factor the polynomial.

10. $x^2 + 2xy - 8y^2$

11. $2x^6 - x^3 - 28$

12. Factor each difference of two squares.

   a. $x^2 - 16$ **b.** $4x^2 - y^2$ **c.** $36 - z^2$

13. Solve each equation by factoring.

   a. $x^2 - 12x + 32 = 0$

   b. $x^2 - 3x = 10$

   c. $2x^2 + 7x + 3 = 0$

14. Factor the following polynomials in steps. First look for a common monomial factor. Then factor by grouping, by splitting a middle term if necessary, or by using the difference of two squares.

   a. $2x^3 - 6x^2 - 36x$

   b. $5xy - 20x - 10y + 40$

   c. $6 - 24x^2$

15. The trinomial $x^2 + x - 2$ factors into $(x + 2)(x - 1)$. The two expressions look entirely different but are, indeed, equivalent.

   a. Demonstrate their equivalence by evaluating both expressions for $x = ^-2$ and $x = 1$.

   b. Graph either expression in the $\boxed{Y=}$ menu with a $\boxed{\text{ZOOM}}$ 4: ZDecimal setting. $\boxed{\text{TRACE}}$ to the points on the graph that correspond to $x = ^-2$ and $x = 1$. What is the name for the line both points lie on?

   c. Notice the choices of $^-2$ and 1 as values of x that produce an output of zero in the factored polynomial $(x + 2)(x - 1)$. What values of x do you suppose produce an output of zero in the factored polynomial $(x - 6)(x + 3)$?

   d. Explain why it is helpful to factor a polynomial in order to find where the graph of a function crosses the x-axis. In the next chapter we examine this question in greater detail.

Skills and Review 6.4

16. Expand each product.

   a. $(x - 6)(3x + 7)$

   b. $(2x - 1)(x^2 + 4x + 3)$

17. Use an area model to show why $(x + 3)^2$ is not equal to $x^2 + 9$.

18. Expand each of the following.

   a. $(2x + 5)^2$ **b.** $(3x - 4)^2$

19. Solve the equation $7x^2 - 21x = 0$.

20. Simplify the expression and write your answer with only positive exponents.

$$\left(\frac{x^{-2}y^4}{x} \right)^2$$

21. Linda and Lucy are $\frac{3}{4}$ mile apart. At 5 P.M. Linda starts running toward Lucy at the rate of $\frac{1}{8}$ mile/minute. At 5:03 P.M. Lucy begins riding her moped toward Linda at the rate of $\frac{1}{4}$ mile/minute. When will Linda and Lucy meet?

22. The price of a collectible went from \$42 to \$197. Find the percent increase.

23. Recall that a system of linear equations in two variables has no solutions if the lines are parallel. Show by demonstrating equal slopes or by an algebraic method (substitution or elimination) that the following system of two equations has no solutions.

$$x + \tfrac{1}{2}y = 6$$

$$y = {}^{-}2x + 10$$

24. Write the equation $2x - 4y = 8$ in slope-intercept form.

25. Solve the equation $11 - (x + 2) = 5(x - 7)$.

    a. Write your solution as a simplified fraction.

    b. Write your solution as a decimal rounded to the nearest thousandth.

6.5 Factoring the Sum and Difference of Two Cubes (Optional)

AFTER STUDYING THIS SECTION YOU WILL BE ABLE TO

■ Factor the sum or difference of two cubes.

■ Use the sum or difference of two cubes to factor more complex polynomials completely.

In Section 6.4 we observed that the difference of two squares may be factored using the pattern

$$a^2 - b^2 = (a - b)(a + b)$$

We also noticed that the *sum* of two squares $a^2 + b^2$ cannot be factored.

    You may be surprised to learn that *both* the sum and the difference of two cubes may be factored. The technique of splitting zero middle terms that you used for the difference of two squares may be extended to expressions involving cubes. Figure 29 suggests how formulas for the sum and difference of two cubes may be found by splitting the terms a^2b and ab^2.

	a^2	^-ab	b^2
a	a^3	$^-a^2b$	ab^2
b	a^2b	$^-ab^2$	b^3

	a^2	ab	b^2
a	a^3	a^2b	ab^2
^-b	$^-a^2b$	$^-ab^2$	$^-b^3$

Figure 29

The Sum or Difference of Two Cubes

$a^3 + b^3$ can be factored as $(a + b)(a^2 - ab + b^2)$.

$a^3 - b^3$ can be factored as $(a - b)(a^2 + ab + b^2)$.

Observe that for the sum of two cubes, the binomial $a + b$ is also a sum. For the difference of two cubes, the binomial $a - b$ is a difference. The middle term of the second factor is $+ab$ or $-ab$. Its sign is the *opposite* of the sign of b in the first factor.

In order to use these patterns, you must recognize expressions that contain sums and differences of two cubes.

EXAMPLE 1 Factor these expressions.

a. $x^3 - 8$
b. $64x^3 + 125y^3$
c. $z^6 + 27$

Solution **a.** x^3 is the cube of x and 8 is the cube of 2. We have the difference of two cubes.

$$x^3 - 8 = x^3 - 2^3$$

$$= (\mathbf{x} - \mathbf{2})(\mathbf{x}^2 + \mathbf{2x} + \mathbf{2}^2)$$ *Using the difference of two cubes with $a = x$ and $b = 2$*

$$= (x - 2)(x^2 + 2x + 4)$$

The work may be checked by expanding $(x - 2)(x^2 + 2x + 4)$ with an area model, as shown in Figure 30.

	x^2	$2x$	4
x	x^3	$2x^2$	$4x$
$^-2$	$^-2x^2$	^-4x	$^-8$

Figure 30

b. $64x^3$ is the cube of $4x$ and $125y^3$ is the cube of $5y$. We have the sum of two cubes.

$$64x^3 + 125y^3 = (\mathbf{4x})^3 + (\mathbf{5y})^3$$

$$= (\mathbf{4x} + \mathbf{5y})((\mathbf{4x})^2 - \mathbf{4x} * \mathbf{5y} + (\mathbf{5y})^2)$$ *Using the sum of two cubes with $a = 4x$ and $b = 5y$*

$$= (4x + 5y)(16x^2 - 20xy + 25y^2)$$ *Using the power-of-a-product law*

c. z^6 is the cube of z^2 and 27 is the cube of 3. We have the sum of two cubes.

$$z^6 + 27 = (z^2)^3 + 3^3$$

$$= (z^2 + 3)((z^2)^2 - 3z^2 + 3^2) \qquad \textit{Using the sum of two cubes with } a = z^2 \textit{ and } b = 3$$

$$= (z^2 + 3)(z^4 - 3z^2 + 9) \qquad \textit{Using the power-of-a-power law}$$

The sum or difference of two cubes may be used in connection with other factoring techniques. As a general rule, look for common factors or the difference of two squares before you apply the patterns for the sum and difference of two cubes.

EXAMPLE 2   Factor completely:

a. $24x^3 + 3$

b. $x^6 - 64$

Solution   **a.** The two terms have a common factor, 3. Therefore, $24x^3 + 3 = 3(8x^3 + 1)$. We now observe that the binomial factor, $8x^3 + 1$, is the sum of two cubes because $8x^3$ is the cube of $2x$ and 1 is the cube of 1. So,

$$24x^3 + 3 = 3(8x^3 + 1)$$

$$= 3((2x)^3 + 1^3)$$

$$= 3(2x + 1)((2x)^2 - 2x + 1^2) \qquad \textit{Using the sum of two cubes with } a = 2x \textit{ and } b = 1$$

$$= 3(2x + 1)(4x^2 - 2x + 1) \qquad \textit{Using the power-of-a-product law}$$

b. The two terms have no common factor, but we may consider this expression as the difference of two squares. x^6 is the square of x^3 and 64 is the square of 8. Once we have factored the difference of two squares, we find that we have a sum of two cubes and a difference of two cubes.

$$x^6 - 64 = (x^3)^2 - 8^2$$

$$= (x^3 - 8)(x^3 + 8) \qquad \textit{Using the difference of two squares with } a = x^3 \textit{ and } b = 8$$

$$= (x^3 - 2^3)(x^3 + 2^3)$$

$$= (x - 2)(x^2 + 2x + 4)(x + 2)(x^2 - 2x + 4) \qquad \textit{Using the sum and difference of two cubes with } a = x \textit{ and } b = 2$$

You may be surprised that this polynomial with two terms can be expressed as the product of four polynomials.

Exercises 6.5

1. Use the sum or difference of two cubes to factor.
   a. $y^3 + 125$ **b.** $27 - 8x^3$
   c. $x^3 - 216$ **d.** $1000z^3 + 1$
   e. $x^6 - y^3$

2. Factor completely.
   a. $2z^3 + 54$ **b.** $40x^3 - 5y^3$
   c. $z^6 - 1$ **d.** $x^6 - y^6$

3. Some of these expressions are prime—that is, they cannot be factored with integer coefficients. Identify those that are prime and factor those that can be factored.
   a. $x^2 + 25$ **b.** $x^3 + 729$
   c. $x^4 + 16$ **d.** $x^6 - 729$
   e. $x^6 + 512$

CHAPTER 6 ■ KEY CONCEPTS ■

Checking with Specific Values   This technique lets us check that our algebraic manipulations have been done correctly. If we substitute specific values for each variable in the original expression and in our simplified form, we should get the same result. If not, we have made a mistake somewhere. It is a good idea to choose small numbers to check with, but avoid 1 and 0. (Page 210)

Product Law for Exponents   This rule lets us simplify expressions involving a product and exponents.

$$a^m a^n = a^{m+n} \qquad \text{(Page 211)}$$

Power-of-a-Power Law for Exponents   This rule lets us simplify expressions involving a power of a power.

$$(a^m)^n = a^{mn} \qquad \text{(Page 212)}$$

Power-of-a-Product Law for Exponents   This rule lets us simplify expressions involving a power of a product.

$$(ab)^m = a^m b^m \qquad \text{(Page 212)}$$

Negative Integer Exponents   A negative integer exponent is another way to represent a quantity in the denominator of a fraction: $a^{-n} = \frac{1}{a^n}$. If a negative exponent appears in a factor in a denominator, then that factor can be moved to the numerator and the exponent becomes positive. (Page 213)

Quotient Law for Exponents   This rule lets us simplify expressions involving quotients and exponents.

$$\frac{a^m}{a^n} = a^{m-n} \qquad \text{(Page 216)}$$

Power-of-a-Quotient Law for Exponents   The rule which lets us simplify expressions involving the power of a quotient.

$$\left(\frac{a}{b}\right)^m = \frac{a^m}{b^m} \qquad \text{(Page 216)}$$

Monomials   A monomial is any single algebraic expression involving a product of numbers and variables raised to positive integer powers. (Page 221)

Polynomials A polynomial is any combination of monomials by addition and subtraction. Polynomials with two terms are called **binomials** (page 221) and with three terms are called **trinomials**. (Page 221)

Area Models An area model is a useful tool to help expand or factor polynomials. The monomials in one factor are written as the rows on one side of a rectangle, and the monomials in the other factor are written at the tops of columns on the other side. The product of the two factors is the area of the rectangle. (Pages 221–223)

Greatest Common Factor (GCF) The GCF is the largest factor common to all of the monomials in a polynomial. This can be either the largest monomial common factor or a common binomial factor. (Page 224)

The Zero-Product Property If the product of two numbers is zero, then at least one of the numbers must be zero. This property can be used to solve **quadratic equations**. (Page 228)

The Square of a Binomial The square of a binomial has a distinctive form.

$$(a + b)^2 = a^2 + 2ab + b^2 \qquad \text{(Page 232)}$$

Factoring by Grouping A technique for factoring polynomials by grouping the monomials according to which pairs have common factors. (Page 233)

Prime Polynomial A polynomial is prime if it cannot be factored into two or more polynomial (or monomial) factors with only integer coefficients. (Page 233)

The Diagonal Test for Grouping This test tells us if a polynomial with four terms may be factored into two binomials with integer coefficients. If the product of two terms equals the product of the other two terms, then the polynomial may be factored; otherwise it cannot. (Page 235)

Splitting the Middle Term This technique allows us to factor trinomials by splitting the middle term into two terms in such a way that the diagonal test for grouping works and the polynomial can be factored.

$$x^2 + 5x + 6 = x^2 + 2x + 3x + 6 \qquad 2x * 3x = x^2 * 6, \text{ so it factors}$$
$$= x(x + 2) + 3(x + 2)$$
$$= (x + 2)(x + 3) \qquad \text{(Page 239)}$$

The Difference of Two Squares This special binomial is the difference of two perfect squares, $a^2 - b^2$. It factors easily as $a^2 - b^2 = (a + b)(a - b)$. (Page 244)

Exploration

The method of multiplying using squares shown in the chapter opener can be used to find the product of two even numbers or two odd numbers. For example, you can multiply $23 * 55$ using this method. (A table of squares is provided here.)

$$\text{Step 1} \quad x = \frac{23 + 55}{2} = \frac{78}{2} = 39$$

$$\text{Step 2} \quad y = \frac{55 - 23}{2} = \frac{32}{2} = 16$$

$$\text{Step 3} \quad x^2 - y^2 = 1521 - 256 = 1265$$

Number	Square	Number	Square	Number	Square
1	1	21	441	41	1681
2	4	22	484	42	1764
3	9	23	529	43	1849
4	16	24	576	44	1936
5	25	25	625	45	2025
6	36	26	676	46	2116
7	49	27	729	47	2209
8	64	28	784	48	2304
9	81	29	841	49	2401
10	100	30	900	50	2500
11	121	31	961	51	2601
12	144	32	1024	52	2704
13	169	33	1089	53	2809
14	196	34	1156	54	2916
15	225	35	1225	55	3025
16	256	36	1296	56	3136
17	289	37	1369	57	3249
18	324	38	1444	58	3364
19	361	39	1521	59	3481
20	400	40	1600	60	3600

a. Use the method of squares to multiply $82 * 46$.

b. Use algebra to explain why this method works. (*Hint:* Let the larger number be m and the smaller number be n. Show that $x + y = m$ and $x - y = n$.)

c. Why does this method work only if both numbers are odd or both are even?

d. The method can be modified to multiply an odd number by an even number. To multiply $77 * 44$, first multiply $76 * 44$ and then add 44 to the result. Explain why this works.

CHAPTER 6 ▪ REVIEW EXERCISES

Section 6.1 The Laws of Exponents

1. Use repeated multiplication to simplify each expression.
   a. $x^4 * x^5$
   b. $(y^2)^4$
   c. $(x * y)^5$

2. Use the laws of exponents to simplify each expression.
   a. $(2xy^3)^6$
   b. $4y * 7y^5$
   c. $(z^2)^4$

3. The side of a cube measures $2.1 * 10^4$ inches. Find the volume of the cube in cubic inches. A formula for the volume of a cube is volume = side^3.

4. Use the laws of exponents to simplify each expression. Write your answer using only positive exponents.
   a. x^4x^{-7}
   b. $x^{-4}x^7$
   c. $(x^3)^{-3}$
   d. $(x^{-2}y)^{-6}$

5. At room temperature sound travels at a speed of $1.13 * 10^3$ feet/second. One microsecond is one millionth of a second, or 10^{-6} seconds. How far does sound travel in 1 microsecond?

6. Simplify each expression and write with only positive exponents.

a. $\dfrac{x^7}{x^3}$

b. $\dfrac{x^3}{x^7}$

c. $\left(\dfrac{x}{y}\right)^6$

7. Match each expression (a)–(e) with its equivalent simplified expression (1)–(5). Also, name the law or laws of exponents used in simplifying each expression.

     a. $\dfrac{x^3}{x^2}$ b. $(x^3)^2$ c. $\dfrac{x^2}{x^3}$ d. x^3x^2 e. $\dfrac{1}{x^{-3}}$

     1. x^5 2. $\dfrac{1}{x}$ 3. x 4. x^3 5. x^6

8. Use the laws of exponents to simplify each expression. Write your answer using only positive exponents.

a. $\dfrac{x^5 y}{x^2 y^4}$

b. $\left(\dfrac{4x^2}{y}\right)^3$

c. $\left(\dfrac{x^3 y^2}{x^7 y}\right)^4$

d. $\left(\dfrac{2x^7}{3x^3 y^2}\right)^{-3}$

Section 6.2 Products and Factors

9. Use an area model to find the product of $4x^3$ and $5x + 2x^4 y$.

10. Find each product.
  a. $5x(6x - 1)$
  b. $2xz(4x + 7y - 3)$
  c. $^-(x^2 - 8x + 2)$

11. Find the greatest common factor (GCF) for each group of expressions.
  a. xy^4 and $x^5 y$
  b. $18x^2 y$, $3x^3 z^5$, and $9x^4$
  c. $60x$ and $105y$

12. Use an area model to factor $8y^2 + 12y$.

13. Factor completely the expression $5x^2 yz^3 - 15x^3 y^4 + 10x^5 y^2$.

14. Factor each expression so that the first term of the binomial factor has a positive coefficient.
  a. $^-8x^2 + 10x$ **b.** $^-9x - 12y$

15. Factor each expression.

a. $4xz - 3z$

b. $4x(y + 7) - 3(y + 7)$

c. Show how (a) and (b) are related to each other.

16. Solve each equation by factoring and using the zero-product property.
  a. $x^2 + 5x = 0$ **b.** $x^2 - 8x = 0$

Section 6.3 Factoring by Grouping

17. Use an area model to expand each product.
  a. $(x + 4)(x + 2)$
  b. $(x - 3)(4x^2 + 5x - 6)$

18. Factor each polynomial by grouping. Factor with an area model and then factor symbolically.
  a. $2x - 9y + xy - 18$
  b. $^-4y + 3z - 12yz + 1$

19. Use the diagonal test for grouping to determine if each polynomial can be factored, and if it can be, factor it.
  a. $4x^3 + 10x^2 - 2x - 5$ **b.** $x^3 - 6x^2 - 5x + 2$
  c. $3x + 8y + 6xy + 4$

20. In this section you learned a formula for squaring a binomial: $(a + b)^2 = a^2 + 2ab + b^2$. Use this formula to find each of the squares.
  a. $(x + y)^2$ **b.** $(x + 2y)^2$
  c. $(5x - 3y)^2$

Section 6.4 Factoring Quadratic Trinomials

21. Follow these steps below to factor the trinomial $x^2 + 11x + 24$.
  a. Find the diagonal product.
  b. List all the factor pairs of the diagonal product.
  c. Choose the factor pair that has a sum equal to the middle term.
  d. Rewrite the trinomial with a split middle term.
  e. Create an area model and factor your four-term polynomial from (d).

22. Factor each trinomial by splitting the middle term.
  a. $x^2 - 5x - 14$ **b.** $5x^2 + 9x - 2$
  c. $3x^2 - 11x - 4$ **d.** $7x^2 - 8 + 26x$

23. Show that each trinomial cannot be factored by trying to split the middle term.
  a. $x^2 - 2x + 5$ **b.** $2x^2 + x + 6$

24. Factor each trinomial. See Example 4.
  a. $x^2 + 10xy + 21y^2$ **b.** $2x^4 - x^2 - 15$

25. Factor each difference of two squares.
  a. $x^2 - 25$ **b.** $9 - y^2$

c. $4x^2 - 81y^2$

26. Factor the following polynomials in steps. First look for a common monomial factor. Then attempt more factoring by grouping, splitting a middle term, or using the difference of two squares.

    a. $18x^2 - 36x + 16$

    b. $xy^2 - xy + 2y^2 - 2y$

    c. $3x^2y - 300y$

27. Solve each equation by factoring.

    a. $x^2 + 13x + 40 = 0$ **b.** $x^2 + 2x = 3$

c. $3x^2 - 19x + 6 = 0$

Section 6.5 Factoring the Sum and Difference of Two Cubes (Optional)

28. Use the sum or difference of two cubes to factor:

    a. $x^3 + 64$ **b.** $1 - y^3$

    c. $8x^3 + 1000y^3$ **d.** $y^3 + 27z^6$

29. Factor completely:

    a. $6 - 48z^3$ **b.** $250x^3 + 2y^3$ **c.** $64 - y^6$

CHAPTER 6 ▪ TEST

For Exercises 1–3, use the laws of exponents to simplify each expression. Write your answer using only positive exponents.

1. $(xy^3z^{-4})^2$

2. $\dfrac{6xy^{-3}}{20x^{-2}}$

3. $\left(\dfrac{3x^4y^2}{xy^2}\right)^{-3}$

4. Suppose the human brain sends $2.0 * 10^7$ signals through its neurons each second. How many signals are sent in one day? *Note:* There are $8.64 * 10^4$ seconds in one day. Perform your work using the laws of exponents. (http://vadim.www.media.mit.edu)

5. Find each product.

    a. $3a * (a + 4)$

    b. $^-6xy^2 * (^-x^2 - 2xy + 5y^2)$

6. Completely factor $^-6ab^2c^3 - 3bc^2 - 12a^3b^4c^3$.

7. Solve $2x^2 - 10x = 0$.

8. Expand each expression.

    a. $(2x + 5)(x - 7)$

    b. $(x - 4)(3x^2 - x + 6)$

9. Factor each polynomial.

    a. $2x + 4xy + 3 + 6y$ **b.** $6x^3 - 9x - 2x^2 + 3$

10. Square the binomial $(2x - 7y)^2$.

11. Factor each trinomial.

    a. $4x^2 - 23x - 6$ **b.** $x^2 + 2xy - 35y^2$

12. Factor the binomial $64x^2 - y^2$.

13. Completely factor each polynomial.

    a. $2x^2y + 6xy^2 - 80y^3$ **b.** $12 - 3x^2$

14. Solve $6x^2 - 17x + 5 = 0$.

12.1 Inequalities and the Number Line

AFTER STUDYING THIS SECTION YOU WILL BE ABLE TO

- Represent inequalities in one variable on a number line.
- Represent inequalities in one variable with set-builder notation.
- Solve linear inequalities in one variable.

There are many real-world situations that cannot be modeled mathematically using equations but instead require the use of **inequalities**. Problems with solutions that involve a *range* of values cannot be modeled using an equation.

Methods of Solving Inequalities

Examples 1–3 illustrate how to solve inequalities.

EXAMPLE 1   Let's return to Gridville in Section 2.3. Suppose Melissa lives on the corner of Street 0 (the x-axis) and Avenue 2. Melissa likes to walk only along Street 0, and she never gets farther than 4 blocks from her house. Where can Melissa go? Show the answer on a number line.

Solution   Because Melissa walks only along Street 0, we have to keep track only of her x-coordinate. If she walks 4 blocks west, she will be at Avenue $^-2$, and if she walks 4 blocks east, she will be at Avenue 6. We can show this by shading in her possible locations on a number line (see Figure 1). We can also write this set of points as $\{x \mid {}^-2 \leq x \text{ and } x \leq 6\}$. A more compact way to show the set is $\{x \mid {}^-2 \leq x \leq 6\}$.

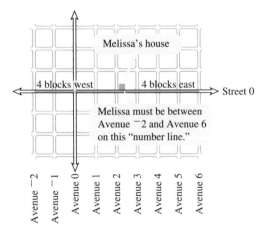

Figure 1   Melissa's position stays between $^-2$ and 6 on the x-axis.

EXAMPLE 2   Ms. Chang's cellular phone company charges her 10¢ per minute, and they give her a free gift if she spends more than $20 per month. Ms. Chang always wants to get the free gift, but she can't afford to spend more than $40 per month on phone calls. How many minutes of calls should Ms. Chang make each month? Show the answer on a number line.

Solution   Because Ms. Chang always wants to get the free gift, she has to spend more than $20. Each minute costs 10¢, so we can work out how many minutes cost $20 = 2000¢ by division:

$$\frac{2000¢}{10¢/\text{minute}} = 200 \text{ minutes}$$

To get her free gift, Ms. Chang has to spend more than 200 minutes on the phone. We can also determine how many minutes cost $40 = 4000¢: $\frac{4000}{10} = 400$. We can then plot the allowable number of minutes on a number line (see Figure 2). In set-builder notation, this is shown as $\{x \mid 200 < x \le 400\}$.

■ ■ ■

Minutes used

Figure 2   Ms. Chang must use more than 200 minutes and no more than 400 minutes.

EXAMPLE 3   A water main breaks at the corner of Avenue 3 and Street 2 in Gridville, flooding Avenue 3 for 6 blocks in either direction. Buses that run along Avenue 3 must stay either north or south of the flooding. Which streets can Avenue 3 buses reach? See Figure 3.

Solution   Because the buses stay on Avenue 3, we need to keep track only of their y-coordinate, and we can mark the streets they can travel to on a number line. The center of the flooding is Street 2, so 6 blocks north is Street 8, and 6 blocks south is Street ⁻4. Therefore, the y-coordinate of the position of any bus on Avenue 3 must be either greater than 6 if they stay north of the flooding or less than ⁻4 if they stay south of the flooding. The possible bus positions can be marked on a y number line (see Figure 4).

We can also express the answer algebraically using set-builder notation (page 304). First, we need to write inequalities using the variable y and the information we have about the flooding. The flooding starts on Street 2 and goes 6 blocks in both directions, and the buses must stay *out* of the flooded area; in other words, they must be either north of the flood **or** south of the flood. North of the flood translates to at least 6 blocks north of street 2, so $y \ge 2 + 6 = 8$. South of the flood becomes $y \le 2 - 6 = $ ⁻4. The set of streets the buses can travel is, therefore, $\{y \mid y \le $ ⁻4 or $8 \le y\}$.

■ ■ ■

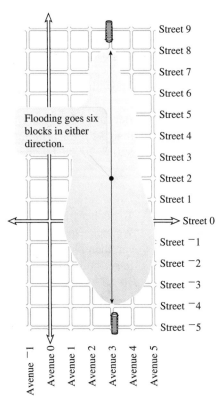

Figure 3 The flooding keeps buses away from the corner of Avenue 3 and Street 2 for 6 blocks in either direction.

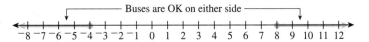

Figure 4 Buses cannot get too close to $y = 2$.

The solutions to Examples 1 and 2 are different than the solution to Example 3. In the first two examples, the possible values of the variable x-coordinate (or number of minutes) are within a given range. The variable must satisfy both conditions put on it, for example the number of minutes must be greater than 200 *and* no more than 400. On the other hand, in Example 3, the variable (y-coordinate) can satisfy either one *or* the other condition; either the bus is north of the flooding *or* it is south of it.

Inequalities that involve *and*, such as Examples 1 and 2, often have solutions that look like Figures 1 and 2, with a bounded range of values shaded. Inequalities that involve *or*, such as Example 3, often have solutions that look like Figure 4, with two (or more) regions shaded (the regions might overlap). We can specify the solution to a single inequality or to a set of inequalities using either a number line or set-builder notation.

EXAMPLE 4 Suppose the number of people who will sign up to take a writing workshop is given by the function $N = 180 - 2x$, where x is the price in dollars charged for the workshop. If the organizers want to make sure at least 30 people sign up and the room the workshop will be in will hold no more than 75 people, how much can they charge for the workshop?

Solution Here, we have a formula, $N = 180 - 2x$, that must satisfy two conditions, so we should use *algebraic* methods to try to obtain a solution. We can write

$$30 \leq 180 - 2x \quad \text{and} \quad 180 - 2x \leq 75$$

Algebraically, we can treat inequalities *almost* the same way we treat equations. If we are given an inequality, we can add the same term on both sides or multiply on both sides by the same *positive* number and still have a valid inequality. Multiplying by a negative number on both sides is a little trickier, as we soon see.

Let's try this with the two inequalities.

$$30 \leq 180 - 2x$$

$$0 \leq 150 - 2x \qquad \textit{Subtracting 30 on both sides}$$

$$2x \leq 150 \qquad \textit{Adding 2x on both sides}$$

$$x \leq 75 \qquad \textit{Multiplying on both sides by } \tfrac{1}{2}$$

Using the first inequality, we know that the charge can be no more than \$75. The second inequality gives

$$180 - 2x \leq 75$$

$$^-2x \leq\ ^-105 \qquad \textit{Subtracting 180 on both sides}$$

The next step is to multiply both sides by $-\tfrac{1}{2}$, but so far we can multiply only by a positive number. What happens if we multiply both sides of an inequality by a negative number?

We can think of an inequality as living on a number line; if x is greater than some number, then it is *to the right of it* on the number line, and if x is less than some number, then it is *to the left of it*. If we multiply by a negative number, then positive numbers become negative, and negative numbers become positive; in other words, the number line *rotates*. So, if x is to the right of a number, after the rotation it is to the left of it, and vice versa. (See Figure 5.) Therefore, if we multiply an inequality by a negative number on both sides, we need to *reverse* the inequality symbol, so $<$ becomes $>$, $\leq$ becomes $\geq$, etc.

Going back to our algebraic manipulation,

$$^-2x \leq\ ^-105 \qquad \textit{Multiplying on both sides by } ^-\tfrac{1}{2}$$

$$x \geq 52.5 \qquad \textit{Reversing the direction of the inequality symbol}$$

Therefore, the organizers must charge at least \$52.50 to keep the crowd small enough to fit into the room.

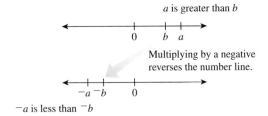

a is greater than b

Multiplying by a negative
reverses the number line.

$-a$ is less than $-b$

Figure 5   Multiplying an inequality by a negative reverses the relationship.

The solution to this example involves two inequalities, $x \geq 52.5$ and $x \leq 75$, and there is a set of x-values that solve the problem. Therefore, we can specify the solution set of the problem using either a number line or set-builder notation. In set-builder notation, the inequalities $x \geq 52.5$ and $x \leq 75$ become the solution set $\{x \mid 52.5 \leq x \leq 75\}$.

Manipulating Inequalities

In the previous example we discovered the following facts about manipulating inequalities.

Manipulating Inequalities

You can add the same quantity (which might be negative) to both sides of an inequality. You can multiply both sides of an inequality by a *positive* number (which might be less than 1). If you multiply both sides of an inequality by a *negative* number, you must reverse the direction of the inequality symbol.

Example 5 illustrates how to apply these ideas.

EXAMPLE 5 ■ Find the solution set if x must satisfy $2x + 3 \geq 5$ and $5x < 10$.

Solution   First, we solve each inequality.

$$2x + 3 \geq 5 \quad \text{and} \quad 5x < 10$$

$$2x \geq 2 \quad \text{and} \quad x < \tfrac{10}{5}$$

$$x \geq 1 \quad \text{and} \quad x < 2$$

Because x must satisfy *both* inequalities, the solution set in set-builder notation is $\{x \mid 1 \leq x < 2\}$.

Exercises 12.1

1. In Example 1 the entire solution set was shown on a number line.

   a. Give four individual solutions from the number line.

   b. Are ⁻2 and 6 solutions to this problem? Explain.

2. Suppose a laser beam is shot east along Street 0 beginning at Avenue 1. *Note:* Assume a laser beam can travel an infinite distance.

   a. Use a number line to show all the points on Street 0 that this laser beam will cross.

   b. Express your answer in set-builder notation.

3. Review Example 2.

   a. Give two individual values that are solutions to Example 2.

   b. Are $x = 200$ minutes and $x = 400$ minutes solutions to this problem?

4. The number of spectators attending a college basketball game is between 3000 and 5000 people.

   a. Show the solution set on a number line.

   b. Write the solution set in set-builder notation.

5. Fill in the blank with each phrase below and choose the correct inequality symbol ($<, >, \leq, \geq$). The first four have been done for you. A number x is __4.

   a. Less than: $x < 4$

   b. Greater than: $x > 4$

   c. Less than or equal to: $x \leq 4$

   d. Greater than or equal to: $x \geq 4$

   e. At most

   f. At least

   g. No more than

   h. No less than

   i. Above

   j. Below

6. It is illegal for a motorist to travel less than 40 miles/hour or more than 65 miles/hour on many interstate highways.

   a. Show the speeds that are illegal on a number line.

   b. Write your answer from part (a) in set-builder notation.

7. Show the solution set for each condition on a number line.

   a. ⁻5 < x and $x \leq 20$

   b. $x \leq$ ⁻5 or 20 < x

8. Write the set indicated on each number line in set-builder notation.

   a.

   b.

9. Review Example 4 and describe what happens to an inequality when you multiply or divide by a negative number. Demonstrate by solving the inequalities.

   a. ⁻3$x \leq$ 18

   b. ⁻$\frac{1}{2}x >$ ⁻7

In Exercises 10–14, use algebra to solve each inequality.

10. $2x - 3 < 15$

11. $4 + x \geq 2 - (7x + 1)$

12. Write the solution set in set-builder notation if
$$\frac{x}{2} - 6 > 4 \quad \text{and} \quad \frac{x}{2} - 6 < 8$$

13. Write the solution set as a single inequality in set-builder notation if $5 \leq 20 - 3x$ and $20 - 3x < 12$.

14. Show the solution set on a number line if $4x - 12 >$ ⁻5 or $4x - 12 \leq$ ⁻10.

15. A rectangular region surrounded by a fence is 40 m wide (see the figure). The perimeter of the region is at least 200 m and no more than 300 m.

   a. Write an expression for the perimeter of the rectangle.

   b. Use your expression to write two inequalities, one with the minimum perimeter and one with the maximum perimeter.

c. Should the inequalities be connected by *and* or *or* in order to describe the possible lengths of the rectangle?

d. Solve the inequalities to find the possible lengths of the rectangle.

Skills and Review 12.1

16. y varies indirectly as the square of x and $y = 1.25$ when $x = 2$. Find y when $x = \sqrt{5}$.

17. y varies directly as the cube root of x and $y = 21$ when $x = 1000$. Find x when $y = 4.2$.

18. Simplify the rational expression

$$\frac{7 - b}{b^2 - 49}.$$

19. Solve for x: $\frac{2}{x} - \frac{3}{x-4} = \frac{5}{2}$.

20. Show the domain and range of the function $f(x) = \frac{1}{x} + 1$ in set-builder notation.

21. Solve for y: $10^{y+3} = 100$.

22. Solve for c: $6c^{1/5} - 1 = 17$.

23. Use a graphing method to solve for x: $x^3 = 2$.

24. Let $y = (x + 3)^2 - \frac{15}{7}$. Notice that this function is modified from the basic quadratic $y = x^2$. Every point on the graph of $y = x^2$ is moved 3 units left and $\frac{15}{7}$ units down. Given that the vertex for the basic quadratic function is $(0, 0)$, mentally find the vertex for this modified function.

25. The revenue R that a company generates is modeled by the equation $R = {}^-3.2P^2 + 64P$, where P is the price of the product in dollars.

a. Use factoring to find the price(s) at which the company generates zero revenue.

b. Recall that the x-coordinate of the vertex for a parabola is midway between the roots. Use this fact to find the vertex.

c. Review the facts about parabolas to determine if this parabola opens upward or downward.

d. Use the information from parts (a)–(c) to either sketch the graph by hand or find a suitable window for viewing the graph on your calculator.

Transition to Intermediate Algebra

Use this guide as a reference to review material from Chapters 1–6 in preparation for Chapters 7–12.

A. Evaluating Expressions

Topic	Main Ideas	Introduced	Forward Links
Signed numbers	Know the rules for addition, subtraction, multiplication and division of signed numbers	Sec. 1.1	Throughout book
Exponents	Positive Integer Exponents represent repeated multiplication	Sec. 1.3	Chap. 9
Zero and negative exponents	$a^0 = 1$ $a^{-n} = \frac{1}{a^n}$	Sec. 1.3	Chap. 9
Scientific notation	$a * 10n$ where $1 \le a < 10$ and n is an integer. Notice how scientific notation appears of calculators with the letter E	Sec. 1.3	Throughout book
Square roots	Use mental math to find square roots of perfect squares between 1 and 100 and to estimate square roots of other positive numbers less than 100. If a positive integer is not a perfect square, then its square root is an irrational number.	Sec. 1.3	Chap. 7
Properties of numbers	Addition and multiplication are commutative: $a + b = b + a$ and $a * b = b * a$: Addition and multiplication are associative: $(a + b) + c = a + (b + c)$ and $(a * b) * c = a * (b * c)$	Sec.1.4 and 2.1	Throughout book
Distributive property	$a * (b + c) = (a * b) + (a * c)$ Demonstrate with area model Expand and Factor	Sec. 2.1	Chap. 7 Chap. 11
Order of operations (very important!)	1. Do operations inside grouping symbols first ( ) 2. Evaluate exponents and roots from left to right $\wedge \sqrt{}$ 3. Perform multiplication and division from left to right $* /$ 4. Perform negation, addition, and subtraction from left to right $^- + -$	Sec. 2.1	Throughout book

B. Equivalent Expressions

Topic	Main Ideas	Introduced	Forward Links
Equivalent expressions	Two expressions are equivalent if when any values are substituted for the variable (or variables), the results are the same, e.g., $2(x + 1)$ is equivalent to $2x + 2$.	Sec. 2.2	Throughout book
Like terms	An application of the distributive property is combining like terms: e.g., $3x + 9x = 12x$.	Sec. 2.2	Throughout book
Procedure for simplifying an expression	1. Use the special properties of 1 and $^{-}1$ if necessary 2. Remove parentheses using the distributive property 3. Group like terms using the commutative property 4. Combine like terms	Sec. 3.2	Throughout book
Laws of exponents	$a^m * a^n = a^{m+n}$ $(a^m)^n = a^{mn}$ $(ab)^m = a^m * b^m$ $\dfrac{a^m}{b^m} = a^{m-n}$ $\dfrac{a}{b^m} = \dfrac{a^m}{b^m}$	Sec.6.1	Chap. 9
Negative exponent in denominator	$\dfrac{1}{a^{-n}} = a^n$	Sec. 6.1	Chap. 9 Chap. 10

C. Solving Equations

Topic	Main ideas	Introduced	Forward Links
Equation solving (very important)	BASIC FACT: If we are given an equation, we can add the same term on both sides or multiply by the same number on both sides and still have a valid equation. Think of subtraction as adding an opposite. Think of division as multiplying by a reciprocal.	Sec. 3.1	Throughout book
Procedure for solving linear equations	1. If necessary, simplify expression on left side. 2. If necessary, simplify expression on right side. 3. If necessary, add same terms on both sides until you have a variable term on one side and a constant term on the other side. 4. If necessary, multiply both sides by the reciprocal of the coefficient of the variable.	Sec. 3.2	Throughout book
Cross-multiplying	If $\frac{a}{b} = \frac{c}{d}$ then $ad = bc$	Sec. 5.1	Chap. 11
Substitution method for solving systems	1. Put one equation in slope intercept form $y = mx + b$ 2. Substitute $mx + b$ for y in the second equation. 3. Solve for x. 4. Substitute for x in first equation to find y.	Sec. 4.4	Chap. 12
Elimination method for solving systems	1. Put both equations in standard form $Ax + By = C$ 2. If necessary multiply one or both equations by the same number on both sides to get x or y terms to be opposites. 3. Add the two equations to get an equation in one variable. Solve for that variable. 4. Substitute back into one of the original equations and solve for the other variable.	Sec. 4.4	Chap. 12
Zero product property	Suppose $a * b = 0$. Then either $a = 0$ or $b = 0$.	Sec. 6.2 Sec. 6.4	Chap. 7

D. Functions and Their Representations

Topic	Main Ideas	Introduced	Forward Links
Functions	Dependent (output) variable is often y. Independent (input) variable is often x. The value of the output variable depends upon the value of the input variable.	Sec. 2.4	Chap. 8
Representing functions	The Rule of Four states that functions may be represented by: 1. description of the situation in words 2. a formula 3. a table of values 4. a graph	Sec. 2.4	Chap. 7 Chap. 8
Functions on calculators	Use Y=, WINDOW, and GRAPH to draw a graph. Use Y=, TblSet, and TABLE to make a table.	Sec. 2.4	Chap. 7
Friendly windows	For TI-82 and TI-83 calculators, PIXELWIDTH = (Xmax − Xmin)/94 PIXELHEIGHT = (Ymax − Ymin)/62 Friendly Windows give nice values for PIXELWIDTH	Sec. 2.4	Chap. 7

E. Linear Equations in Two Variables

Topic	Main Ideas	Introduced	Forward Links
Slope of a line	$\text{Slope} = \frac{\text{change in output}}{\text{change in input}}$ $\text{Slope} = \frac{\text{rise}}{\text{run}}$ Slope represents rate of change	Sec. 4.1	Sec. 7.1
Linear equations	Straight lines have constant slope	Sec. 4.1	Sec. 7.1
Slope-intercept form for a linear equation	$y = mx + b$ y is the dependent variable x is the independent variable m is the slope (rate of change) b is the y-intercept (initial value)	Sec. 4.2	Chap. 8
Graph a linear equation with a calculator	If necessary, solve for y in terms of x.	Sec. 4.2	Throughout book
System of two linear equations in two variables	Solution is the intersection point (if it exists).	Sec. 4.3	Chap. 12
Inconsistent system	Lines are parallel. There is no solution.	Sec. 4.3	Chap. 12

F. Expanding and Factoring with an Area Model

Topic	Main Ideas	Introduced	Forward Links
Mulitiplying monomial by polynomial	Use the distributive property Illustrate with area model	Sec. 6.2	Chap. 7
Factor out a monomial	Use the distributive property (in reverse) Illustrate with area model	Sec. 6.2	Chap. 7
Finding the greatest common factor (GCF)	1. List all variables and prime factors of coefficients. 2. When a variable or prime factor does not appear include that factor to the zero power. 3. Take the smallest power of each to form the GCF.	Sec. 6.2	Sec. 11.1
Zero product property	Suppose $a * b = 0$, then either $a = 0$ or $b = 0$ Some quadratic equations may be solved using this property	Sec. 6.2 Sec. 6.4	Sec. 7.2
Multiplying polynomials	Use area model	Sec. 6.3	Chap. 7
Factor by grouping	Use the diagonal test. A polynomial with four terms may be factored by grouping if the product of one pair of terms is equal to the product of the other two terms.	Sec. 6.3	Chap. 7
Squaring a binomial	$(a + b)^2 = a^2 + 2ab + b^2$	Sec. 6.3	Sec. 7.2
Factor quadratic trinomials	One method is to split the middle term and use an area model to factor by grouping.	Sec. 6.4	Sec. 7.2 Sec. 11.1

G. Problem Solving

Topic	Main Ideas	Introduced	Forward Links
Seven steps to problem solving (very important)	1. Understand 2. Visualize 3. Assign variable(s) 4. Write equation(s) 5. Solve equation(s) 6. Answer the question 7. Check the answer.	Sec. 3.3	Throughout book
Perimeter and area	Perimeter measures the distance around the outside of the figure and is measured in linear units such as feet. Area measures the surface enclosed by a plane figure and is measured in square units such as square feet.	Sec. 1.4	Chap. 7
Geometry formulas	Area of rectangle, parallelogram, triangle, trapezoid Circumference and area of circles	Sec. 1.4	Chap. 7
Distance-Rate-Time	$\frac{\text{Distance}}{\text{Time}} = \text{Rate}$ miles divided by hours = miles per hour, etc. Distance = Rate $*$ Time (miles = miles per hour $*$ hours, etc.)	Sec. 1.2	Sec. 11.3
Work rate problems	$\frac{\text{Work}}{\text{time}} = \text{work rate}$ Work rate is often expressed in jobs per hour, etc.	Sec. 1.2	Sec. 11.3
Percent change	percent change $= \frac{\text{change}}{\text{original}}$ New amount = original $\pm$ change (refer to number line model)	Sec. 5.2	Chap. 10
Linear combinations	Typically a system of equations with $x + y = \text{something}$ something $* x +$ something $* y = \text{something}$ Applications to solutions, mixtures, interest problems	Sec. 5.3	Sec. 12.3
Simple interest	Interest = Principal $*$ rate $*$ time	Sec. 5.3	Sec. 10.1

Friendly Windows for Graphing Calculators

Friendly Windows for TI-83 and TI-84 Calculators

PIXEL WIDTH	FOUR-QUADRANT WINDOWS			FIRST QUADRANT WINDOWS	
	Xmin	Xmax	Shortcut for square windows	Xmin	Xmax
.1	⁻4.7	4.7	ZOOM 4 ZDecimal	0	9.4
.2	⁻9.4	9.4	ZOOM 4 ZDecimal	0	18.8
			ZOOM 3[b] ZoomOut ENTER		
.5	⁻23.5	23.5	ZOOM 8 ZInteger[a]	0	47
			ZOOM 2[b] Zoom In ENTER		
1	⁻47	47	ZOOM 8 ZInteger[a]	0	94
2	⁻94	94	ZOOM 8 ZInteger[a]	0	188
			ZOOM 3[b] Zoom In ENTER		
5	⁻235	235		0	470
10	⁻470	470		0	940

Suggested values for Xscl: Xscl = 10∗ PIXELWIDTH
[a]ZInteger will always give a screen with PIXELWIDTH = 1 and PIXELHEIGHT = 1. The center of the screen depends upon the last location of the cursor. If necessary, first activate ZOOM 6 ZStandard before pressing ZOOM 8 ZInteger.
[b]To use ZOOM 2 and ZOOM 3, set ZoomFactors = 2

Feature	TI-82/83	TI-85/86	TI-89
Set Xmin, Xmax, Ymin, Ymax	WINDOW	GRAPH F2	diamond F2
Create special windows	ZOOM	GRAPH F3	diamond F2 F2
Display graph	GRAPH	GRAPH F5	diamond F3
Enter function	Y =	GRAPH F1	diamond F1
Set up table	2nd TblSet	TABLE F2 (86 only)	diamond F4
Display table	2nd TABLE	TABLE F1 (86 only)	diamond F5
Trace points on a graph	TRACE	GRAPH F4	diamond F3 F3
Find point of intersection	2nd CALC 5:Intersect	GRAPH MORE F1	diamond F3 F5 5:Intersect
Find turning points	2nd CALC 3:Min and 4:Max	GRAPH MORE F1	diamond F3 F5 3:Min and 4:Max

Friendly Windows for TI-85 and TI-86 Calculators

PIXEL WIDTH	FOUR-QUADRANT WINDOWS			FIRST QUADRANT WINDOWS	
	Xmin	Xmax	Shortcut for square windows	Xmin	Xmax
.1	-6.3	6.3	ZOOM 4 ZDecimal	0	12.6
.2	-12.6	12.6	ZOOM 4 ZDecimal	0	25.2
.5	-31.5	31.5	ZOOM 3[b] ZoomOut ENTER ZOOM 8 ZInteger[a] ZOOM 2[b] Zoom In ENTER	0	63
1	-63	63	ZOOM 8 ZInteger[a]	0	126
2	-126	126	ZOOM 8 ZInteger[a] ZOOM 3[b] Zoom In ENTER	0	252
5	-315	315		0	630
10	-630	630		0	1260

Friendly Windows for TI-89 Calculators

PIXEL WIDTH	FOUR-QUADRANT WINDOWS			FIRST QUADRANT WINDOWS	
	Xmin	Xmax	Shortcut for square windows	Xmin	Xmax
.1	-7.9	7.9	ZOOM 4 ZDecimal	0	15.8
.2	-15.8	15.8	ZOOM 4 ZDecimal	0	31.6
.5	-39.5	39.5	ZOOM 3[b] ZoomOut ENTER ZOOM 8 ZInteger[a] ZOOM 2[b] Zoom In ENTER	0	79
1	-79	79	ZOOM 8 ZInteger[a]	0	158
2	-158	158	ZOOM 8 ZInteger[a] ZOOM 3[b] Zoom In ENTER	0	316
5	-395	395		0	790
10	-790	790		0	1580

Suggested values for Xscl: Xscl $= 10*$ PIXELWIDTH

[a]ZInteger will always give a screen with PIXELWIDTH $= 1$ and PIXELHEIGHT $= 1$. The center of the screen depends upon the last location of the cursor. If necessary, first activate ZOOM 6 ZStandard before pressing ZOOM 8 ZInteger.

[b]To use ZOOM 2 and ZOOM 3, set ZoomFactors $= 2$

Answers to Exercises

Chapter 1 Geometry and Numbers

1. a. $^+6 + {}^-4 = {}^+2$

   b. $^+5 + {}^-9 = {}^-4$

3. a. $(^-)(^-)(^-)(^-)(^-)(^-)$
   $(+)(+)(+)(+)(+)(+)(+)$
   $^+1$

   b. $(^-)(^-)(^-)(^-)(^-)(^-)(^-)(^-)$
   $(+)(+)$
   $^-6$

   c. $(^-)(^-)(^-)(^-)(^-)(^-)$
   $(^-)(^-)$
   $^-8$

   d. $(+)(+)(+)(+)(+)$
   $(+)(+)(+)(+)$
   $^+9$

   e. $(^-)(^-)(^-)(^-)(^-)(^-)$
   $(+)(+)(+)(+)(+)(+)$
   0

5. a. $^-14°C$

   b. $^-6 + {}^-8 = {}^-14$

7. a. $^+\$275$

   b. $^+100 + {}^-250 + {}^+475 + {}^-50 = {}^+275$

9. a. $^+5 + {}^-13 = {}^-8$

   b. $^-37 + {}^-42 = {}^-79$

   c. $^+11.8 + {}^-5.7 = {}^+6.1$

   d. $-\frac{2}{5} + {}^+\frac{1}{10} = -\frac{3}{10}$

11. An odd number of negatives results in a negative number. An even number of negatives results in a positive number.

13. a. Starting position: 5; final position: $^-3$; change: $^-8$

   $^-3 - 5 = {}^-3 + {}^-5 = {}^-8$

   b. Starting position: $^-3$; final position: 5; change: 8

   $5 - {}^-3 = 5 + 3 = 8$

   c. Starting position: 6; final position: 2; change: $^-4$

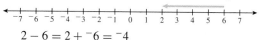

   $2 - 6 = 2 + {}^-6 = {}^-4$

   d. Starting position: $^-3$; final position: 4; change: 7

   $4 - {}^-3 = 4 + 3 = 7$

15. a. $^+6 \div {}^+2 = {}^+3$. The temperature rose $^+3$ degrees per hour. The numbers $^-6$ and $^+2$ are the same sign so the quotient is positive.

   b. $^-6 \div {}^+2 = {}^-3$. The temperature rose $^-3$ degrees per hour. The numbers $^-6$ and $^+2$ are opposite signs so the quotient is negative.

   c. $^-6 \div {}^-2 = {}^+3$. The temperature rose $^+3$ degrees per hour. The numbers $^-6$ and $^-2$ are the same sign so the quotient is positive.

   d. $^+6 \div {}^-2 = {}^-3$. The temperature rose $^-3$ degrees per hour. The numbers $^+6$ and $^-2$ are opposite signs so the quotient is negative.

1.1 Skills and Review

17. a. 1

   b. Do not add denominators.

   c. 1

   d. Multiplication is repeated addition. Adding five one-fifths is the same as multiplying one-fifth by 5.

19. a. 10 m/s

   b. $\frac{1}{2} * 4$ miles = 2 miles

   c. $68 + 6 = 74$

   d. $81 - 9 = 72$

21. a. $\frac{-21}{10}$ **b.** 2   **c.** $^-.9$

23. 5400 seconds

25. .1 is greater. The digit 1 in .1 is in the tenths place, whereas the digit 7 in .07 is in the hundreths place.

1.2 Exercises

1. a.

   b. 57 miles/hour

3. You will travel 3 times as far in 1 hour as you will in $\frac{1}{3}$ of an hour.

5. a. 125 apples/hour

   b. $\frac{1}{4}$ house/day

   c. $\frac{1}{3}$ bike/hour

7. a. $= \frac{3}{4}$ **b.** $= \frac{2}{5}$ **c.** $= \frac{7}{10}$

   d. $\approx \frac{1}{3}$ **e.** $= \frac{5}{8}$ **f.** $\approx \frac{2}{3}$

9. Error division by 0. Division by 0 is undefined.

11.

13. a. $\frac{13}{20}$ **b.** $\frac{31}{25}$ **c.** $\frac{23}{40}$

   d. $\frac{2}{5}$ **e.** $\frac{201}{250}$

15. a. $.3 = \frac{3}{10}$

   b. $.33 = \frac{33}{100}$

   c. $.333 = \frac{333}{1000}$

   d. $.3333 = .3333$

   e. $.3333333333 = .3333333333$

   f. $.333333333333 = \frac{1}{3}$ (*Caution:* This is an approximation by the calculator.)

   g. No. $\frac{1}{3} = .\overline{3}$. There must be an infinite number of 3s for the decimal to equal $\frac{1}{3}$.

1.2 Skills and Review

17. If the signs are the same, the product is positive. If the signs are opposite, the product is negative.

19. a. $\frac{-2}{5}$ **b.** 0   **c.** $\frac{-1}{6}$

21. a. Starting position: 6; change: $^-8$; final position: $^-2$

$6 + {}^-8 = {}^-2$

   b. Starting position: $^-5$; change: 9; final position: 4

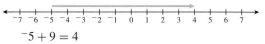

$^-5 + 9 = 4$

   c. Starting position: 4; final position: $^-2$; change: $^-6$

$^-2 - 4 = {}^-6$

   d. Starting position: $^-1$; final position: 3; change: 4

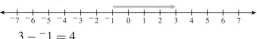

$3 - {}^-1 = 4$

23. $\frac{4 \text{ yards}}{1} * \frac{3 \text{ feet}}{1 \text{ yard}} * \frac{12 \text{ inches}}{1 \text{ foot}} = 144$ inches. Write the original quantity as a fraction. Use the facts given in the hint to set up ratios. The ratios should be set up so that when you multiply, all the units cancel except the units to which you are converting.

25. $\frac{1}{2}$. Convert to fractions with common denominators.

$$0, \frac{1}{2}, \frac{2}{3}, 1 \qquad \frac{0}{6}, \frac{3}{6}, \frac{4}{6}, \frac{6}{6}$$

$\frac{4}{6}$ is closer to $\frac{3}{6}$ than $\frac{6}{6}$, so $\frac{1}{2}$ is the answer.

1.3 Exercises

1. a. $3 + 3 + 3 + 3 = 12$

   b. $3 * 3 * 3 * 3 = 81$

3. a. 16   **b.** 1

   c. $\frac{1}{16}$ **d.** 9

   e. $^-27$

5. a. 1

   b. Any nonzero real number raised to the zeroth power equals 1.

7. a. The numbers in c, d, and e are different but are so close to 0 that they appear to lie in the same spot on the number line.

b. 0

c. No. The numbers will get closer to 0 but never become negative. Conclusion: Negative powers do not make negative numbers.

9. a. $1.089 * 10^3$ feet/second

b. $4.84 * 10^8$ miles

c. $2.0 * 10^{-9}$ mile

11. a. $9.59 * 10^{-5} = .0000959°F/day$

b. $1.581 * 10^{10} = 15,810,000,000$ g/day

13. c

15. a. 3.1   **b.** 6.5   **c.** 8.9

1.3 Skills and Review

17. a. $\frac{1}{4} = .25$ hour   **b.** 0 hour

c. $\frac{1}{2} = .5$ hour   **d.** 1 hour

19. a. 19.304 cm

b. $\frac{7.6 \text{ inches}}{1} * \frac{2.54 \text{ cm}}{1 \text{ inch}} = 19.304$ cm

21. 2 cars/day

23. a. 21.0 m

b. 21 feet/minute

c. 927.6 cm

25. 543 feet

1.4 Exercises

1. Perimeter is the distance around the outside of the figure. Area is the space inside the figure.

3. Answers may vary.

5. a. 14 cm

b.

Area $= 11.25$ cm^2, answers may vary slightly.

c. Area $= 11.25$ cm^2

d. The areas are the same. (Estimates within 2 cm^2 are good.)

7. a. $\frac{1}{8}$

b. $\frac{1}{8}$ mile^2; the answers from (a) and (b) are the same.

c. $P = 1\frac{1}{2}$ miles $= 1.5$ miles

d. $A = 12,800$ rods^2, $P = 480$ rods

e. 80 acres

f. 80 acres

9. a. $A = 25.2$ square feet

b. $P = 28$ feet

11. a. $A \approx 24$ cm^2 **b.** $A = 24$ cm^2

13. Circumference is the perimeter of a circle and Carl was running around the perimeter of the circle.

15. $C = 2 * \pi * r \approx 2 * (3.14) * (8.5) = 53.38$ m
$C = \pi * d \approx 3.14 * (17) = 53.38$ m

1.4 Skills and Review

17. a. Reorder the multiplication: $5 * 7 = 7 * 5 = 35$.

b. Most of the facts in the multiplication table are duplicates if you use the commutative property.

19. a. 6   **b.** 10   **c.** 100   **d.** .9   **e.** $\frac{3}{5}$

21. 7000

23. $\frac{1}{25} = .04$

25. e

Chapter 1 Exploration

a. $^-335.58$

b. 9589.67

c. Use the formula start + change = final.
$9925.25 + {}^-335.58 = 9589.67$

Chapter 1 Review Exercises

1. a. $(+)(+)(+)$
$(+)(+)(+)(+)$
$^+3 + {}^+4 = {}^+7$

b. $(+)(+)$
$(^-)(^-)(^-)(^-)(^-)$
$^+2 + {}^-5 = {}^-3$

c. ($^-$)

$(+)(+)(+)$

$^-1 + {}^+3 = {}^+2$

d. $(^-)(^-)(^-)(^-)$

$(^-)(^-)$

$^-4 + {}^-2 = {}^-6$

2. a. The numbers have opposite signs. Subtract the absolute value of the numbers ($71.2 - 2.5 = 68.7$) and take the sign of the number with the larger absolute value ($^+71.2$). The answer is 68.7.

b. The numbers have the same sign. Add the absolute value of the numbers ($15.1 + 56.76 = 71.86$) and keep the sign. The answer is $^-71.86$.

3. a. $^+6 - {}^+5 = {}^+6 + {}^-5 = {}^+1$

b. $^+18 - {}^-7 = {}^+18 + {}^+7 = {}^+25$

c. $\frac{^-3}{8} - \frac{^+1}{4} = \frac{^-3}{8} + \frac{^-1}{4} = \frac{^-5}{8}$

d. $^-12.1 - {}^-4.3 = {}^-12.1 + {}^+4.3 = {}^-7.8$

4. 45 feet

5. $^-120$ feet

6. a. 6   **b.** $^-200$

c. $\frac{^-2}{3}$ **d.** 8

7. a. 2   **b.** $^-51$

c. $\frac{^-1}{15}$ **d.** 3

8. a. 70 km/h   **b.** 12 km/h   **c.** 8 km/h

9. a. 8 feet^2/minute   **b.** $\frac{1}{3}$ job/hour

c. $\frac{1}{4}$ job/hour   **d.** $\frac{7}{12}$ job/hour

10. a. 1.8   **b.** .567   **c.** .057

11. a. 180%   **b.** 56.7%   **c.** 5.7%

12.

13. a. 64   **b.** 81   **c.** 8

d. $\frac{1}{32}$ **e.** 1

14. a. $^-3$ **b.** 9

c. $^-27$ **d.** 81

15. a. $\frac{1}{16}$ **b.** $\frac{1}{15}$ **c.** 1

16. a. $3.48 * 10^8$ **b.** $7.4 * 10^{-4}$

c. $5.772 * 10^3$

17. a. $1.39128 * 10^{10} = 13,912,800,000$

b. $5.0 * 10^{-4} = .0005$

18. a. 3   **b.** 8   **c.** 6

19. a. 2.8   **b.** 6.1   **c.** 8.5

20. $s \approx 6.9$ inches

21. $P = 20$ cm

$A = 21$ cm^2

22. $P = 20$ cm

$A = 21$ cm^2

23. $P = 28$ cm

$A = 23$ cm^2

24. $3 + 27 + 18 + 2 = 50$

25. $2 * 5 * 16 = 160$

26. $P = 34$ inches, $A = 55$ inches^2

27. $C \approx 43.96$ feet

Chapter 1 Test

1. $^-3$

2. $^-10$

3. 25°C

4. a. $^-4$

b. $^-6$

c. $\frac{1}{4} = .25$

5. $\frac{8}{3} \approx 2.67$ ounces/hour

6. a. $.40 = 40\%$ **b.** $.75 = 75\%$

c. $.30 = 30\%$ **d.** $\approx .333 = 33.3\%$

e. $2.25 = 225\%$

7. $2^0, 145\%, \frac{3}{2}, 1.512, 1\frac{5}{8}$

8. a. 8   **b.** $^-8$ **c.** $\frac{1}{8}$

d. 1   **e.** 1

9. a. $1.15 * 10^5$ **b.** $7.4 * 10^{-6}$

10. a. $1.664 * 10^{-6}$ mm^2 **b.** $.000001664$ mm^2

11. 7.2

12. $P = 22$ cm, $A = 24$ cm^2

13. $14 + 16 + 33 + 7 + 2 + 8 = 80$

14. ≈ 1758.4 mm

15. 11.2 feet

Chapter 2 Algebraic Expressions

2.1 Exercises

1. a.

   b. 7.64 mm + (5.2 mm + 4.8 mm)

   c. 17.64 mm

3. $220 * 891 = 220 * (198 + 297 + 396)$

$= 220 * 198 + 220 * 297 + 220 * 396$

$= 196{,}020$ feet^2

5. a. $4 * 512 = 4 * (500 + 12) = 4 * 500 + 4 * 12 = 2048$

   b. 4433

7. Expansion

9. Division before subtraction; 1

11. a. $\frac{21}{4} = 5.25$

   b. $(3 + 24 - 6)/(6 - 2)$

13. Answers may vary.

15. a. $a + b - 8 - c$ **b.** $^-y - 6 + z$ **c.** $3 - s - t$

2.1 Skills and Review

17. 31.4 inches

19. a. 81   **b.** $\frac{1}{8}$ **c.** 1

   d. 1   **e.** $\frac{1}{81}$

21. a. $\frac{1}{2^{10}}$

   b. $9.765625 * 10^{-4}$

   c. .0009765625

23. a. 50 feet^2/hour

   b. $\frac{5}{6}$ feet^2/minute

   c. $\frac{1}{9}$ wall/hour

25. 19. One morning the temperature was $^-3°$F. By afternoon the temperature had risen to 16°F. What was the change in temperature?

2.2 Exercises

1. a. 1   **b.** 4   **c.** 4

   d. 9.42   **e.** 15   **f.** 5

3. a. 0   **b.** 14   **c.** 20 cm^2

   d. 48 mm^2 **e.** 10 inches   **f.** 75.36 feet^2

5. a. $\frac{7}{3} = 2\frac{1}{3}$ cups

   b. $S * \frac{1}{3} = \frac{1}{3}S$ cups

   c. $F = \frac{1}{3}S$ or $F = \frac{S}{3}$

7. $12 * 1 - 12 * 1 \neq 1$

9. a. $C = .13 * M + .3 * M$ or $C = .13\,M + .3\,M$

   b. $C = .43 * M$ or $C = .43\,M$

   c. 43 cents

   d. \$4.30

11. a.

   b. Let B represent the length of the base; then the height is $B - 5$.

   c. $B * (B - 5) = B^2 - 5 * B$

   d. 300 inches^2

13. 30 feet

15. a. 125 miles   **b.** Highway

2.2 Skills and Review

17. $^-23$

19. 3

21. a. $2 * 5 - 3$ **b.** 7 inches

   c. 35 inches^2 **d.** 24 inches

23. a. 64   **b.** 1   **c.** 1

   d. $\frac{1}{25} = .04$ **e.** 16

25. a. 3   **b.** $^-9$

   c. $^-2$ **d.** 11

2.3 The Coordinate Plane

1.

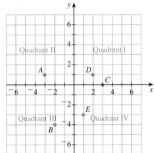

3. $(^-5, 4)$

5. a. Answers may vary; $(^-5, ^-3)$, $(^-2, ^-3)$, $(0, ^-3)$, $(4, ^-3)$.

   b. The y-coordinate is always $^-3$.

   c. The x-coordinate varies.

7. a. x **b.** increase

9. Run $= 1$, rise $= 9$; run $= {}^-1$, rise $= {}^-9$

11. a.

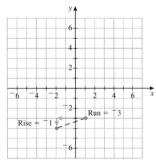

   b. run $= {}^-3$, rise $= {}^-1$

   c. $\sqrt{10} \approx 3.16$

13. $\sqrt{17} \approx 4.12$

15. 9 square units

2.3 Skills and Review

17. a. $12y$ **b.** $5x$

   c. $3x + 3$ **d.** $^-2x^2 + x$

19. $\frac{3}{2} = 1.5$

21. 400

23. a. 32   **b.** 9

   c. $^-9$ **d.** $\frac{1}{25} = .04$

   e. $^-1$

25. a. $^-3$ **b.** 3

   c. 13   **d.** $^-13$

2.4 Exercises

1. The variable cost is the part of the total cost that depends upon the value of the independent variable. The fixed cost is the part of the total cost that remains constant and is not affected by the value of the independent variable.

3. b. $c = 42t + 75$ **c.** Yes   **d.** $159.00

5. a. No, you can't have a negative number of boxes.

   b.

Cost of Office Supplies

c. yes

d. 14-box shipment costs $165.00.

7. a. Answers may vary

$$\text{Xmin} = {}^-23.5, \text{Xmax} = 23.5, \text{Xscl} = 5,$$
$$\text{Ymin} = {}^-50, \text{Ymax} = 50, \text{Yscl} = 10$$

   b. A straight line passing through quadrants I, II, and III

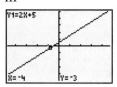

   c. $Y = {}^-3$

9. a. $C = \frac{5}{9} * (F - 32)$

   b.

°Fahrenheit	°Celsius
10	$^-12.2$
30	$^-1.1$
50	10
70	21.1
90	32.2

   c. **Converting Fahrenheit to Celsius Temperatures**

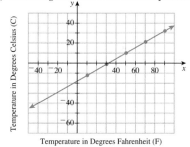

11. a. Answers may vary. Let i represent the interest (in dollars) and p represent the principal.

   b. $i = .06 * p$

   c.

Investment ($)	Interest Earned ($)
500	30
1000	60
1500	90
2000	120
2500	150

d.

Interest Earned on a 6% Investment

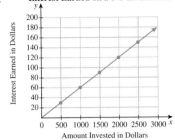

13. a. Let V represent the value of the product and t represent the age of the product (in years).

Formula: $V = 10{,}000 - 1500t$

Table of values:

Age of Product (years)	Value of Product ($)
0	10,000
1	8500
2	7000
3	5500
4	4000
5	2500
6	1000

Graph:

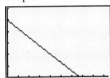

b. 0 to about 6.67 years

c. $0 to $10,000

d. Pick friendly values for Xmin and Xmax that include the range of years. Ymin and Ymax should include the range of product values.

15. a. A four-quadrant window shows both positive and negative values for x and y. A first-quadrant window shows only nonnegative values for x and y.

b. Cost of office supplies: first quadrant;

$y = 2x + 5$: four quadrant;

Fahrenheit and Celsius temperatures: four quadrant;

Paint required to cover walls: first quadrant

2.4 Skills and Review

17. $(^-2, 3)$

19. a. $4x + 2.8$ **b.** 18 inches

21. a. The commutative property states that for any numbers a and b, $a + b = b + a$. Because $50 - 4x = 50 + {}^-4x$, we have $50 - 4x = {}^-4x + 50$.

b. Number substitutions may vary.

When $x = 1$, both expressions equal 46.

When $x = 2$, both expressions equal 42.

When $x = 7$, both expressions equal 22.

23. 6.4

25. a. 3 miles/hour   **b.** 6 miles/hour

    c. 9 miles/hour   **d.** 15 miles/hour

Chapter 2 Exploration

a. $x_2 - x_1 = {}^-10{,}315$

$y_2 - y_1 = {}^-5659$

$z_2 - z_1 = 4978$

b. About 12,775 miles

c. Yes. The closest the automobile could be from the satellite is 11,000 miles. So we expect the distance will exceed that number.

Chapter 2 Review Exercises

1. a. $(6 + 124) + 58 = 188$

b. $189 + (43 + 17) = 249$

2. No; $(30 - 10) - 5 = 20 - 5 = 15$;

$30 - (10 - 5) = 30 - 5 = 25$

3. a. $7 * (8 * 5) = 280$ **b.** $\left(\frac{1}{3} * 3\right) * 467 = 467$

4. No; $(16 \div 4) \div 2 = 4 \div 2 = 2$;

$16 \div (4 \div 2) = 16 \div 2 = 8$

5. a. $3 * 40 + 3 * 7 = 141$

b. $4 * 90 - 4 * 2 = 352$

c. $6 * 8 + 6 * 10 = 108$

d. $2 * x + 2 * y = 2x + 2y$

e. $9 * a - 9 * b = 9a - 9b$

f. $8 * x - 8 * y = 8x - 8y$

6. a. $4 * (52 + 8) = 240$ **b.** $3 * (9 + 81) = 270$

c. $5 * (x + y)$ **d.** $7 * (a - b)$

7. a. 9   **b.** 19   **c.** $^-1$

8. $(5 + 11) \div (6 - 8) = {}^-8$

9. a. $^-4$ **b.** 0   **c.** 1

10. a. Special property of 1, c

b. Special property of $^-1$, c

11. Answers may vary.

12. Answers may vary.

13. Answers may vary.

14. a. $C \approx 12.56$ inches   **b.** $\frac{1}{2}$ ft/second

c. $A \approx 50.24$ square feet **d.** 6

e. 10

15. a. yes

x	$5 * x - 2$	$6 * x - (x + 2)$
4	18	18
3	13	13
$^-2$	$^-12$	$^-12$

b. No, substitution of $^-2$ gives different outputs.

x	$\sqrt{x^2 + 2 * x + 1}$	$x + 1$
4	5	5
3	4	4
$^-2$	1	$^-1$

c. yes

x	$(x - 1) * (x + 1)$	$x^2 - 1$
4	15	15
3	8	8
$^-2$	3	3

16. Area $= \frac{1}{2} * (b_1 + b_2) * h$

Area $= \left(\frac{1}{2} * b_1 + \frac{1}{2} * b_2\right) * h$

Area $= \frac{1}{2} * b_1 * h + \frac{1}{2} * b_2 * h$

17. a. $15y$ **b.** $3x$ **c.** $3a^2 - 12a$

18. a. $\dfrac{11}{a}$ **b.** $\dfrac{12}{a} - \dfrac{5}{9}$

c. $\dfrac{2 + x}{y}$ **d.** $x^2 + x$

19. a. $x + 5$ **b.** $x + 4$ **c.** $x - 4$

d. $x - 2$ **e.** $2x$ **f.** $\frac{1}{3}x$

g. $7x$ **h.** $\frac{x}{6}$ **i.** $\frac{x}{3}$

j. $3x + 4$ **k.** $3x - 4$

20. a. $10x + 6$ **b.** 156 yards

21. 18.03 cm

22.

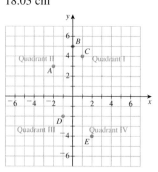

23. Only the y-coordinate varies on a vertical line.

24. They are all 3.

25. a. Run $= ^-4$, rise $= 6$

b. Run $= ^-4$, rise $= ^-9$

26. $(4, ^-2)$

27. $(1, ^-3)$

28. Xmin $= ^-4.7$, Xmax $= 4.7$, Xscl $= 1$, Ymin $= ^-3.1$, Ymax $= 3.1$, Yscl $= 1$

29. The corners of the screen are located at $(10, 10)$, $(^-10, 10)$, $(^-10, ^-10)$, and $(10, ^-10)$.

30. 5

31. a. 2nd $\sqrt{((^-6 - 2) \wedge 2 + (7 - ^-1) \wedge 2)}$

b. 11.31

32. $300

33. a. $y = .25x + 100$

b. x (the number of travel miles)

c. y (the cost of the trip)

34.

$x = $ number of miles traveled	$y = $ cost of trip (in $)
0	100
100	125
200	150
300	175
400	200

35.

Cost of Flying on Nomystery Airline

36. a. $Y1 = .25X + 100$

b. TblStart $= 0$, Δ Tbl $= 100$

c. Xmin $= 0$, Xmax $= 470$, Xscl $= 50$, Ymin $= 0$, Ymax $= 250$, Yscl $= 25$

Chapter 2 Test

1. a. $(^-8 + ^-2) + 51 = 41$

b. $9 * (5 * 6) = 270$

c. $9 + (^-73 + 73) = 9$

2. a. $5 * 3 - 5 * 8 = {}^-25$ **b.** $6 * (a + b)$

  c. $7 * a + 7 * b$ **d.** $2 * (x - y)$

3. a. 6   **b.** 81   **c.** 4

4. a. 0   **b.** 0

  c. $\frac{1}{5}$ **d.** $^-1$

5. a. $y = 21$ **b.** $A = 20$ cm^2

6. Yes

x	$x + 4 * x$	$x * (1 + 4)$
5	25	25
2	10	10
$^-3$	$^-15$	$^-15$

7. $A = P + P * r * t$

8. a. $6x$ **b.** $\dfrac{3}{x} + \dfrac{1}{8}$

  c. $a - 5$ **d.** $\dfrac{11}{a}$

9. a. $4w + 270$ **b.** 1170 feet

10. 340 feet

11.

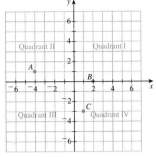

12. a. run $= {}^-1$, rise $= 2$

    b. run $= 4$, rise $= 1$

13. 10

14. Let C represent the monthly charge in dollars and t represent the number of minutes of calls; $C = .07t + 4.95$.

15.

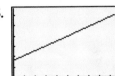

16.

Chapter 3 Linear Equations

3.1 Exercises

1. $t = 2.5$ hours

3. $x = 7$

5. $b = -\frac{34}{9}$

7. $x = 2$

9. $3x + 20 + {}^-20 = 6x + 2 + {}^-20$ *Adding $^-20$ on both sides*

            $3x = 6x + {}^-18$ *Combining like terms*

    $3x + {}^-6x = 6x + {}^-18 + {}^-6x$ *Adding ^-6x on both sides*

              $^-3x = {}^-18$ *Combining like terms*

            $\dfrac{^-3x}{^-3} = \dfrac{^-18}{^-3}$ *Dividing by $^-3$ on both sides*

                $x = 6$ *Solution*

The health club costs the same for 6 visits per month.

11. $x = {}^-24$

13. $x = {}^-\frac{1}{4} = {}^-.25$

15. a. provider one: $12 + 2h$; provider two: $15 + 1.5h$

    b. $12 + 2h = 15 + 1.5h$

    c. $h = 6$

    d. Both Internet providers charge the same amount for 6 hours of use.

3.1 Skills and Review

17. a. Y1 $= 7 + 5$X

    b.

c.

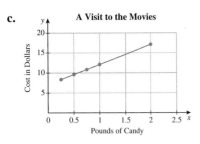

A Visit to the Movies

19. Run = $^-3$, rise = 8
21. $^-9$
23. $^-4$
25. **b.** $^-25$

3.2 Exercises

1. Distributive property: $5(x + 3) = 5 * x + 5 * 3 = 5x + 15$
3. $\frac{3}{5}x - \frac{1}{10}x + 2 - 6 = \frac{1}{2}x - 4$
5. $8x + 23$
7. **a.** $^-c^2 + 11c - 5$
   b. $^-4x + 5$
   c. 9 inches$^2 + 5$ inches
   d. $5x - 5$
   e. $\frac{8}{3}x - 14$
9. **a.** $x = \frac{19}{4} = 4.75$ **b.** $x = ^-7$
   c. $x = ^-1.2$ **d.** $x = \frac{3}{4} = .75$
11. **a.** $40t, 55t$
    b. $40t + 55t = 57$
    c. $t = \frac{3}{5}$ hour or 36 minutes
13. **a.**

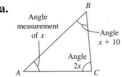

   b. $x + x + 10 + 2x = 180$
   c. $x = 42.5°$
15. The measure of angle A is 47.5°, B is 100°, and C is 32.5°.

3.2 Skills and Review

17. $2 * 1 - 5 = ^-10 * 1 + 7$
    $^-3 = ^-3$ *OK*
19. Yes, $\frac{1}{3}x + \frac{8}{5} = \frac{5x}{15} + \frac{24}{15} = \frac{5x + 24}{15}$
21. $^-10°C$
23. $^-13; ^-8 + ((^-1) \wedge 19 + 6)/(9 - 10)$

25. $\dfrac{^-16\text{ feet}}{\text{sec}^2}(4 \text{ sec}^2) + \dfrac{50\text{ feet}}{\text{sec}}(2 \text{ sec}) + 150 \text{ feet}$
    Evaluating exponents

   $\dfrac{^-64\text{ feet} * \text{sec}^2}{\text{sec}^2} + \dfrac{100\text{ feet} * \text{sec}}{\text{sec}} + 150 \text{ feet}$
   Performing multiplication

   $^-64$ feet $+ 100$ feet $+ 150$ feet
   Canceling units of measurement

   186 feet
   Performing addition and subtraction

3.3 The Problem Solving Process

1. **(1)** *Understand* the problem.
   (2) *Visualize* the problem.
   (3) *Assign* variable(s).
   (4) *Write* equation(s).
   (5) *Solve* equation(s).
   (6) *Answer* the question.
   (7) *Check* your answer.
3. **(1)** Find the dimensions of a rectangle with perimeter 900 feet and length twice the width.
   (2) See Figure 9 on page 108.
   (3) Let $x =$ the width (in feet); then $2x =$ the length.
   (4) $900 = x + 2x + x + 2x$
   (5) $150 = x$
   (6) The width is 150 feet and the length is 300 feet.
   (7) 150 feet $+$ 300 feet $+$ 150 feet $+$ 300 feet $=$ 900 feet, the answer checks.
5. No, we need to answer the question in the problem and check the answer. Although $t = 3$ hours is the solution to the equation, the answer to the question is that Jacob catches Ruth at noon.
7. **(4)** $10x - 5(11 - x) = 8$
   (5) $x = \frac{21}{5} = 4.2$
   (6) The smaller number is 4.2 and the larger number is 6.8.
   (7) $4.2 + 6.8 = 11$ and $10 * 4.2 - 5(11 - 4.2) = 8$. The answer checks.
9. **(3)** Let $w =$ the width of the rectangle, then $4w =$ the length.
   (4) $100 = w + 4w + w + 4w$
   (5) $10 = w$
   (6) The width is 10 meters and the length is 40 meters.

(7) $10 \text{ m} + 40 \text{ m} + 10 \text{ m} + 40 \text{ m} = 100 \text{ m}$. The answer checks.

11. 58 minutes

13. a. (2)

	Rate (miles/hour)	Time (hours)	Distance (miles)
Train A	$R + 5$	2	$2(R + 5)$
Train B	R	2	$2R$
Total	N/A	N/A	370 mi

b. **(3)** Let R = the speed of train B (in miles/hour), then $R + 5$ = the speed of train A.

(4) $2(R + 5) + 2R = 370$

(5) $R = 90$

(6) The average rate of train B is 90 miles/hour and the rate of train A is 95 miles/hour.

(7) Train B travels 2 hours at a rate of 90 miles/hour, for a distance of 180 miles. Train A travels 2 hours at a rate of 95 miles/hour, for a distance of 190 miles. The sum of the distances is 370 miles, so the answer checks.

15. Kyle bought 20 tickets, Missy bought 32 tickets.

3.3 Skills and Review

17. $6x - 30$

19. $x = 4$

21. $y = {}^-6$

23. ${}^-4$

25. run $= 5$, rise $= 3$

3.4 Exercises

1. a. Multiply each term by 2 to find the next term: 16, 32, 64.

b. Add 10 to each term to find the next term: 53, 63, 73.

c. Subtract 2 from each term to find the next term: 33, 31, 29.

d. Starting at 50, successive terms are found by adding 1, subtracting 2, adding 3, subtracting 4, adding 5, etc.: 47, 54, 46.

3. a. $a_1 = 17, d = 3$

b. $a_1 = 85, d = {}^-5$

c. $a_1 = 15, d = 2.5$

d. $a_1 = 1, d = {}^-3$

5. 15 posts

7. Yes, 76th term

Chapter 3 Exploration

a. $6H_2O$

b. $6CO_2$

c. $6O_2$

d. $6H_2O + 6CO_2 = 6O_2 + 1C_6H_{12}O_6$

e.

	Atoms on Left Side	Atoms on Right Side
Carbon (C)	6	6
Hydrogen (H)	12	12
Oxygen (O)	18	18

f. Answers may vary.

Chapter 3 Review Exercises

1. a. $x = 1$　　**b.** $x = \frac{{}^-4}{5} = {}^-.8$

c. $x = {}^-6$　　**d.** $x = 1$

e. $x = \frac{{}^-3}{2} = {}^-1.5$　　**f.** $x = \frac{21}{2} = 10.5$

g. $x = 9$　　**h.** $x = 21$

2. $2 * 9 - 3 = 9 + 6$

$15 = 15$　　*OK, the solution $x = 9$ checks.*

3. a.

Time (hours)	Distance (miles)
1	50
2	100
3	150
4	200
t	$50t$

b. Distance = rate * time; the rate is 50 miles/hour and the time is t. Therefore, distance = $50t$.

c. The solution represents the number of hours that it takes to travel a distance of 120 miles at a rate of 50 miles/hour.

d. $t = \frac{12}{5} = 2.4$ hours

4. a. $373 = C + 273$

b. $C = 100$; water boils at $100°C$.

5. $28 = 3S + 1$

$S = 9$; a row made of 28 toothpicks has 9 squares.

6. a. $2.50 + 1.50d$

b. $4 + 1d = 2.50 + 1.50d$

c. $d = 3$; the fees of each club are the same when exactly 3 CDs are purchased.

7. a. $2x - 3$　　**b.** $5x - 2$

c. $7x - 6$　　**d.** $x^2 + 6x - 24$

e. $3x^2 + 2y$

f. $3x + \frac{1}{2}$

g. $\frac{1}{6}x$

h. $x + 6$

8. The special property of $^-1, c$ on page 53 lets us change the subtraction in front of the left parenthesis to addition if we insert a $^-1$; $4x$.

9. a.
$$3x + 8 = 32 \qquad LS$$
$$\underline{+^-8 \quad +^-8}$$
$$3x = 24 \qquad A$$
$$\frac{3x}{3} = \frac{24}{3} \qquad M$$
$$x = 8 \qquad LS, RS$$

b.
$$5x - 10 + 9 = 7x + 21 \qquad LS, RS$$
$$5x - 1 = 7x + 21 \qquad LS$$
$$\underline{+^-5x \quad +^-5x}$$
$$^-1 = 2x + 21 \qquad A$$
$$\underline{+^-21 \quad +^-21}$$
$$^-22 = 2x \qquad A$$
$$\frac{^-22}{2} = \frac{2x}{2} \qquad M$$
$$^-11 = x \qquad LS, RS$$

10. a. $x = 5$

b. $x = 1$

c. $x = 35$

d. $x = 40$

e. $x = \frac{1}{4} = .25$

f. $x = ^-9$

g. $x = \frac{^-5}{13}$

h. $x = \frac{3}{2} = 1.5$

11. $L = 6$; the rectangle has a length of 6 inches.

12. $x = \frac{3}{4}$

13. a. Less than 1 hour; in 1 hour the combined distance of the trains is 100 miles.

b. $45t$

c. $45t + 55t = 36$

d. $t = \frac{9}{25} = .36$; 2:22 P.M.

14. a. Angle B is $x + 20$; angle C is $x + 70$

b. $x + x + 20 + x + 70 = 180$

c. $x = 30$

d. The measure of angle A is $30°$, B is $50°$, and C is $100°$.

15. a. $90 + x + x = 180$

b. $x = 45$

c. Both unknown angles measure $45°$.

16. a.

b. $x + x + x = 180$; $x = 60$; each angle measures $60°$.

17. a. Find the total distance the pilot flies.

b.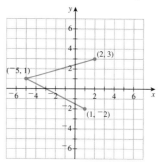

c. Let $d_1 = $ the distance (in blocks) from $(2, 3)$ to $(^-5, 1)$.

Let $d_2 = $ the distance from $(^-5, 1)$ to $(1, ^-2)$.

d. $d_1 = \sqrt{(^-7)^2 + (^-2)^2}$

$d_2 = \sqrt{6^2 + (^-3)^2}$

e. $d_1 \approx 7.3$

$d_2 \approx 6.7$

f. The pilot flew approximately 14 blocks.

g. The answer checks with an approximate count of the blocks in the picture.

18. (1) Find the dimensions of a tennis court with perimeter 228 feet and a length that is 6 feet more than twice the width.

(2)

(3) Let $x = $ width, then $2x + 6 = $ length.

(4) $228 = x + 2x + 6 + x + 2x + 6$

(5) $36 = x$

(6) The width is 36 feet and the length is 78 feet.

(7) 36 feet + 78 feet + 36 feet + 78 feet = 228 feet, so the answer checks.

19. About 478 minutes

20. a. 12.9 seconds

b. 113.52 m

c. Marion Jones

21. a. Arithmetic: 22, 26, 30

b. 405, 1215, 3645

c. 0, 17, 0

d. Arithmetic: 11, 9, 7

22. a. $a_{10} = 64$

b. $d = 1$

c. $a_1 = 8$

Chapter 3 Test

1. $x = {}^-2$

2. $x = \frac{-5}{3}$

3. $6\left(\frac{3}{2}\right) - 1 \stackrel{?}{=} 2\left(\frac{3}{2}\right) + 5$

$\qquad 8 = 8 \qquad\qquad OK!$

Therefore, $x = \frac{3}{2}$ is a solution to the equation.

4. $2x + 9 - 5x = 4(x - 3)$

$\qquad\qquad x = 3$

5. $C = \frac{290}{9} \approx 32.2°$

6. a. $20 - \frac{x}{13}$

   b. Approximately 19.6 gallons

   c. 260 miles

7. a. Let $t =$ the number of hours it took for the boats to meet.

   b. $15.5t + 1.5t = 58$

   c. $t = \frac{58}{17} \approx 3.41$; the boats met at about 3:50 A.M.

8. c. Angle A measures 36° and angles B and C measure 72°.

9. a. 1.625 hours or 1 hour 37 minutes 30 seconds

   b. Yes. Lance runs about 8 miles/hour. In 15 minutes, or one-quarter of an hour, Lance gets about a 2-mile head start on Doug. Doug is faster than Lance by a little more than 1 mile/hour. Therefore, in less than 2 hours Doug will have made up Lance's 2-mile head start.

10. The length of each leg is 3.2 cm and the remaining side is 13.6 cm.

Chapter 4 Systems of Linear Equations

4.1 Exercises

1.

Variable Cost	Fixed Cost	Rate of Change
a. .25 * (number of minutes)	$1.25	$.25 per minute
b. .20 * (number of ounces)	$.25	$.20 per ounce
c. .25 * (number of miles)	$8.	$.25 per mile

3. a. Answers may vary; (0, 1000), (100, 1002)

   b. .02

   c. Ordered pairs may vary; (200, 1004), (1000, 1020). Slope = .02

   d. The slopes from (b) and (c) are the same. Although the elevation changes, the slope of the hill is always .02.

5.

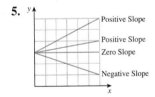

Positive Slope
Positive Slope
Zero Slope
Negative Slope

7. a. (5, 7)   **b.** (3, ⁻6)

   c. (2, 9)   **d.** (1, 4), (3, 5)

9. a. ⁻1   **b.** $\frac{-11}{5}$ **c.** $\frac{3}{4}$ **d.** 0

11. a. $1000

   b. No. In the first year the investment increased $100. In the second year it increased $110.

   c. No, the rate of change is not constant.

   d. Although both investments have an initial value of $1000 and a first year growth of $100, this investment is better because it increases by a larger amount every year thereafter.

13. a. 1.09

   b. 1.09 > 1.00; no, the company did not tell the truth.

15. a.

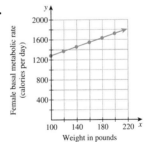

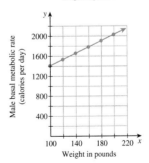

   b. Female BMR: 4.4, Male BMR: 6.2

   c. A female needs 4.4 more calories per day for every 1-pound increase in weight. A male needs 6.2

more calories per day for every 1-pound increase in weight.

4.1 Skills and Review

17. **(1)** Find the number of minutes at which the two phone plans cost the same.

(2) Example 2 of Section 3.2 is a similar problem.

(3) Let t = the number of calling minutes.

(4) $.07t + 22.95 = .03t + 28.45$

(5) $t = 137.5$

(6) At 137.5 minutes the two cellular phone plans cost the same.

(7) Plan A: At 7 cents per minute, 137.5 minutes costs $9.63. Add the fixed cost of $22.95 for a total of $32.58.

Plan B: At 3 cents per minute, 137.5 minutes costs $4.13. Add the fixed cost of $28.45 for a total of $32.58. The answer checks.

19. $^-4 * 5 + 23 = 2 * 5 - 7$

$\qquad\qquad 3 = 3 \qquad\qquad OK.\ x = 5\ is\ a\ solution$

21. $r = \frac{11}{12}$ cm $\approx .92$ cm

23. $11c^2 - 6d + 16$

25. 4 inches/second

4.2 Exercises

1. $^-8x + y = ^-10$ or $8x - y = 10$

$y = ^-x + 7$

$y = 3x - \frac{7}{2}$

3. a. Slope-intercept form **b.** $m = ^-3$

c. y-intercept = $(0, 5)$ **d.** x-intercept = $(\frac{5}{3}, 0)$

5. a. x-intercept = $(2, 0)$, y-intercept = $(0, ^-4)$

b.

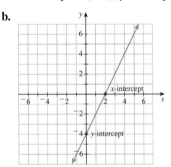

c. $m = 2$

d. $y = 2x - 4$

7. a. $y = \frac{3}{5}x + 4$ **b.** $y = 2x - 1$

c. $y = 7$ **d.** $y = ^-\frac{1}{2}x$

9. a. $y = ^-x + 4$ **b.** $y = x + 3$

c. $y = ^-\frac{1}{2}x - 3$ **d.** $y = 4$

11. a. $y = 3500$ feet

b. y will decrease by 22.

c. $y = ^-22x + 3500$

13. a.

Hour of Day	Elapsed Hours since 2 P.M.	Temperature (°F)
10:00 P.M.	8	75
11:00 P.M.	9	73.5
12:00 A.M.	10	72
1:00 A.M.	11	70.5
2:00 A.M.	12	69
3:00 A.M.	13	67.5
4:00 A.M.	14	66

From the table, the low temperature is 66°F.

b. $y = ^-1.5x + 87$ for elapsed times between 0 and 14 hours.

c. Windows may vary: Xmin = 0, Xmax = 18.8, Xscl = 2, Ymin = 65, Ymax = 90, Yscl = 4

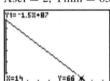

From the trace of the graph, the low temperature is 66°F.

d. The exact low temperature is 66°F.

15. a. $\frac{1}{3}x$

b. $\frac{1}{2}y$

c. $\frac{1}{3}x + \frac{1}{2}y = 6$

d. $y = ^-\frac{2}{3}x + 12$

e. Friendly windows may vary: Xmin = 0, Xmax = 18.8, Xscl = 2, Ymin = 0, Ymax = 15, Yscl = 2, Y1 = ($^-$2/3)X + 12

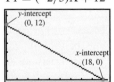

f. The x-intercept is $(18, 0)$. It takes Paul 18 hours to complete 6 jobs alone. The y-intercept is $(0, 12)$. It takes Joan 12 hours to complete 6 jobs alone.

g. The slope is $-\frac{2}{3}$. For each 3-hour increase in Paul's hours, Joan's hours decrease by 2, or for each 3 hour decrease in Paul's hours, Joan's hours increase by 2.

4.2 Skills and Review

17. a. Run = 4, rise = 5
   b. $\frac{5}{4}$
   c. Distance = $\sqrt{41} \approx 6.4$

19. $x = 33$

21. a. Diagonal ≈ 10.8 m
   b. Diagonal = $\sqrt{117}$ m

23. $4 * (83 - 3) = 320$

25. 0

4.3 Exercises

1. Intersection: $(^-1, 1)$

$$
\begin{array}{ll}
y = {}^-x & y = x + 2 \\
1 \overset{?}{=} {}^-(^-1) & 1 \overset{?}{=} (^-1) + 2 \\
1 = 1 \quad OK & 1 = 1 \quad OK
\end{array}
$$

The solution $(^-1, 1)$ checks.

3. a. Answers may vary; statement 1: $(1, 9), (2, 8), (3, 7)$; statement 2: $(10, 5), (9, 4), (8, 3)$.

   b. and **c.**

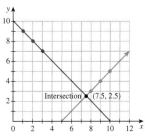

   d. The intersection must satisfy both statements; the pair of numbers must sum to 10 and have a difference of 5.

   e. $(7.5, 2.5)$; see above graph.

5. $(2, {}^-1)$

7. No solution (inconsistent system). These are two different lines that have the same slope of 1. Therefore, the lines are parallel and the system has no solution.

9. $(.25, 0)$

11. $(1, 7)$

13. a.

Miles Driven	Pinnacle's Cost	Competitor's Cost
50	\$20.50	\$22.50
60	\$23.00	\$23.00
70	\$25.50	\$23.50

   b. 60 miles

   c. Intersection point

15. a. $(500, 85)$

   b. At 500 miles, both companies charge \$85.

   c. Udrive is cheaper for rentals of more than 500 miles. Each additional mile at Udrive is 10 cents, whereas for Mile Rent-a-Car it is 15 cents.

4.3 Skills and Review

17. a. Look at the table and find Pinnacle's cost when 0 miles are driven.

   b. The rate of change is constant, so pick any two points to find the slope.

$$m = \frac{10.50 - 8.00}{10 - 0} = .25,$$

so the rate of change is \$.25 per mile.

19. a. $m = {}^-3$, y-intercept = $(0, 2)$
   b. $m = \frac{3}{2}$, y-intercept = $(0, {}^-3)$

21. $^-750$ vehicles/hour

23. $W = 3$ cm

25. a. $^-5x + 10$
   b. 25
   c. 25
   d. yes

4.4 Exercises

1. (c) and (d) are complete solutions.

3. a. We need both an x- and y-value to be a solution of a system of two equations.

   b. The solution is $(^-1, 3)$.

5. $(^-2, \frac{^-4}{15})$

7. a. Multiplying the second equation by 3 leads to a ^-6y term when the equations are added. We want to eliminate the y-term in the resulting equation.

   b.
$$
\begin{array}{ll}
4x - 3y = 22 & \\
\underline{{}^-9x + 3y = {}^-42} & \text{\textit{Multiplying on both sides of the}} \\
 & \text{\textit{second equation by }}{}^-3 \\
{}^-5x = {}^-20 & \text{\textit{Adding the equations}}
\end{array}
$$

$$x = 4$$

$$3 * 4 - y = 14 \quad \textit{Substituting 4 for x into}$$
$$3x - y = 14$$

$$y = {}^-2 \quad \textit{Solving for y}$$

Solution: $(4, {}^-2)$

9. $(7, 2)$

11. a. Elimination. The equations are in standard form. Multiply one of the equations by $^-1$ and add the equations to eliminate the y-term.

b. $\left(0, -\frac{4}{3}\right)$

13. $({}^-10, 7)$

Check the solution in both equations:

$$^-10 + 2 * 7 \overset{?}{=} 4 \qquad\qquad ^-({}^-10) \overset{?}{=} 7 + 3$$
$$4 = 4 \quad OK \qquad\qquad 10 = 10 \quad OK$$

The solution $({}^-10, 7)$ checks.

15. No solution (inconsistent system); the graphs form parallel lines.

4.4 Skills and Review

17. Approximately $(1.18, 5.55)$

19. a. x-intercept $= (3, 0)$, y-intercept $= (0, {}^-2)$

b.

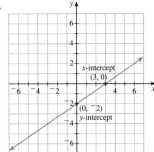

21. $^-5$; the larger the absolute value of the slope, the steeper the road.

23. a. $\sqrt{52}$ **b.** about 7.2

25. a. 2   **b.** 1   **c.** $\frac{1}{2}$

     d. $^-4$ **e.** .15

4.5 Exercises

1. $m_1 = m_2 = 2$

3. The lines are parallel, $m_1 = m_2 = 1$.

5. a. None of these

     b. Parallel

     c. Perpendicular

d. Same

7. Yes. Although the lines appear to be parallel, the slopes are different ($m_1 = 1, m_2 = .99$). Lines with unequal slopes intersect.

Chapter 4 Exploration

a.

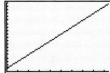

Friendly window ($0 \leq X \leq 9.4, 0 \leq Y \leq 2000$)

b. 199

c. 199 per year

d. 3876 lives saved

e. $^-502$; the function yields a negative number, which does not make sense in the context of the problem.

Chapter 4 Review Exercises

1. a. $m = 4$ **b.** $m = \frac{^-8}{3}$ **c.** $m = {}^-1$

     d. $m = 0$ **e.** $m = \frac{^-1}{2}$

2. a. 0 inches

     b. 2 inches/hour

     c.

Time (hours)	Amount of Snow on Ground (inches)
0	0
1	2
2	4
3	6

     d.

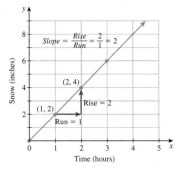

$m = 2$; the slope and rate of change (2 inches/hour) are the same.

3. a. $-\frac{100}{3}$ supplements per dollar

b. For every $3 decrease in price, Vitomax can sell 100 more supplements. Apply this rate of change to the first ordered pair. $20 − $3 = $17, and 5000 + 100 = 5100, giving a second ordered pair of (17, 5100).

c. (14, 5200)

d. $m = -\frac{100}{3}$

4. $m = \frac{3}{2}$

5. a ⇔ 4, b ⇔ 3, c ⇔ 1, d ⇔ 2

6. a.

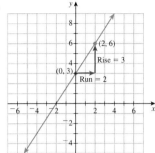

7. a. 5 inches of snow

   b. 2 inches/hour

   c. $y = 2x + 5$

8. a. $y = -300x + 1800$

9. a. $y = 6x + 2$ **b.** $y = \frac{1}{3}x + 4$

   c. $y = 2x + 1$ **d.** $y = -5x + \frac{1}{2}$

   e. $y = x - 3$ **f.** $y = -x + 5$

10. a. $m = 4$, y-intercept $= (0, 3)$

    b. $m = -1$, y-intercept $= (0, -1)$

    c. $m = 3$, y-intercept $= (0, -5)$

    d. $m = 1$, y-intercept $= (0, -3)$

    e. $m = -\frac{2}{3}$, y-intercept $= (0, 4)$

    f. $m = -1$, y-intercept $= (0, 2)$

11. $y = \frac{3}{4}x - 3$

12. a. $y = 5x + 11$ **b.** $y = x + 9$

    c. $y = -3x + 7$ **d.** $y = \frac{1}{2}x - 4$

13. a. $y = 2x + 2$ **b.** $y = 4x - 17$

    c. $y = \frac{-7}{2}x + 13$ **d.** $y = -\frac{1}{3}x + 4$

14. a. $\frac{4}{1}$

    b. $4y$

    c. $3x + 4y = 12$

    d. $\frac{9}{4}$ or $2\frac{1}{4}$ months

    e. x-intercept $= (4, 0)$, y-intercept $= (0, 3)$. To complete the album, the first musician must write songs for 4 months when the second musician writes for 0 months. To complete the album, the second musician

must write songs for 3 months when the first musician writes for 0 months.

f.

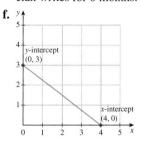

15. a. x-intercept: (5, 0), y-intercept: (0, 5)

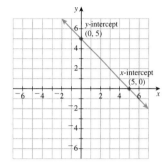

    b. (4, 0) (0, −2)

    c. (2, 0) (0, 3)

    d. (20, 0) (0, −2)

    e. (2, 0) (0, −12)

    f. $\left(\frac{9}{4}, 0\right) \left(0, \frac{9}{5}\right)$

16. a.

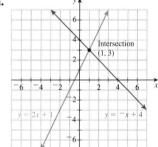

    b. Intersection point

    c. (1, 3)

17. (1, 4)

18. (−2, −3)

19. No solution (inconsistent system)

20. Approximately (1.02, −7.49)

21. Approximately (3.67, 1.33)

22. The numbers are 53.75 and 24.45.

23. The newspapers charge the same amount for 10 lines of advertising.

24. $\left(\frac{11}{3}, \frac{4}{3}\right)$

25. $(^-2, ^-9)$

26. $\left(\frac{1}{2}, \frac{3}{2}\right)$

27. $(5, ^-2)$

28. $(5, ^-1)$

29. $(^-1, 2)$

30. $(0, ^-6)$

31. $\left(^-4, \frac{3}{4}\right)$

32. a. $x + y = 180$

    b. $y = 2x - 30$

    c. smaller angle: 70°; larger angle: 110°

33. The cat will catch the mouse in $1\frac{1}{2}$ seconds.

34. a. parallel

    b. perpendicular

    c. same

    d. none of these

35. perpendicular

Chapter 4 Test

1. $m = ^-\frac{1}{4}$

2. a.

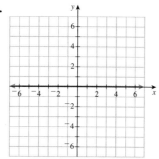

   b.

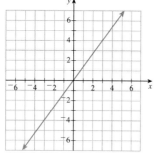

c.

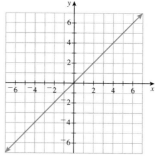

d.

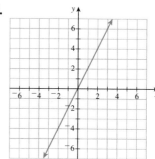

3. a. $\frac{5}{2}$ inches/year

   b.

Time (years)	Height (inches)
0	250
2	255
4	260

4. $y = \frac{5}{2}x + 250$

5. a. $m = ^-\frac{2}{3}$

   b. y-intercept $= (0, 2)$

6. $y = ^-\frac{3}{4}x + 2$

7. $y = 5x - 7$

8. x-intercept: $(5, 0)$, y-intercept: $(0, ^-4)$

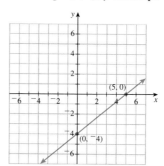

9. Both companies charge the same amount when their trucks are driven 100 miles.

10. Approximately $(.67, ^-.14)$

11. $\left(\frac{2}{3}, -\frac{1}{7}\right)$

12. $(^-6, 1)$

13. Smaller angle: 52.5°; larger angle: 127.5°

14. The lines are parallel.

Chapter 5 More Applications of Linear Equations

5.1 Exercises

1. Two of several proportions produce the same cross product.

$$\frac{2}{50} = \frac{6}{150} \qquad \frac{6}{2} = \frac{150}{50}$$
$$2 * 150 = 50 * 6 \qquad 6 * 50 = 2 * 150$$
$$300 = 300 \qquad\quad 300 = 300$$

3. $x = \frac{76}{3} \approx 25.33$

5. Length of AD $= \frac{21}{2}$ cm $= 10.5$ cm

7. D

9. Two of several proportions: $\frac{x}{84} = \frac{6}{7}$ and $\frac{84}{x} = \frac{7}{6}$

11. $\frac{10}{7} \approx 1.4$ minutes

13. $\frac{725}{3}$ minutes ≈ 242 minutes

15. 85 penguins

5.1 Skills and Review

17. Smaller angle: 34°; larger angle: 146°

19. a. $m = \frac{4}{3}$ **b.** $y = \frac{4}{3}x - \frac{17}{3}$

21. $x = \frac{^-5}{13} \approx ^-.38$

23. 36π inches^2

25. 77 mm^2

5.2 Exercises

1. a.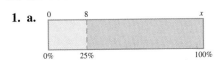

b. $x = 32$

c. $x = 32$

3. About 48.1%

5.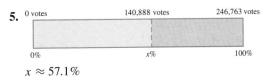

$x \approx 57.1\%$

7.

Sodium chloride: 22.5 g; water: 227.5 g

9.

$6890

11.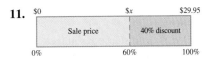

$x = \$17.97$

13. a. About 24.6%

b. About 10.0%

c. Compare each state's change in population with its 2000 population. Although California had a larger change in population its change relative to the 2000 population was less than Arizona's.

15. a. approximately .124 gallons

b. approximately 15.8 ounces

5.2 Skills and Review

17. a. $\frac{4}{3} = \frac{x}{10}$ or $\frac{x}{4} = \frac{10}{3}$

b. $x = \frac{40}{3} \approx 13.33$

19. approximately (1.91, .55)

21. The equation is in slope-intercept form, $y = mx + b$. Therefore, the slope is the coefficient of x; $m = 3$.

23.

Days Rented	Charge (\$)
1	$3 + 1 * 1 = 4$
2	$3 + 1 * 2 = 5$
4	$3 + 1 * 4 = 7$

25. 21

5.3 Exercises

1. a. $2.80 per pound

b. Peanuts

c. Peanuts, because $2.80 is closer to the $2 peanut price than it is to the $5 cashew price.

3. a.

b. $x + y = 30$

c. $.15x + .40y = .25(30)$

d. (1) Solve each equation for y in terms of x.

(2) Enter the equations in the $\boxed{Y =}$ menu on the calculator.

(3) Find a window that includes the intersection of the two lines.

(4) Use $\boxed{\text{TRACE}}$ or $\boxed{2^{nd}}$ CALC 5: intersect to find the intersection.

5. Distance equation: $4x$ is the distance Jason travels, $10y$ is the distance Nathan travels, and 16 is their combined distance.

Time equation: x is the number of hours Jason travels, y is the number of hours Nathan travels, and $\frac{1}{2}$ hour is Nathan's later start time.

7. a. Let x = the amount of chocolate raspberry, in pounds. Let y = the amount of French vanilla, in pounds.

b.

	Chocolate Raspberry	French Vanilla	Mixture
Rate ($/pound)	4	6	
Weight (pounds)	x	y	3
Cost ($)	$4x$	$6y$	13

c. $x + y = 3$ *weight equation*

$4x + 6y = 13$ *money equation*

d. $x = \frac{5}{2} = 2\frac{1}{2} = 2.5$, $y = \frac{1}{2} = .5$

e. Chocolate raspberry: $2\frac{1}{2}$ pounds, French vanilla: $\frac{1}{2}$ pound

9. a.

b. Let x = the amount (in mL) of 10% solution.

Let y = the amount (in mL) of 40% solution.

c. $x + y = 600$ *solution equation*

$.10x + .40y = .31(600)$ *alcohol equation*

d. $x = 180$, $y = 420$

e. 10% solution: 180 mL, 40% solution: 420 mL

f. Quick check: There should be quite a bit more of the 40% solution in the mixture because 31% is much closer to 40% than it is to 10%. *Thorough check:* The numbers should meet the conditions of the problem.

11. a.

b. Let x = the time in hours Thelma drives.

Let y = the time in hours Louise drives.

$x + y = 6.5$ *time equation*

$61x + 72y = 446$ *distance equation*

c. $x = 2$, $y = 4.5$

d. Thelma: 2 hours; Louise: 4.5 hours

13. Ordinary seats: 520; special seats: 80

15. 7.5% source: $4100, 11.25% source: $1500

5.3 Skills and Review

17. Hydrochloric acid: 18 g; water: 282 g

19. $x \approx {}^{-}10.97$

21. x-intercept $= (4, 0)$, y-intercept $= (0, {}^{-}9)$

23. $x = \frac{3}{11} \approx .27$

25. 10 inches

5.4 Exercises

1. 12 quarters, 8 dimes, 4 pennies

3. 5 small colonials, 3 big colonials, 3 split-levels

Chapter 5 Exploration

a. $\frac{119}{500} = \frac{x}{18500}$; $x = 4403$; estimate: 4403 people

b. 23.8%

c. Between 20.1% and 27.5%

d. Minimum students: 3718; maximum students: 5088

Chapter 5 Review Exercises

1. **a.** $x = 45$ **b.** $x = \frac{27}{2} = 13.5$
   c. $x = 15$ **d.** $x = \frac{11}{5} = 2.2$

2. Two possible proportions:

$$\frac{6 \text{ gallons}}{9 \text{ dollars}} = \frac{20 \text{ gallons}}{c \text{ dollars}} \quad \text{or} \quad \frac{c \text{ dollars}}{9 \text{ dollars}} = \frac{20 \text{ gallons}}{6 \text{ gallons}}$$

3. 68°F

4. one gallon: \$3.90; 150 gallons: \$585

5. 21.25 feet

6. 10 gallons

7. **a.** The time it takes for two people to complete a job is less than the fastest person working alone.
   b. $1\frac{1}{2} = 1.5$ hours

8. Estimate; 103 deer

9. **a.** Part = percent ∗ whole
   b. whole = $\frac{\text{part}}{\text{percent}}$

10.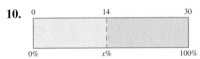

11. estimate: 50%

12. About $46\frac{2}{3}\%$

13. **a.**
    b. estimate: 25%
    c. 26.25%

14. 10.8

15. 200

16. 30%

17. 3 g

18. 25,000 mg

19. **a.** The *solute* is the substance that is dissolved in another.
    b. The *solvent* is the substance in which another is dissolved.
    c. The *solution* consists of the solute and the solvent mixed together.

20. 9%

21. \$33.36

22. 27.38%

23. approximately 10,684 people

24. **a.** Let x = the amount of peanut butter fudge, in pounds.
    Let y = the amount of vanilla fudge, in pounds.
    b. $x + y = 2$ *weight equation*
    $5x + 7y = 13$ *money equation*
    c. $Y = {}^-X + 2$
    $Y2 = ({}^-5/7)X + 13/7$
    d. Peanut butter fudge: .5 pounds, vanilla fudge: 1.5 pounds

25. 10% solution: 80 mL, 30% solution: 120 mL

26. Approximately \$112.90 was deposited in the checking account.
    Approximately \$587.10 was deposited in the savings account.

27. $x = {}^-22.33$, $y = 4.83$, and $z = {}^-9.5$

28. 6 pennies, 24 nickels, and 1 quarter

Chapter 5 Test

1. $x = \frac{80}{3} \approx 26.67$

2. about \$233.10

3. $\frac{24}{7} \approx 3.43$ hours ≈ 3 hours 26 minutes

4. approximately 38 polar bears

5.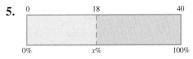

6.
   $x = 45\%$

7.
   $x = 170$
   $x \approx 57.14$

8. 80%

9. 12.5%

10. The 15% solution contains more sulfuric acid.

11. Almonds: $1\frac{1}{3}$ pounds; peanuts: $2\frac{2}{3}$ pounds

12. AAA bonds: \$3000; CD: \$2000

13. 1.75 L

Chapter 6 Exponents and Factoring

6.1 Exercises

1. a. x^7 **b.** y^{12} **c.** $x^6 y^{12}$

3. a. $12a^9$; product law $a = a, m = 4, n = 5$

  b. b^{18}; power-of-a-power law $a = b, m = 3, n = 6$

  c. $a^{14} b^{28}$; power-of-a-product law and power-of-a-power law $a = a^2, b = b^4, m = 7$

  d. $64b^3$; power-of-a-product law $a = 4, b = b$, and $m = 3$

5. a. k^4 **b.** $\dfrac{1}{k^4}$ **c.** $\dfrac{1}{j^{15}}$ **d.** $\dfrac{j^{20}}{k^8}$

7. a. y^4 **b.** $\dfrac{1}{y^6}$ **c.** $\dfrac{y^9}{z^9}$

9. $\dfrac{(2x^3 y^4)^3}{x^{-2} y^{12}} = \dfrac{8x^9 y^{12}}{x^{-2} y^{12}}$
$$= 8x^{11} y^0$$
$$= 8x^{11}(1)$$
$$= 8x^{11}$$

11. xy^3

13. $\dfrac{4x^2}{y}$

15. $^-2$

6.1 Skills and Review

17. a. $x + y = 6$ weight equation: x is the weight of the plain chocolate, y the weight of the deluxe chocolate, and 6 is the weight of the mixture, in pounds.

  $3x + 5y = 27$ money equation: $3x$ is the cost of the plain chocolate, $5y$ is the cost of the deluxe chocolate, and 27 is the cost of the mixture, in dollars.

  b. $x = 1.5$ and $y = 4.5$. The mixture contains 1.5 pounds of plain chocolate and 4.5 pounds of deluxe chocolate.

19. $x = 3.6$

21. $x = {}^-6$

23. The height is 4 cm.

25. 53

6.2 Exercises

1.

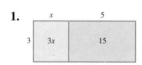

3. $40z^2 - 24z$

5. $x^2 - 9x + 5$

7. a.

	$5x$	$^-3$
2	$10x$	$^-6$

  b. GCF $= 18$; $18(3y + 4)$

  c. GCF $= 7x$; $7x(2x^2 + y - 6x)$

  d. $7x(2x^2 + y - 6x) = 14x^3 + 7xy - 42x^2$

9. a. $6x^3(3x^2 + 1)$ **b.** $3xy^3(7x - 5y)$

11. $2\pi r(h + r)$

13. a. $(x + 3)$ **b.** $(x + 3)(4y + 9)$

15. a. $x = 0$ or $x = {}^-4$

  b. $x = 0$ or $x = 11$

6.2 Skills and Review

17. $\frac{x^8}{9}$

19. .5 L

21. The width of the enlargement is 9 inches and the length is 15 inches.

23. a. $m = \frac{-5}{6}$

  b. x-intercept: $(14, 0)$, y-intercept: $\left(0, \frac{35}{3}\right) = \left(0, 11\frac{2}{3}\right)$

25. 13

6.3 Exercises

1. a. $(x + 6)(3x^2 + 1) = 3x^3 + 18x^2 + x + 6$

  b. $3x^3 + 18x^2 + x + 6$

  c. Answers may vary. Let $x = 3$, then $(x + 6)(3x^2 + 1) = 252$ and $3x^3 + 18x^2 + x + 6 = 252$.

3. $4x^2 + 19x - 63$

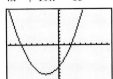

The graph of Y1 is the same as the graph of Y2, so the expansion is correct.

5. $x^2 + 8xy + 16y^2$

7. Expansion is the reverse of factoring.

9. $2y^2 + 7x + 2xy + 7y = (y + x)(2y + 7)$

11. a

13. The expression can be factored because the diagonal test for grouping works,

$$6x^3 * 5 = {}^-2x^2 * {}^-15x$$

$$6x^3 - 2x^2 - 15x + 5 = (2x^2 - 5)(3x - 1)$$

15. a. $\frac{1}{2}ab$

   b. $2ab$

   c. $2ab + c^2$

   d. $a^2 + 2ab + b^2$

   e. $2ab + c^2 = a^2 + 2ab + b^2$

   f. Subtract $2ab$ from both sides.

6.3 Skills and Review

17. $6x^3 - 12x^2 + 66x$

19. Randy should invest \$3125 in the 8.2% annuity and \$1875 in the 5% CD.

21. 257,600

23. $x = \frac{13}{8} = 1\frac{5}{8} = 1.625$

25. $\frac{15}{4} = 3\frac{3}{4} = 3.75$

6.4 Exercises

1. a. $x^2 + x - 6$; quadratic trinomial

   b. $x^3 - x + 6$

   c. $x^2 + 3$

   d. $4x^2 - x + 5$; quadratic trinomial

3.

	$2x$	1
x	$2x^2$	$1x$
3	$6x$	3

$2x^2 + 7x + 3 = (2x + 1)(x + 3)$

5. a. $(x^2)(6) = ({}^-3x)({}^-2x) = 6x^2$

   b.

	x	$^-3$
x	x^2	^-3x
$^-2$	^-2x	6

$x^2 - 5x + 6 = (x - 3)(x - 2)$

   c. George made his mistake in the grouping of the second step: $^-2x + 6 \neq {}^-(2x + 6)$. Use the rule for subtraction to write the four terms as a sum.

$$x^2 - 5x + 6 = x^2 - 3x - 2x + 6$$
$$= x^2 + {}^-3x + {}^-2x + 6$$
$$= (x^2 + {}^-3x) + ({}^-2x + 6)$$
$$= x(x + {}^-3) + {}^-2(x + {}^-3)$$
$$= (x + {}^-3)(x + {}^-2)$$
$$= (x - 3)(x - 2)$$

7. $(3x + 2)(2x - 5)$

9. Prime: No factor pairs of $40x^2$ add to ^-3x:

$$^-1x + {}^-40x = {}^-41x \quad No$$
$$^-2x + {}^-20x = {}^-22x \quad No$$
$$^-4x + {}^-10x = {}^-14x \quad No$$
$$^-5x + {}^-8x = {}^-13x \quad No$$

11. Diagonal product $= (2x^6)({}^-28) = {}^-56x^6$

	$2x^3$	7
x^3	$2x^6$	$7x^3$
$^-4$	$^-8x^3$	$^-28$

$$1x^3 + {}^-56x^3 = {}^-55x^3 \quad No$$
$$2x^3 + {}^-28x^3 = {}^-26x^3 \quad No$$
$$4x^3 + {}^-14x^3 = {}^-10x^3 \quad No$$
$$7x^3 + {}^-8x^3 = {}^-1x^3 \quad Yes$$

$2x^6 - x^3 - 28 = (2x^3 + 7)(x^3 - 4)$

13. a. $x = 4$ or $x = 8$

   b. $x = {}^-2$ or $x = 5$

   c. $x = {}^-3$ or $x = -\frac{1}{2}$

15. a. $x^2 + x - 2 = (x + 2)(x - 1)$

$$(^-2)^2 + {}^-2 - 2 \overset{?}{=} (^-2 + 2)(^-2 - 1)$$

$$0 = 0 \quad OK$$

$$1^2 + 1 - 2 \overset{?}{=} (1 + 2)(1 - 1)$$

$$0 = 0 \quad OK$$

b.

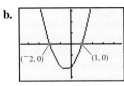

x-axis

c. $x = 6$ or $x = {}^-3$

d. It's easy to recognize the values of x that give an output of 0 in a factored polynomial.

6.4 Skills and Review

17.

	x	3
x	x^2	$3x$
3	$3x$	9

$(x + 3)^2 = x^2 + 6x + 9$

19. $x = 0$ or $x = 3$

21. 5:04 P.M.

23. Method 1: Place both equations in *slope-intercept* form and compare slopes.

$$y = {}^-2x + 12$$

$$y = {}^-2x + 10$$

The equations have the same slope but have different y-intercepts, so the lines are parallel and the system has no solution.

Method 2: Solve algebraically. Substitute the second equation into the first equation.

$$x + \tfrac{1}{2}({}^-2x + 10) = 6$$

$$x - x + 5 = 6$$

$$5 = 6 \qquad \textit{But } 5 \neq 6, \textit{ so there is no}$$
$$\textit{solution to this system of}$$
$$\textit{equations.}$$

25. a. $x = \tfrac{22}{3}$ **b.** $x \approx 7.333$

6.5 Exercises

1. a. $(y + 5)(y^2 - 5y + 25)$

b. $(3 - 2x)(9 + 6x + 4x^2)$

c. $(x - 6)(x^2 + 6x + 36)$

d. $(10z + 1)(100z^2 - 10z + 1)$

e. $(x^2 - y)(x^4 + x^2 y + y^2)$

3. a. Prime

b. $(x + 9)(x^2 - 9x + 81)$

c. Prime

d. $(x - 3)(x^2 + 3x + 9)(x + 3)(x^2 - 3x + 9)$

e. $(x^2 + 8)(x^4 - 8x^2 + 64)$

Chapter 6 Exploration

a. Step 1 $x = 64$

Step 2 $y = 18$

Step 3 $82 * 46 = x^2 - y^2 = 4096 - 324 = 3772$

b. By Step 1, $x = \frac{m+n}{2}$

By Step 2, $y = \frac{m-n}{2}$

Then

$$x + y = \frac{m + n}{2} + \frac{m - n}{2} = m$$

and

$$x - y = \frac{m + n}{2} - \frac{m - n}{2} = n.$$

Therefore, $m * n = (x + y)(x - y) = x^2 - y^2$. This is Step 3 of the algorithm.

c. When both numbers are odd or both are even, the sum is divisible by 2 and the difference is divisible by 2. This is necessary because the table has squares only of whole numbers.

d. We may write 77 as the sum of 76 and 1, then multiply by 44. This gives a product that can be found with the algorithm multiplying using squares on page 209.

$$77 * 44 = (76 + 1) * 44$$

$$= 76 * 44 + 44 \qquad \textit{Using the distributive}$$
$$\textit{property}$$

Chapter 6 Review Exercises

1. a. x^9 **b.** y^8 **c.** $x^5 y^5$

2. a. $64x^6 y^{18}$ **b.** $28y^6$ **c.** z^8

3. volume $= 9.261 * 10^{12}$ inches^3

4. a. $\dfrac{1}{x^3}$ **b.** x^3

   c. $\dfrac{1}{x^9}$ **d.** $\dfrac{x^{12}}{y^6}$

5. $1.13 * 10^{-3}$ feet $= .0013$ feet

6. a. x^4 **b.** $\dfrac{1}{x^4}$ **c.** $\dfrac{x^6}{y^6}$

7. $a \Leftrightarrow 3$ Quotient law

    $b \Leftrightarrow 5$ Power-of-a-power law

    $c \Leftrightarrow 2$ Quotient law and definition of negative integer
       exponents

    $d \Leftrightarrow 1$ Product law

    $e \Leftrightarrow 4$ Negative exponent in the denominator

8. a. $\dfrac{x^3}{y^3}$ **b.** $\dfrac{64x^6}{y^3}$

   c. $\dfrac{y^4}{x^{16}}$ **d.** $\dfrac{27y^6}{8x^{12}}$

9.

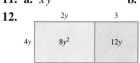

$4x^3(5x + 2x^4y) = 20x^4 + 8x^7y$

10. a. $30x^2 - 5x$ **b.** $8x^2z + 14xyz - 6xz$

   c. $^-x^2 + 8x - 2$

11. a. xy **b.** $3x^2$ **c.** 15

12.

$8y^2 + 12y = 4y(2y + 3)$

13. $5x^2y(z^3 - 3xy^3 + 2x^3y)$

14. a. $^-2x(4x - 5)$ **b.** $^-3(3x + 4y)$

15. a. $z(4x - 3)$

   b. $(y + 7)(4x - 3)$

   c. (a) and (b) are basically the same. Let z replace
      $(y + 7)$ in part (b).

16. a. $x = 0$ or $x = {}^-5$ **b.** $x = 0$ or $x = 8$

17. a.

$(x + 4)(x + 2) = x^2 + 6x + 8$

b.

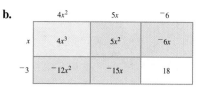

$(x - 3)(4x^2 + 5x - 6) = 4x^3 - 7x^2 - 21x + 18$

18. a.

$2x - 9y + xy - 18 = (y + 2)(x - 9)$

   b.

$^-4y + 3z - 12yz + 1 = (^-4y + 1)(3z + 1)$

19. a. Factorable: $(4x^3)(^-5) = (10x^2)(^-2x) = {}^-20x^3$;
      $(2x + 5)(2x^2 - 1)$

   b. Not factorable because we can't pair terms to make
      the product of one pair equal the product of the other
      pair.

   c. Factorable: $(3x)(8y) = (6xy)(4) = 24xy$;
      $(2y + 1)(3x + 4)$

20. a. $x^2 + 2xy + y^2$ **b.** $x^2 + 4xy + 4y^2$

   c. $25x^2 - 30xy + 9y^2$

21. a. $24x^2$

   b. $1x$ and $24x$, $2x$ and $12x$, $3x$ and $8x$, $4x$ and $6x$

   c. $3x + 8x = 11x$

   d. $x^2 + 3x + 8x + 24$

   e.

$(x + 3)(x + 8)$

22. a. $x^2 + 2x - 7x - 14 = (x + 2)(x - 7)$

   b. $5x^2 - 1x + 10x - 2 = (5x - 1)(x + 2)$

   c. $3x^2 + 1x - 12x - 4 = (3x + 1)(x - 4)$

   d. $7x^2 - 2x + 28x - 8 = (7x - 2)(x + 4)$

23. a. Prime, no factor pairs of $5x^2$ sum to ^-2x.

$$^-1 * {}^-5 \qquad ^-1x + {}^-5x = {}^-6x \qquad \textit{No}$$

b. Prime, no factor pairs of $12x^2$ sum to $1x$.

$$1 * 12 \qquad 1x + 12x = 13x \qquad \textit{No}$$

$$2 * 6 \qquad 2x + 6x = 8x \qquad \textit{No}$$

$$3 * 4 \qquad 3x + 4x = 7x \qquad \textit{No}$$

24. a. $(x + 3y)(x + 7y)$ **b.** $(2x^2 + 5)(x^2 - 3)$

25. a. $(x - 5)(x + 5)$ **b.** $(3 - y)(3 + y)$

 c. $(2x - 9y)(2x + 9y)$

26. a. $2(9x^2 - 18x + 8) = 2(9x^2 - 6x - 12x + 8)$

$$2(3x(3x - 2) - 4(3x - 2)) = 2(3x - 2)(3x - 4)$$

 b. $y(xy - x + 2y - 2) = y(x(y - 1) + 2(y - 1))$

$$= y(y - 1)(x + 2)$$

 c. $3y(x^2 - 100) = 3y(x - 10)(x + 10)$

27. a. $x = {}^-5$ or $x = {}^-8$ **b.** $x = {}^-3$ or $x = 1$

 c. $x = \frac{1}{3}$ or $x = 6$

28. a. $(x + 4)(x^2 - 4x + 16)$

 b. $(1 - y)(1 + y + y^2)$

 c. $(2x + 10y)(4x^2 - 20xy + 100y^2)$

 d. $(y + 3z^2)(y^2 - 3yz^2 + 9z^4)$

29. a. $6(1 - 2z)(1 + 2z + 4z^2)$

b. $2(5x + y)(25x^2 - 5xy + y^2)$

c. $(2 - y)(4 + 2y + y^2)(2 + y)(4 - 2y + y^2)$

Chapter 6 Test

1. $\frac{x^2 y^6}{z^8}$

2. $\frac{3x^3}{10y^3}$

3. $\frac{1}{27x^9}$

4. $1.728 * 10^{12}$ signals

5. a. $3a^2 + 12a$

 b. $6x^3 y^2 + 12x^2 y^3 - 30xy^4$

6. $^-3bc^2(2abc + 1 + 4a^3 b^3 c)$

7. $x = 0$ or $x = 5$

8. a. $2x^2 - 9x - 35$

 b. $3x^3 - 13x^2 + 10x - 24$

9. a. $(1 + 2y)(2x + 3)$ **b.** $(3x - 1)(2x^2 - 3)$

10. $4x^2 - 28xy + 49y^2$

11. a. $(4x + 1)(x - 6)$ **b.** $(x - 5y)(x + 7y)$

12. $(8x - y)(8x + y)$

13. a. $2y(x - 5y)(x + 8y)$ **b.** $3(2 - x)(2 + x)$

14. $x = \frac{1}{3}$ or $x = \frac{5}{2}$

Chapter 7 Solving Quadratic Equations

7.1 Exercises

1. a. See Figure 2. Note that some data is rounded.

 b. No

 c. No, linear models have constant slope. The graph of these data has changing slope.

3. 8 inches

5. a. $x = \pm 3$

 b. $s = \pm 5$

 c. $s = \pm \sqrt{26}$

 $s \approx \pm 5.1$. (a) and (b) are exact, but (c) is approximate; 9 and 25 are perfect squares, but 26 is not.

7. $d = \pm \sqrt{\frac{1000}{3}}$; exact

 $d \approx \pm 18.26$; approximate, $\frac{1000}{3}$ is not a perfect square.

9. $x \approx \pm 4.08$

11. $2x - 3 = 0 \qquad 2x^2 - 3 = 0$

$$2x = 3 \qquad\quad 2x^2 = 3$$

$$x = \tfrac{3}{2} \qquad\quad x^2 = \tfrac{3}{2}$$

$$x = \pm\sqrt{\tfrac{3}{2}}$$

Solving quadratic equations of the form $ax^2 + c = 0$ uses the same process as solving linear equations, with the extra step of taking a square root on both sides of the equation.

13. a. $x = {}^-1$ or $x = {}^-3$ **b.** $x = 1$ or $x = 2$

 c. $y = 2$ or $y = {}^-7$ **d.** $x = 2$ or $x = 9$

 e. $x = {}^-2$ or $x = {}^-3$

15. a. $x = \pm \frac{7}{2}$

 b. $x = \frac{7}{2}$ or $x = \frac{-7}{2}$

 c. The answers are the same.

7.1 Skills and Review

17. $x = 8$ or $x = {}^-8$

19. $4x^2 - 12x + 9$

21. a. $x + y = 212$

   b. $x - y = 83$

   c. Graphical solutions are approximate: 147.5 and 64.5.

23. $z = \frac{15}{8} = 1.875$

   $\frac{9}{8} = \frac{9}{8}$;   *OK, the answer checks*

25. 4

7.2 Exercises

1. y-intercept, x-intercepts (if any), and the vertex.

3. a. y-intercept   **b.** y-intercept

   c. y-intercept   **d.** $x = 0$

5. a. $x \approx .7$ or $x \approx 4.3$ **b.** $(0, 3)$

   c. $(2.5, {}^-3.25)$ **d.** Minimum

7. a.

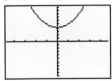

No x-intercept

   b.

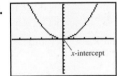

One x-intercept

   c.

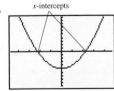

Two x-intercepts

9. a. ${}^-16(x^2 - 2x - 3)$

      ${}^-16(x - 3)(x + 1)$

   b. $x = 3$ or $x = {}^-1$

   c. Windows may vary: Xmin $= {}^-4.7$, Xmax $= 4.7$

   d. Ymin $= {}^-3.1$, Ymax $= 70$

11. a. Between 5 and 6 seconds

   b. Between 2 and 3 seconds

13. a. No

   b. The water will reach an approximate height of 104 feet.

15. The football will remain airborne approximately 4.6 seconds.

7.2 Skills and Review

17. a. $y = {}^-20$

   b. $x = \frac{3}{2}$ or $x = {}^-5$

19. $x = 4$ or $x = {}^-7$

21. $4y^2 - 9$

23. $\dfrac{y^2}{4x^2}$

25. a. Area $= 93.5$ inches^2

   b. Perimeter $= 39$ inches

7.3 Exercises

1. a. Greatest common factor (GCF) and zero-product property (ZPP); the expression on the left side of the equation factors so that the ZPP can be used.

   b. Factor and ZPP; the expression on the left side of the equation factors into the product of two binomials allowing the use of ZPP.

   c. Graphing; find approximate solutions with the graphing calculator.

   d. Square root principle; the equation is of the form $ax^2 + c = 0$.

   e. Quadratic formula; the expression on left side of the equation does not factor with integer coefficients and we need exact solutions.

3. a. $a = 2, b = 12, c = {}^-5$

   b. $x = {}^-3 \pm \dfrac{\sqrt{184}}{4}$ *This square root simplifies (we learn more about simplifying radicals in Chapter 9).*

      $x = {}^-3 + \dfrac{\sqrt{184}}{4}$ or $x = {}^-3 - \dfrac{\sqrt{184}}{4}$

      $x \approx .39$ or $x \approx {}^-6.39$

5. $x = {}^-1$

7. a. $x = -\dfrac{b}{2a}$ **b.** $x = -\dfrac{3}{2} = {}^-1.5$

   c. $y = -\dfrac{29}{2} = {}^-14.5$ **d.** x-intercepts

9. a., b.

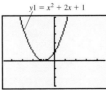

$y1 = x^2 + 2x + 1$

$b^2 - 4ac = 0$

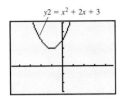

$$b^2 - 4ac = {}^-8$$

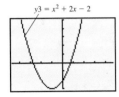

$$b^2 - 4ac = 12$$

c. The quadratic equation $0 = ax^2 + bx + c$ has

  1. No real root when the discriminant is negative;

  2. One real root when the discriminant is zero;

  3. Two real roots when the discriminant is positive.

11. a.

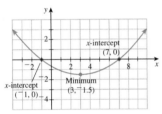

b. $(7, 0)$

13. No solution

15. a. $x = \frac{1}{5}$ or $x = {}^-1$

  b. $x = \frac{1}{5}$ or $x = {}^-1$

  c. $x = .2 = \frac{1}{5}$ or $x = {}^-1$

7.3 Skills and Review

17. $x \approx .22$ or $x \approx 3.33$

19. a. Cheese $= 1.3d^2$

b.

Diameter (inches)	Cheese (grams)
6	47
10	130
14	255

c.

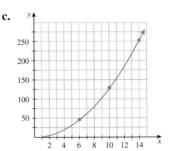

21. $\frac{4y^2}{x^{10}}$

23. $b_1 = \frac{7}{2}$ cm $= 3.5$ cm

25. a. $\frac{73}{100}$

  b. 73%

7.4 Exercises

1. In a real-life maximum problem, such as Example 1, Xmax can be found by doubling the x-coordinate of the vertex and choosing the next-higher friendly value. Set Ymax slightly larger than the y-coordinate of the vertex.

3. x-intercepts

5. We want the width that maximizes the area (vertex), not the width that makes zero area (x-intercepts).

7. Step 1 The stopping distance of a car is given by the quadratic equation $y = ax^2 + bx$, where $a = .04$ and $b = .2$. Determine the speed of a car that leaves a skid mark 200 feet long.

  Step 2 See Figure 22.

  Step 3 Let $x =$ the speed of the car in miles/hour and $y =$ the stopping distance in feet.

  Step 4 $200 = .04x^2 + .2x$

  Step 5 $x \approx 68.25$ or $x \approx {}^-73.25$

  Step 6 The speed of the car was approximately 68 miles/hour.

  Step 7 Substitute 68 for x in the equation from step 4. The answer checks.

9. The speed of the car was approximately 58.79 miles/hour.

11. a. The spaceship is 1,056,000 feet from the sun.

  b. The probe would hit the sun in approximately 48.6 seconds.

  c. The probe would melt in approximately 34.3 seconds.

13. a.

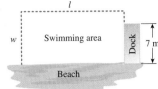

b. $l + w + w - 7 = 30$

c. $l = 37 - 2w$

d. $A = lw$, substituting the expression for l gives $A = {}^-2w^2 + 37w$.

e. The area is maximized with a width of 9.25 m and a length of 18.5 m.

f. The maximum swimming area is 171.125 m².

15. a. Prices of \$0 or approximately \$27.59 generate zero revenue.

b. Revenue is maximized at a price of approximately \$13.79.

c. Prices of approximately \$9.57 or \$18.02 generate \$500 of revenue.

7.4 Skills and Review

17. $b^2 - 4ac = {}^-79$; ${}^-79 < 0$, no x-intercept.

19. $x \approx {}^-12.43$ or $x \approx 6.43$

21. $\dfrac{y^3}{x^9}$

23. $x = {}^-3$

25.

7.5 Exercises

1. a. $(x - 6)(x^2 - 9) = 0$

b. $(x - 6)(x - 3)(x + 3) = 0$

c. $x = 6$ or $x = 3$ or $x = {}^-3$

3. The calculator displays 6.

Chapter 7 Exploration

a.

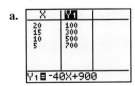

b. $y = {}^-40x^2 + 900x$

c. $x = 11.25$; a price of \$11.25 maximizes revenue.

d. The charity will make \$3562.50 profit.

Chapter 7 Review Exercises

1. The slope of a linear equation remains constant. The slope of a quadratic equation changes.

2. a. Linear **b.** Quadratic **c.** Other

3. $x \approx {}^-.83$ or $x = 1.2$

4. $x = \pm\sqrt{8}$

$x \approx \pm 2.83$

5. $x = \pm\sqrt{\dfrac{3}{7}}$

$x \approx \pm.65$

6. $x = 0$ or $x = {}^-\dfrac{4}{3}$

7. $x = 5$ or $x = {}^-\dfrac{3}{2}$

8. $x = 0$ or $x = {}^-2$

9. a. The pizza is approximately 13.1 inches.

b. The pizza is exactly $\sqrt{\dfrac{180}{1.05}} = \sqrt{\dfrac{1200}{7}}$ inches.

10. a. A parabola given by the equation $y = ax^2 + bx + c$ opens upward when $a > 0$ and opens downward when $a < 0$.

b. The turning point is the vertex. The x-coordinate is $\dfrac{{}^-b}{2a}$ and the y-coordinate is found by evaluating the quadratic when $x = \dfrac{{}^-b}{2a}$.

c. If the discriminant, $b^2 - 4ac$, is

1. Positive, there are two x-intercepts;

2. Zero, there is one x-intercept;

3. Negative, there is no x-intercept.

d. The y-intercept is the point where the graph intersects the y-axis. This point is $(0, c)$.

11. y-intercept: $(0, {}^-4)$

x-intercepts: $(1, 0), ({}^-1.33, 0)$

Vertex: minimum at $({}^-.17, {}^-4.08)$

12. y-intercept: $(0, 0)$

x-intercept: $(0, 0)$

Vertex: maximum at $(0, 0)$

13. y-intercept: $(0, 15)$

x-intercepts: none

Vertex: minimum at $({}^-2.5, 2.5)$

14. a.

b. Windows may vary: Xmin = 0, Xmax = 4.7, Ymin = 0, Ymax = 25

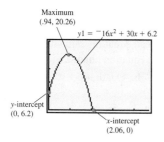

c. The ball hits the ground in approximately 2.06 seconds.

d. Approximate maximum at (.94, 20.26)

e. (0, 6.2); this is the height of the ball at release.

15. The larger x-intercept is used to set Xmax and the y-coordinate of the vertex is used to set Ymax. Xmin and Ymin are usually set at zero.

16. a. The x-intercepts are the points where the graph intersects the x-axis. These occur when $y = 0$.

b. $(1, 0)$, $\left(-\frac{4}{3}, 0\right)$

17. $x = {}^-6 \pm \sqrt{38}$

18. $x = -\frac{1}{6} \pm \frac{\sqrt{97}}{6}$

19. $x = \frac{1}{6}$ or $x = \frac{-1}{2}$

20. a. $(3, 14)$

b. x-intercepts: $\left(3 + \frac{\sqrt{56}}{2}, 0\right)$, $\left(3 - \frac{\sqrt{56}}{2}, 0\right)$

21. a.

b. Let s = the length of a side of the square in centimeters; $s^2 + s^2 = 150^2$.

c. $s = \pm\sqrt{11250}$

d. Each side of the square is $\sqrt{11250} \approx 106.1$ cm.

22. a. The width is approximately 1.67 m and the length is 6 m.

b. The width is $\frac{5}{3} = 1\frac{2}{3}$ m and the length is 6 m.

23. a. Vertex: maximum $\approx (6.1, 34.49)$

b. Approximately 6.1 seconds after release, the ball is 34.49 m above the surface of the moon.

c. x-intercept $\approx (12.58, 0)$

d. The astronaut's throw hits the moon approximately 12.58 seconds after it is released.

24. The ball is 18 m high at exactly

$$\frac{10}{1.64} + \frac{\sqrt{54.08}}{1.64} \text{ seconds}$$

or

$$\frac{10}{1.64} - \frac{\sqrt{54.08}}{1.64} \text{ seconds}$$

after release.

25. a.

b. Let w = the width of the table top in inches; then $w + 16$ is the length. Equation: $w^2 + (w + 16)^2 = 72^2$

c. $w = {}^-8 + \frac{\sqrt{10112}}{2} \approx 42.3$

d. The table top is approximately 42.3 inches wide by 58.3 inches long.

26. The area of the space is maximized with a width of 51 feet and a length of 102 feet.

27. The vehicle was traveling exactly

$$\frac{{}^-.22}{.09} + \frac{\sqrt{31.5484}}{.09}$$

miles/hour or approximately 60 miles/hour.

28. a. $1 + 4i$

b. $9 - 4i$

c. $^-41 + 23i$

d. 34

29. a. $x = \pm 2i$

b. $x = 3 \pm 4i$

c. $x = -\frac{5}{2} + \frac{\sqrt{11}}{2}i$

d. $x = {}^-3 \pm \frac{\sqrt{72}}{2}i$

Chapter 7 Test

1. $x = \pm 2$

2. $x = 0$ or $x = {}^-3$

3. $x = 2$ or $x = 6$

4. $x = \frac{1}{4}$ or $x = -\frac{5}{2}$

5. $x = 1$ or $x = {}^-5$

6. $x \approx .98$ or $x \approx {}^-8.18$

7. a. The parabola opens downward so the vertex is a maximum.

b. $\left(-\frac{1}{6}, \frac{109}{12}\right)$

c. $b^2 - 4ac = 109$; $109 > 0$, two x-intercepts

d. $(1.57, 0)$, $(^-1.91, 0)$

e. $(0, 9)$

8. a. y-intercept: $(0, 400)$; x-intercepts: $(10, 0)$, $(40, 0)$; the vertex might vary $\approx (25, ^-225)$

b. Windows may vary: Xmin $= 0$, Xmax $= 47$, Ymin $= ^-300$, Ymax $= 500$

9. a. The water attains a maximum height of approximately 12.98 m.

b. 1.5 m

c. The water hits the ground at exactly

$$\frac{15}{9.8} + \frac{\sqrt{254.4}}{9.8} \text{ seconds}$$

or approximately 3.16 seconds after it is shot.

10. The TV has a height of 3 feet and a width of 4 feet.

11. a. A price of $13.46 (rounded to the nearest penny) generates zero revenue.

b. A price of $6.73 (rounded to the nearest penny) generates maximum revenue.

12. The driver was not speeding. The driver's approximate speed was 59.3 miles/hour.

Chapter 8 What Is a Function

8.1 Exercises

1. a.

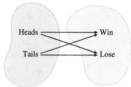

b. A function requires that each input be associated with one and only one output. This is not a function; each input is associated with two outputs, win and lose.

3. a. Function; domain: {lab, husky, poodle}; range: {dog}

b. Not a function

5. a. 0 seconds and 2.5 seconds

b. Domain: $\{x | 0 \leq x \leq 2.5\}$

Domain

0   2.5

c. 0 feet and 100 feet

d. Range: $\{x | 0 \leq y \leq 100\}$

Range

0   100

e. In a real-life problem, the limits of the domain are used to set Xmin and Xmax and the limits of the range are used to set Ymin and Ymax.

f. Quadrant I; the domain and range are both nonnegative.

7. $f(0) = 0$

$f(2) = 12$

$f(3) = 27$

9. a. $f(2) = ^-3$ **b.** $g(^-4) = 28$

c. $h(3) = ^-9.1$

11. $f(^-2.15) = ^-16.641$

13. a. Domain: $\{x | ^-\infty < x < \infty\}$; range: $\{y | y \leq 2\}$

b. Domain: $\{x | ^-\infty < x < \infty\}$; range: $\{y | y \geq ^-2\}$

c. Domain: $\{x | ^-\infty < x < \infty\}$; range: $\{y | y = 5\}$

15. a. Range: $\{y | y \geq 0\}$; the outputs will be nonnegative so the graph will appear only in Quadrants I and II.

b. The absolute value of any real number results in an output greater than or equal to zero.

8.1 Skills and Review

17. The width is 45 feet and the length is 90 feet.

19. a. $x = ^-4$ **b.** $x = ^-4$ **c.** $x = ^-4$

21. $x = \pm\sqrt{35}$

$x \approx 5.92$

23. a. x^2 **b.** $\frac{1}{x^2}$

25. $k = \frac{3}{2}$

8.2 Exercises

1. Not a function

3. Function

5. Not a function

7. a.

x	y
$^-4$	$^-2$
$^-1$	$^-1$
0	0
$^-1$	1
$^-4$	2

b.

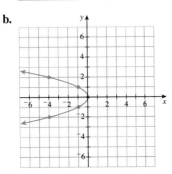

c. Not a function; the graph fails the vertical-line test.

9. a. Yes; there is one and only one output associated with each input.

b. (1996, 52), (1997, 53), (1998, 56), (1999, 56), (2000, 56), (2001, 55)

c. Domain: {1996, 1997, 1998, 1999, 2000, 2001}; range: {52, 53, 55, 56}

11. a. 3   **b.** 1   **c.** 2

13.

Domain: $\{x | 4 \leq x < \infty\}$

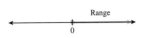

Range: $\{y | 0 \leq y < \infty\}$

15.

Domain: $\{x | x \neq ^-6\}$

Range: $\{y | y \neq 0\}$

8.2 Skills and Review

17. Domain: {31, 32, 33, 34, 35}; range: {Packers, Broncos, Rams, Ravens}

19. Step 1 Find the price(s) of a product that generate zero revenue.

Step 2 A graph of the revenue function, $R = ^-5p^2 + 90p$

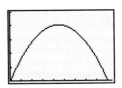

Step 3 Let p = price of the product in dollars and R = revenue in dollars.

Step 4 $0 = ^-5p^2 + 90p$

Step 5 $p = 0$ or $p = 18$

Step 6 Prices of $0 or $18 generate zero revenue.

Step 7 Substitute 0 and then 18 into the equation from step 4. The answers check.

21. a. $x = 2$ **b.** $x = 3$ or $x = ^-4$

23. $\dfrac{25x^8}{y^2}$

25. $^-23a^2 + 48a - 16$

8.3 Exercises

1.

Basic Function	Function	Graph
Linear	$f(x) = x$	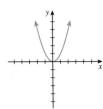
Quadratic	$f(x) = x^2$	
Cubic	$f(x) = x^3$	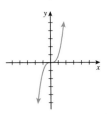

1. (*continued*)

Basic Function	Function	Graph
Square root	$f(x) = \sqrt{x}$	
Absolute value	$f(x) = |x|$	
Reciprocal	$f(x) = \frac{1}{x}$	

3. a. The square of any number is nonnegative.

   b. Vertex $= (0, 0)$

   c. The graph is symmetric about the y-axis.

5. a. We can't take the square root of a negative number in the real number system.

   b. The domain excludes negative values: domain: $\{x | 0 \le x\}$.

7. Both graphs are symmetric about the y-axis.

9. The graph has two branches with the same shape, one in the first quadrant and the other in the third.

11. a. $(3.01, {}^-4.21)$

   b. $({}^-.34, 3.32)$

13. a. \$91.25

   b. $c(g(x)) = 50 + .0825x$

15. a. $f(g(3)) = 0$

   b. $f(g(x)) = x^2 - 4x + 3$

   c. $g(f({}^-1)) = 2$

   d. $g(f(x)) = x^2 - 2x - 1$

8.3 Skills and Review

17. Domain: $\{x | {}^-\infty < x < \infty\}$; range: $\{y | {}^-3 \le y\}$

19. $x = 0$ or $x = 6$

21. a. $a > 0$, opens upward

   b. y-intercept: $(0, {}^-28)$

   c. x-intercepts: $({}^-4, 0), (7, 0)$

   d. Vertex: minimum $\left(\frac{3}{2}, \frac{{}^-121}{4}\right)$

   e.

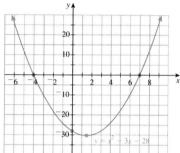

23. a. $3x^3 + 7x^2 - 5x$

   b. $2x^2 + 13x - 24$

25. $x = \frac{{}^-5}{2}$

8.4 Exercises

1. Stretching a function stretches the graph away from the x-axis. Compressing a function compresses the graph toward the x-axis.

3. a. $c > 1$

   b. $0 < c < 1$

   c. $c = 1$

5. The original function is reflected (flipped) across the x-axis.

7. The graph of $f(x) = 0$ is a line on the x-axis. Reflecting $f(x)$ across the x-axis does not change the graph.

9. The table shows that values of Y2 correspond to values of Y1 one row earlier. Typical of this movement is the x-intercept. The table shows that the x-intercept occurs when $x = 0$ for Y1 and when $x = 1$ for Y2.

11. a. 2   **b.** 3   **c.** 4   **d.** 1

13. a. $g(x) = |x - 2|$

   b. $g(x) = \sqrt{x + 2}$

   c. $g(x) = x^3 - 1$

   d. $g(x) = (x + 1)^2 + 1$

15. Vertex: $(9.5, 52)$

8.4 Skills and Review

17.

Basic Function	Function	Graph	Domain and Range
Linear	$f(x) = x$		Domain: $\{x \mid {}^{-}\infty < x < \infty\}$ Range: $\{y \mid {}^{-}\infty < y < \infty\}$
Quadratic	$f(x) = x^2$		Domain: $\{x \mid {}^{-}\infty < x < \infty\}$ Range: $\{y \mid 0 \leq y\}$
Cubic	$f(x) = x^3$		Domain: $\{x \mid {}^{-}\infty < x < \infty\}$ Range: $\{y \mid {}^{-}\infty < y < \infty\}$
Square root	$f(x) = \sqrt{x}$		Domain: $\{x \mid 0 \leq x\}$ Range: $\{y \mid 0 \leq y\}$
Absolute value	$f(x) = |x|$		Domain: $\{x \mid {}^{-}\infty < x < \infty\}$ Range: $\{y \mid 0 \leq y\}$
Reciprocal	$f(x) = \frac{1}{x}$		Domain: $\{x \mid x \neq 0\}$ Range: $\{y \mid y \neq 0\}$

19. a. Yes, the graph of the function passes the vertical-line test.

b. $\left(\frac{5}{2}, \frac{11}{4}\right) = (2.5, 2.75)$

c. Range: $\{y | 2.75 \leq y\}$

21.

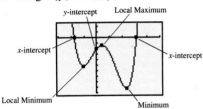

23. $24b(3a^2 - 2b^2)$

25. About $(^-.08, ^-1.85)$

Chapter 8 Exploration

a. The browser links to the page for athletics.

b. The browser remains on the home page.

c. Domain: $\{(x, y) | 110 \leq x \leq 170 \text{ and } 30 \leq y \leq 90\}$

d. Range: set of 18 links.

Chapter 8 Review Exercises

1. A function is a rule that associates to an allowable input value one and only one output value.

2. The set of all allowable inputs to a function is called the *domain* of the function.

The allowable inputs are those that correspond to an output.

The set of possible outputs of a function is the *range* of the function.

3. Yes. Each input has associated with it a unique output value.

a. Domain: $\{\alpha, \beta, \gamma, \varepsilon\}$

b. Range: $\{1, 2, 3\}$

4. No. The input x has two outputs, 3 and 8, associated with it.

5. a.

6. a. $f(x) = x^2 - 3$ **b.** $f(^-2) = 1$

c. $f(1.46) = ^-.8684$

7. a. $f(3) = 4$ **b.** $g(2) = 2$

c. $h(^-1) = ^-35$ **d.** $p(4) = 3$

e. $q(^-2) = ^-28$ **f.** $r(1) = ^-3$

8. Function

9. Not a function

10. Function

11. Domain: $\{A, B, C, D\}$; range: $\{4, 6, 8, 10\}$

12. Domain: $\{^-2, ^-1, 3, 4\}$; range: $\{^-2, ^-1, 1, 2\}$

13. a.

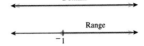

b. Domain: $\{x | ^-\infty < x < \infty\}$; range: $\{y | ^-1 \leq y\}$

14. a. Domain: $\{x | 2 \leq x\}$; range: $\{y | 0 \leq y\}$

b. Domain: $\{x | ^-2 \leq x\}$; range: $\{y | 0 \leq y\}$

c. Domain: $\{x | x \neq ^-2\}$; range: $\{y | y \neq 0\}$

d. Domain: $\{x | x \neq 1\}$; range: $\{y | y \neq 0\}$

15. a. Linear: I, III;

quadratic: I, II;

cubic: I, III;

square root: I;

absolute value: I, II;

reciprocal: I, III

b. Reciprocal

16. Local maximum: $(^-2, 4)$; local minimum: $(1, ^-1)$

17.

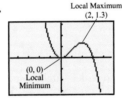

Local minimum: $(0, 0)$;

Local maximum: $(2, 1.3)$ (answers for the y-coordinate may vary slightly)

18. a. It costs $90 to print 4500 pages.

b. It costs $30 * \left(\frac{s}{1500}\right) = \frac{s}{50} = .02s$ dollars to print s pages.

c. $c(p(s)) = .02s$. Yes. We can find the cost in two steps by using the functions $p(s)$ and then $c(p)$, or we can use the composite function $c(p(s))$ to find the cost in one step.

19. a. $f(g(2)) = 2$ **b.** $f(g(3)) = 7$

c. $f(g(x)) = x^2 - 2$ **d.** $g(f(0)) = 0$

e. $g(f(^-2)) = ^-4$ **f.** $g(f(x)) = x^2 + 4x$

20. a. $k(j(^-1)) = ^-4$ **b.** $k(j(x)) = \frac{1}{x} - 3$

c. $j(k(2)) = ^-1$ **d.** $j(k(x)) = \frac{1}{x-3}$

21. a. 4   **b.** 2   **c.** 1   **d.** 5   **e.** 3

22. a. The graph of $f(x)$ moves left 3 units.

b. The graph of $f(x)$ moves down 3 units.

c. The graph of $f(x)$ is reflected (flipped) across the x-axis.

d. The graph of $f(x)$ is compressed toward the x-axis.

23. The basic square root function moves left 4 units and moves down 2 units.

24. The graph of $f(x)$ is stretched away from the x-axis, reflected across the x-axis, and moved right 2 units.

25. The graph of $f(x)$ is moved down 5 units and moved left 1 unit.

Chapter 8 Test

1. The graph passes the vertical-line test.

2. a. $g(x) = x^3 - 3x^2$

  b. $g(2) = {}^-4$

  c. $g({}^-3.27) = {}^-67.044483$

3.

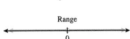

4. a.

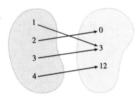

Yes, each input is associated with a single output.

  b.

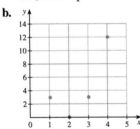

Yes, the graph passes the vertical-line test.

5. No, the graph fails the vertical-line test.

6. a. Yes, there is a single output associated with each input.

  b. Domain: {DSL, cable, 56 Kbs, 33.6 Kbs, 28.8 Kbs}; range: {1000, 2600, 8600, 15,000, 15,500}

7. a. One x-intercept: $(0, 0)$, y-intercept: $(0, 0)$

  b. No

8.

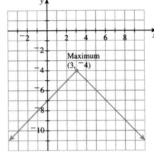

9. a. $c(t(b)) = 45b$ **b.** 78.75 cups of coffee

10. a. $f(g(4)) = \frac{1}{3}$ **b.** $f(g(x)) = \frac{1}{x-1}$

  c. $g(f({}^-3)) = {}^-\frac{4}{3}$ **d.** $g(f(x)) = \frac{1}{x} - 1$

11. The graph of $f(x)$ is stretched away from the x-axis and moved right 3 units.

12. a. The graph of $f(x)$ moves right 2 units.

  b. The graph of $f(x)$ moves up 2 units.

  c. The graph of $f(x)$ is reflected across the x-axis.

  d. The graph of $f(x)$ is stretched away from the x-axis.

Chapter 9 Powers and Roots

9.1 Exercises

1. $16^{-1} = \frac{1}{16}$; $16^0 = 1$; $16^1 = 16$

  a. $1 < 16^{1/2} < 16$

  b. $\sqrt{16}$

  c. ${}^-4$ does not lie between 1 and 16; see part (a).

d. No, the solutions of $x^2 = 16$ are $x = 4$ and $x = {}^-4$, whereas the solution of $x = \sqrt{16}$ is only $x = 4$.

3. a. $\left(\sqrt{7}\right)^5$ or $\sqrt{7^5}$; in simple radical form, $49\sqrt{7}$

  b. $\sqrt[3]{13}$

  c. $5^{3/2}$

  d. $11^{1/5}$

5. $\sqrt{(^-5)^2} = 5;\ \left(\sqrt{^-5}\right)^2$ is undefined.

The two expressions differ in the placement of the parentheses. In the first, we square $^-5$ before taking the square root. In the second, we must attempt the square root of $^-5$ before squaring. Negative numbers, however, do not have real number square roots.

$\sqrt[3]{(^-5)^3} = ^-5;\ \left(\sqrt[3]{^-5}\right)^3 = ^-5$

These two expressions result in a cube root of a negative number. The cube root of a negative number is a negative number. For example, $\sqrt[3]{^-8} = ^-2$ because $(^-2)(^-2)(^-2) = ^-8$. Section 9.2 provides further information on odd and even roots.

7. a. 2 **b.** 6 **c.** 4 **d.** 2

9. Each side of the cube is exactly $\sqrt[3]{20}$ cm or approximately 2.7 cm.

11. a. 9 **b.** 8 **c.** .00032

  d. $\frac{27}{125}$ **e.** 129.64

13. a. $\frac{\sqrt{5}}{5}$ **b.** $\frac{3\sqrt{2}}{2}$ **c.** 2

  d. $\frac{\sqrt{70}}{5}$ **e.** $\frac{\sqrt{21}}{7}$ **f.** $\frac{\sqrt{30}}{6}$

15. a. $49\sqrt{7}$

  b. $7^{5/2} = 49\sqrt{7} \approx 129.64$

9.1 Skills and Review

17. a. 0

  b. 3 is not in the domain of $g(x)$; $g(3) = \sqrt{3-4} = \sqrt{^-1}$, and negative numbers do not have real square roots.

19. ⟵——————|——————⟶
          0

21. $c = ^-3$ or $c = ^-5$

23. a. $(x-4)(x-6)$

  b. $^-4(x-3)(x+3)$

  c. $5x(2x-7)$

25. $x = 6$

9.2 Exercises

1. a. Domain: $\{x\,|\,^-\infty < x < \infty\}$

  b. Range: $\{y\,|\,^-\infty < y < \infty\}$

  c. I and III

  d. $f(x) = x^3,\ f(x) = x^5$. n is odd, the domain and range are the set of real numbers, and the graphs appear in quadrants I and III.

3. a. $x = 2$

  b. $x = ^-3$

  c. $x = ^-1$ or $x = 1$

5. a. $x = \pm\sqrt[4]{25} = \pm\sqrt{5}$

  b. No real solution; you can't take the even root of a negative number.

  c. $x = ^-2$ or $x = 12$

7. a. $x = 27.9841$

  b. No real solution; the graph of Y1 $= X \wedge (1/4)$ does not go below the x-axis. Therefore, the graph of Y1 does not intersect the graph of Y2 $= ^-2.3$.

  c. $x = 18.89568$

  d. $x = ^-18.89568$

9. $x = 0$ or $x = 2.5$

11. a. $f(g(x)) = x$ and $g(f(x)) = x$

  b. $f(g(x)) = x$ and $g(f(x)) = x$

  c. $f(g(x)) = x$ and $g(f(x)) = x$

13. $(3, 4)$ and $(0, ^-2)$

15. a.

  b. Yes; the graph of Y2 appears to be the mirror image of the graph of Y1, with the line $y = x$ as the mirror.

  c. Yes

  d. Yes; when two functions are inverses of each other, each point (x, y) on the graph of one function has a corresponding point (y, x) on the graph of its inverse function.

9.2 Skills and Review

17. $x = \pm 4\sqrt{2}$

19. a. Basic absolute value function

  b. Basic square root function

  c. Basic linear function

  d. Basic reciprocal function

  e. Basic quadratic function

  f. Basic cubic function

21. The graph of $f(x)$ is shifted up 7 units.

23. ⟵——————|——————⟶
          0

25. The vertex is a minimum at $(2, ^-16)$.

9.3 Exercises

1. $y = .407(93)^{1.5};\ y \approx 365$ days

3. a. $y = ax$ **b.** $y = .5x$

  c. $y = 1.5$ **d.** $x = 40$

5. a. $f(x) = ax^{5/2}$ **b.** $f(x) = 1.7x^{5/2}$
   c. $f(4) = 54.4$ **d.** $x = 9$

7. $a = .25$

9. a. 3; the graph looks like the basic linear function, $y = x$.
   b. 1; the graph is similar to the graph of the basic square root function, $y = \sqrt{x} = x^{1/2}$.
   c. 2; the graph is similar to the graph of the basic quadratic function, $y = x^2$.

11. a. Yes

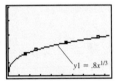

b. Yes. Both table outputs are nearly the same, so our choice of functions is a good one.
   c. $y = 3.2$
   d. $x \approx 11.4$

13. a. $y = ax^{1/3}$
   b. $a \approx .624$, $y = .624x^{1/3}$
   c. $y \approx 2.26$; the radius of the sphere is about 2.3 cm.

15. $g = 32$; the gravitational constant is 32 feet/second^2.

9.3 Skills and Review

17. $x = 1$ or $x = 5$

19. a. $2\sqrt{3}$
   b. $54\sqrt{2}$
   c. $\frac{\sqrt{5}}{5}$

21. $c^{1/3}$

23. a.

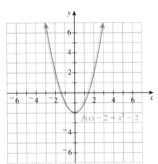

b.

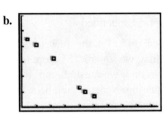

c.

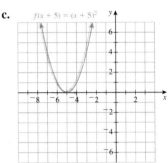

25. $(x + 2)(x - 7)$

9.4 Exercises

1. United States

3. a.

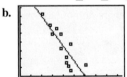

Window: $0 \le X \le 94$, $0 \le Y \le 80$; no.

b.

$y \approx {}^-1.758x + 105$; the line does not fit the points exactly but is close to most of them.

c. (0, 105); 105°F is the predicted average January temperature at 0°N (the equator).

d. ${}^-1.758$ is the rate of change for the temperature. The average January temperature drops about 1.76°F for each increase of 1° in latitude.

e. Other geographic factors, including proximity to large bodies of water and elevation, affect the temperature. For example, Olympia and San Francisco are both located on the Pacific coast and are much warmer than the corresponding inland cities, Bismarck and Charleston.

Chapter 9 Exploration

Note	Number of Half-Steps above Middle C	Frequency in Traditional System	Frequency with Equal Temperament
Middle C	0	264	264
C sharp/D flat	1	278.4	279.7
D	2	297	296.3
D sharp/E flat	3	312.8	314.0
E	4	330	332.6
F	5	352	352.4
F sharp/G flat	6	371.2	373.4
G	7	396	395.6
G sharp/A flat	8	417.6	419.1
A	9	440	444.0
A sharp/B flat	10	469.4	470.4
B	11	495	498.4
High C	12	528	528

a. Middle C and high C

b. Note A

c.

Ratio of Frequencies	Traditional	Equal Temperament
G to middle C	$\frac{396}{264} = 1.50$	$\frac{395.6}{264} \approx 1.498$
A to D	$\frac{440}{297} \approx 1.48$	$\frac{444.0}{296.3} \approx 1.498$
B flat to E flat	$\frac{469.4}{312.8} \approx 1.50$	$\frac{470.4}{314.0} \approx 1.498$

The ratios of frequencies for the traditional system are close to each other, but the ratios of frequencies for the equal temperament are much closer. The ratios of the equal temperament are within .001 of each other.

Chapter 9 Review Exercises

1.

X	Y1	Y2
0	0	0
1	1	1
2	1.1892	1.1892
3	1.3161	1.3161
4	1.4142	1.4142
5	1.4953	1.4953
6	1.5651	1.5651

X=0

$Y1 = 4\sqrt[4]{(X)}$, $Y2 = X \wedge (1/4)$; Y1 and Y2 are the same, so the expressions are equal.

2. a. $\frac{2}{3}$ **b.** 3

3. 1.246

4. a. 125   **b.** 27

c. $\frac{4}{9}$ **d.** 17.78

5. a. $\sqrt{18}$ or $3\sqrt{2}$ **b.** $\sqrt[4]{49}$ or $\sqrt{7}$

c. $\sqrt[5]{3}^2 = \sqrt[5]{9}$ **d.** $\frac{1}{\sqrt{8}}$ or $\frac{\sqrt{2}}{4}$

6. a. $7\sqrt{2}$ **b.** $6\sqrt{3}$ **c.** $\frac{\sqrt{7}}{7}$ **d.** $\frac{\sqrt{6}}{3}$

7. a. $x = \pm 3\sqrt{6}$ **b.** $x = {}^-2 \pm 3\sqrt{2}$

c. $x = 2 \pm \frac{5\sqrt{3}}{3}$

8. a. $x = \pm 2$

b. No real solution; the graph of $Y1 = X \wedge 4$ does not go below the x-axis.

c. $x = 5$

d. $x = {}^-5$

9. a. $x = \pm\sqrt[6]{49} \pm \sqrt[3]{7}$.

b. $x = 5$

c. No real solution; you can't take the even root of a negative number.

10. a. $x = 9$

b. No real solution; the graph of $Y1 = X \wedge (1/2)$ does not go below the x-axis.

c. $x = 10.48576$

d. $x = {}^-10.48576$

11. a. $x = 9$

b. No real solution; $x = 9$ is an extraneous solution because it doesn't satisfy the original equation.

c. $x = 10.48576$

d. $x = {}^-10.48576$

12. a. $x = 3$ or $x = 6$

b. $x = 3$ is an extraneous solution because it doesn't satisfy the original equation. A graph of $Y1 = X - 4$ and $Y2 = \sqrt{(X - 2)}$ shows a single intersection of $X = 6$. Therefore, $x = 3$ is not a solution.

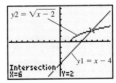

13. $f(g(x)) = x$ and $g(f(x)) = x$

14. The left half of the graph of $Y1 = X \wedge 4$ has no corresponding points on the graph of $Y2 = X \wedge (1/4)$.

15. Jupiter completes one revolution around the sun in about 12 years.

16. $a = \frac{1}{3}$

17. $a = 5$

18. $a = .2$

19. a. $a = \frac{100}{\sqrt{10}} = 10\sqrt{10} \approx 31.62$
  b. $y \approx 63.25$
  c. $x = 4.096$

20. a. $y = ax$
  b. $a = .11, y = .11x$
  c. $x \approx 455$; the resident uses about 455 kWh.

21. a. $y = ax^3$
  b. $a = .13, y = .13x^3$
  c. $y = 2031.25$; the windmill generates 2031.25 W of power.

22.

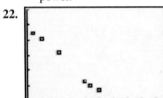

The points show a downward trend; as x increases, y decreases. The points fit fairly closely along a straight line.

23. a. $y \approx {}^{-}3.46x + 97.65$
  b. $y \approx 73.45$

Chapter 9 Test

1. a. 10   **b.** 7   **c.** 2

2. a. 1.3   **b.** 2.5

3. a. 1000   **b.** 25   **c.** 625

4. a. $\sqrt[3]{54}$ **b.** $\sqrt[6]{36}$
  c. $\left(\sqrt[3]{4}\right)^5 = \sqrt[3]{4^5}$

5. a. $4\sqrt{3}$ **b.** $2\sqrt{7}$ **c.** $\frac{\sqrt{10}}{5}$ **d.** $\frac{\sqrt{15}}{5}$

6. a. Two solutions; the graph of $Y1 = X \wedge 2$ intersects the graph of $Y2 = 100$ twice.
  b. One solution; the graph of $Y1 = X \wedge 3$ intersects the graph of $Y2 = {}^{-}27$ once.
  c. No real solution; the graph of $Y1 = X \wedge 2$ doesn't intersect the graph of $Y2 = {}^{-}100$.

7. a. $x = \pm 10$
  b. $x = {}^{-}3$
  c. No real solution; you can't take the square root of a negative number.

8. a. $x = 6$
  b. $x = \pm\sqrt[4]{36} = \pm\sqrt{6}$
  c. No real solution; $x = 256$ is an extraneous solution because it doesn't satisfy the original equation.
  d. $x = {}^{-}1$

9. $x = 2$; $x = {}^{-}3$ is an extraneous solution because it doesn't satisfy the original equation.

10. $f(g(x)) = x$ and $g(f(x)) = x$

11. a. $a = 3$ **b.** $y = 192$ **c.** $x = 1$

12. a. $y = ax$
  b. $a = \frac{\sqrt{3}}{2} \approx .866, y = \frac{\sqrt{3}}{2}x$ or $y = .866x$
  c. $y = .750$; the height of the equilateral triangle is .750 cm.

13. a. $y = ax^2$
  b. $a = 4.9, y = 4.9x^2$
  c. $x = 10$; in 10 s the object drops 490 m.

Chapter 10 Exponential and Logarithmic Functions

10.1 Exercises

1. a. $A_0 = 1000$
  b. $r = 6\%$
  c. $n = 12$
  d. $A(4) = 1000(1 + .06/12) \wedge (12 * 4) \approx 1270.49$

3. a.

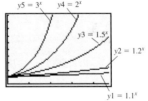

b. y-intercept: $(0, 1)$

c. The greater the base, b, the steeper the graph.

5. $f(x) = \frac{1}{3}(5)^x$

7. a. The outputs increase by the same factor, in this case 1.5. This is the growth factor, b.

b. $f(x) = 5(1.5)^x$

9. $x \approx 4.97$

11. Daily compounding at 5% yields more. Compare $1000 invested for 1 year. After 1 year the 5% investment appreciates to $1051.27, whereas the 5.1% investment appreciates to $1051.00.

13. a.

Year	Number of Years Since 2002	Highest Baseball Salary
2002	0	22,000,000
2003	1	25,740,000
2004	2	30,115,800
2005	3	35,235,486
2006	4	41,225,519
2007	5	48,233,857
2008	6	56,433,612
2009	7	66,027,327
2010	8	77,251,972

b. $A(t) = 22000000(1.17)^t$

c.
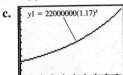

15. About 16 years

10.1 Skills and Review

17. $y = \frac{3}{8}x^{5/2}$

19. $x = 2$

21. $x = {}^-6 \pm \sqrt{52}$

$x = {}^-6 \pm 2\sqrt{13}$ *(Simple radical form)*

23. a.
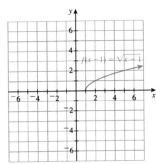

b.
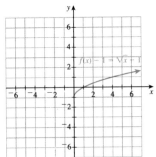

c.
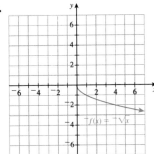

d.
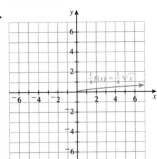

25. The car was traveling 90 miles/hour.

10.2 Exercises

1. a. $b > 1$

b. $0 < b < 1$

3. a. 1 **b.** 5 **c.** .4 **d.** $\frac{1}{2}$

5. The graph of $y = 2(3)^{-x}$ is the mirror image of the graph of $y = 2(3)^x$ with the y-axis as the mirror.

7. Half-life gives a quick method to compare rates of decay. It is the amount of time it takes for a substance to decay to one-half of its initial amount.

9. a. For equal time periods the output decreases by the same factor. In this case, after every 13 days the weight is halved.

b. $y_0 = 1$

c. $b = \frac{1}{2}$

d. $k = \frac{1}{13}$

e. $y = \left(\frac{1}{2}\right)^{(1/13)t} = \left(\frac{1}{2}\right)^{t/13}$

11. a. $y_0 = \$90$

b. $\$45$

c.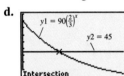

From the table of values, an estimate for the half-life of the video game is between 1 and 2 years.

d.

y1 = $90\left(\frac{2}{3}\right)^x$

y2 = 45

Intersection
X=1.7095113 _Y=45

From the graph, a better approximation for the half-life is 1.7 years.

13. a. $A(t) = 60\left(\frac{3}{4}\right)^{t/10}$

b. In approximately 24 days there is half of the initial amount of thorium 234.

15. The machine is worth half of its initial value in about 5 years.

10.2 Skills and Review

17. The population doubles in about 10.3 years.

19. a. $a = \frac{5}{2}$ **b.** $y = \frac{45}{2} = 22.5$ **c.** $x = 5.2$

21. 3

23. a. $f(g(^-5)) = {^-}11$ **b.** $f(g(x)) = 2x - 1$

c. $g(f(x)) = 2x - 2$

25. $(x - 5)(x + 4)$

10.3 Exercises

1. The graph of $y = \log(x)$ appears to be the mirror image of the graph of $y = 10^x$ with the line $y = x$ as the mirror.

3. a. $10^3 = 1000 \rightarrow \log(1000) = 3$

b. $10^1 = 10 \rightarrow \log(10) = 1$

c. $10^0 = 1 \rightarrow \log(1) = 0$

d. $10^{-2} = \frac{1}{100} \rightarrow \log\left(\frac{1}{100}\right) = {^-}2$

5. $\log(3.2)$ is between 0 and 1.

7. $6(10)^{2x} = 600$

$(10)^{2x} = 100$ *Dividing by 6 on both sides*

$\log(10^{2x}) = \log(10^2)$ *Taking the logarithm on both sides and writing 100 as 10^2*

$2x = 2$ *Common log undoes raising 10 to a power*

$x = 1$ *Dividing by 2 on both sides*

9. a. $x \approx 2.77815$ **b.** $x \approx {^-}.31808$

c. $x \approx {^-}.56632$

11. a. $x = 100$ **b.** $x = 1000$ **c.** $x = 10$

13. $x \approx 501.187$ *Check:* $\log(501.187) \approx 2.7$

15. $t = \frac{\log(.5)}{\log(.97)} \approx 22.76$

10.3 Skills and Review

17. a. $y = 500\left(\frac{3}{4}\right)^x$

b. The item is worth half of its initial value in approximately 2.4 years.

19. a. $A(t) = 750\left(1 + \frac{.038}{12}\right)^{12t}$

b. The account is worth $\$1500$ in approximately 18.3 years.

21. $a = 7$

23. $c = {^-}1$ or $c = {^-}5$

25. $x = 44$

10.4 Exercises

1. The domain of $f(x) = \log(x)$ is the set of positive numbers. There is no number that we can put in the exponent of 10 that will give 0 or a negative number.

3. a. $M(1) = 0$ **b.** $M(100) = 2$

c. $M(100,000) = 5$

5. a. $M(12,843) \approx 4.1$

b. $M(240) \approx 2.4$

c. $M(351,060,000) \approx 8.5$

7.

x	$\log x$
.058	$^-1.2$
.58	$^-.2$
5.8	.8
58	1.8
580	2.8

9. It is hard to distinguish between amplitudes that vary so much. On the other hand, Richter magnitudes usually vary between 1 and 9, making it easier to see differences in earthquake intensity.

11. The lower the pH, the more acidic the substance.

13. a. Lemon juice

   b. 10^9 or 1,000,000,000

15. 10^2 or 100

10.4 Skills and Review

17. a. $x = \pm 3$ **b.** $x = 9$

19. a. $x = \frac{3}{2} = 1.5$ **b.** $x = 10^{-1} = \frac{1}{10} = .1$

21. a. $A(t) = 3\left(\frac{1}{2}\right)^{t/800}$ **b.** $\frac{3}{2} = 1.5$ kg

   c. $\frac{3}{8} = .375$ kg

23. $f(g(x)) = x$ and $g(f(x)) = x$

25. a. $2x(x + 3)$ **b.** $y(x - 4)(x + 4)$

   c. $(x + 4)(x - 1)$

10.5 Exercises

1. The half-life for this material is approximately 44.15 years.

Chapter 10 Exploration

a.

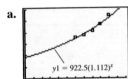

$y1 = 922.5(1.112)^x$

b. If the current rate continues, the number of AIDS cases will double in about 6.4 years.

c. Estimate 7710 AIDS cases in this region in the year 2010.

d. Answers may vary.

Chapter 10 Review Exercises

1. a.

x	y
0	2
1	8
2	32
3	128

   b. $y_0 = 2$

   c. $b = 4$

2. $y = 200(7)^x$

3. a. $A(t) = 2000\left(1 + \frac{.068}{12}\right)^{12t}$ **b.** $A(7) \approx \$3214.92$

4. Between 10 and 11 years

5. 10.2 years

6. Rule of 72: 60 years

7. c

8. a. Half-life is the amount of time it takes for half of a substance to decay.

b. 7.5 g

c. 3.75 g

d.

Time (years)	Amount U-234 (g)
0	15
245,000	7.5
490,000	3.75
735,000	1.875

   e. $A(t) = 15\left(\frac{1}{2}\right)^{t/245,000}$

9. $y = 12(.92)^{t/5}$

10. a. about .9 miles   **b.** 34.3 years

11. Using the definition of negative integer exponents from Section 6.1, we have $6^{-x} = \frac{1}{6^x}$; because 1 to any power is 1, we may write $\left(\frac{1}{6}\right)^x$. Therefore, $20(6)^{-x} = 20\left(\frac{1}{6}\right)^x$.

12. a. $y = 8000\left(\frac{2}{3}\right)^t$ **b.** 1.7 years

13. Domain: $\{x \mid {}^-\infty < x < \infty\}$; range: $\{y \mid 0 < y < \infty\}$

14. a. 2   **b.** 4   **c.** $^-1$

15. a. $^-.699$ **b.** .222   **c.** 1.892

16. $x = 1000$

17. a. $10^{5/4} = 10^{1.25}$ **b.** 17.78

18. a. $x = 2$ **b.** $x = 5$ **c.** $x = 1$

19. $x = 6$

20. a.

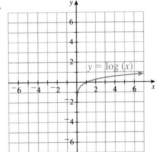

   b. Domain: $\{x \mid 0 < x < \infty\}$; range: $\{y \mid {}^-\infty < y < \infty\}$

21. a. 1.04   **b.** 3.15   **c.** 7.73

22. 1000

23. a. 14   **b.** 3   **c.** 6.9

24. The pH will decrease by 1.

25. The 100-dB sound is 10^8, or 100,000,000, times more intense than the 20-dB sound.

26. The recommended maximum sound at a nightclub is about 30,000 ($10^{4.5} \approx 31,623$) times more intense than the maximum sound outdoors in a residential area at nighttime.

27. The investment doubles in approximately 11.55 years.

28. a. 6

    b. $^-9$

    c. 1.8

    d. 1

    e. $\ln(40) \approx 3.69$

Chapter 10 Test

1. a. $y_0 = 1,998,000$

    b. 3.1%

    c. 3,679,330

    d. Around the year 2015 (by graphing $x \approx 15.4$)

2. a. $A(6) \approx \$15,219.00$

    b. Using the rule of 72 or graphing, we find the investment doubles in about 10 years.

3. Rule of 72: 18 minutes

4. 1600 years

5. a. $A(t) = 8600(.87)^t$

    b. about 4286

6. a. $A(t) = 3000\left(\frac{3}{4}\right)^t$

    b. $A(2) = \$1687.50$

    c. The piece of hardware is worth half its initial value in approximately 2.4 years.

7. a. 1   **b.** 0   **c.** $^-3$ **d.** $^-2$

8. a. $10^{2/3}$ **b.** 4.64

9. $x = \frac{4}{5}$

10. 4.4

11. 7.1

12. The lawn mower sound is 1000 times more intense than the vacuum cleaner sound.

Chapter 11 Rational Expressions

11.1 Exercises

1. A rational expression is a fraction in which both the numerator and denominator are polynomials. Answers may vary:

$$\frac{x + 3}{x^2 - 2x + 5}.$$

3. a. Substituting $^-2$ for x in the expression will give a denominator of 0, and division by 0 is undefined.

    b. $Y1 = (X - 3)/(X + 2)$

    c. ERROR

5. a. 15   **b.** $x^2 y^2$

    c. $x^2 - 8x + 15$

7. a. $\dfrac{17}{36}$ **b.** $\dfrac{3y - 2x}{xy}$

    c. $\dfrac{5x + 9}{(x + 2)(x + 1)}$

9. a. $\dfrac{3}{16}$ **b.** $\dfrac{4x}{5y^2}$ **c.** $\dfrac{x + 2}{x}$

11. Method 1: Compare table outputs. Enter the expressions in the Y= menu. The table outputs for Y1 and Y2 should be equal except at X = 5.

Method 2: Compare graphs. The graph of Y1 should be the same as the graph of Y2.

13. $\dfrac{a}{b^2 x^2 y^3}$

15. $\dfrac{x - 2}{5(x - 8)}$

11.1 Skills and Review

17. $f(g(x)) = 10^{\log(x)} = x$ and $g(f(x)) = \log(10^x) = x$

19. a. 10,000   **b.** .001   **c.** 100,000

21. a. Increasing; because $b > 1 (b = 1.065)$, we have growth.

    b. The initial value is $y_0 = 4449$ eagle pairs.

    c. The eagle pairs are increasing by 6.5% each year.

    d. 10,744 eagle pairs

23. a. The graph of the basic absolute value function $f(x) = |x|$ is shifted to the left 1 unit.

    b. The graph of the basic cubic function $f(x) = x^3$ is reflected across the x-axis.

    c. The graph of the basic square root function $f(x) = \sqrt{x}$ is stretched away from the x-axis.

    d. The graph of the basic reciprocal function $f(x) = \frac{1}{x}$ is shifted up 5 units.

25. a. y-intercept: $(0, ^-8)$

    b. x-intercepts:

$$\left(\frac{3}{2} + \frac{\sqrt{41}}{2}, 0\right), \quad \left(\frac{3}{2} - \frac{\sqrt{41}}{2}, 0\right)$$

c. Vertex (minimum):

$$\left(\frac{3}{2}, \frac{-41}{4}\right)$$

11.2 Exercises

1. a.

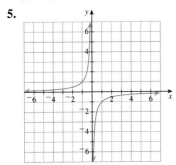

b. As the number of items x increases, the average cost decreases, but the rate of decrease slows.

c. As x gets very large, the average cost approaches \$7 per item.

d. Substituting 0 for x in the average cost function causes division by 0, which is undefined.

3. Horizontal asymptote: $y = 3$; vertical asymptote: $x = 1$.

5.

7. The branches of the graph of $f(x) = \frac{1}{x}$ are reflected across the x-axis and stretched away from the x-axis. The branches now appear in the second and fourth quadrants. Horizontal asymptote: x-axis; vertical asymptote: y-axis.

9. The graph of $f(x)$ is shifted down 1 unit. Horizontal asymptote: $y = -1$; vertical asymptote: y-axis.

11. a. Domain: $\{x \mid x \neq 0\}$; range: $\{y \mid y \neq 0\}$

b. Domain: $\{x \mid x \neq 0\}$; range: $\{y \mid y \neq 0\}$

c. Domain: $\{x \mid x \neq -4\}$; range: $\{y \mid y \neq 0\}$

d. Domain: $\{x \mid x \neq 0\}$; range: $\{y \mid y \neq -1\}$

e. Domain: $\{x \mid x \neq 2\}$; range: $\{y \mid y \neq 6\}$

13. a. Third and fourth quadrants

b. Domain: $\{x \mid x \neq 0\}$; range $\{y \mid y < 0\}$

15. a. No, the function is undefined at $x = -4$.

b. Either graph with a MODE of Dot or graph with a friendly window such as $-9.4 \leq X \leq 9.4$, $-6.2 \leq Y \leq 6.2$.

11.2 Skills and Review

17. $\dfrac{x^2 - 4x - 1}{(x - 3)(x + 3)}$

19.

x	$\log(x)$
.13	$-.9$
1.3	.1
13	1.1
130	2.1
1300	3.1

21. 3.6 years

23. a. $f(-2) = 0$

b. $f(0)$ is undefined due to division by 0.

c. $f(2) = 2$

d. $f(200) \approx 1$

25. $\frac{3}{10} = .3$

11.3 Exercises

1. a. Answers may vary; Ymax $= 1$.

b. $x = 6$; the graphing solution is the same as the algebraic solution.

3. Windows may vary; Xmin $= -9.4$, Xmax $= 9.4$, Ymin $= -10$, Ymax $= 10$; $x = 2.25$

5. The empty pool fills in 3 hours with the outtake pipe shut.

7. $x = \frac{16}{3}$

9. $x = \frac{2}{3}$ or $x = 4$

11. Working together, Joan and her partner detail a car in 2.4 hours, or 2 hours 24 minutes.

13. a. The speed of the river current is 20 m/s.

b. The rowing team travels downstream in 30 s.

15. a. No, the graph of Y1 has a horizontal asymptote of $y = 7$.

b. You get the impossible solution $3 = 0$.

c. There is no solution.

11.3 Skills and Review

17. a.

b. Vertical asymptote: $x = 0$; horizontal asymptote: $y = 1$

19. $-\dfrac{1}{3x}$

21. $^{-}2$

23. $\dfrac{1}{z^{12}}$

25. a. $x = {}^{-}3$ or $x = {}^{-}2$ **b.** $x = 2$

    c. $x = 1$ **d.** $x = \pm 2$

    e. $x = {}^{-}2$

11.4 Exercises

1. As the weight increases, the distance decreases. The distance decreases quickly at first, then the rate of decrease slows.

3. a. 120 pound-feet

    b. Weight

    c. Distance

5. a. Time $*$ Velocity is a constant of 3600.

    b. Velocity $= \dfrac{3600}{\text{time}}$

7. $a = 400$, $R = \dfrac{400}{I}$

9. $F = \dfrac{a}{d^2}$

11. $F = 1250$ newtons

13. a. $y = \dfrac{1}{5}$ **b.** $x = 12$ **c.** $y = 12.5$

15. a. Pressure $= .90125$ atmosphere

    b. Volume ≈ 3.43 L

11.4 Skills and Review

17. $f(x) + 6 = \dfrac{1}{x} + 6$; the basic reciprocal function is shifted up 6 units.

19. $y = 200\left(\dfrac{9}{10}\right)^x$

21. a. $x = 9$; we reject $x = 1$ as extraneous because it doesn't satisfy the original equation.

    b. No, substitution or graphing show that this solution is false.

23. a. 3   **b.** 2   **c.** 5

25. a. $y = \dfrac{60}{x^2}$

    b. $f(x) = \dfrac{60}{x^2}$

    c. $f(2) = 15$

    d. $x = \pm 6$

11.5 Exercises

1. a. $x + 5$

    b. $x + 5 - \dfrac{5}{x+7}$

    c. $x + 5 + \dfrac{3}{x+7}$

3. a. $Y1 = (X \wedge 2 - 14X + 48)/(X - 6)$

       $Y2 = (X \wedge 2 - 14X + 30)/(X - 6)$

       $Y3 = (X \wedge 2 - 14X + 60)/(X - 6)$

    b.

c. The graph of Y1 is a straight line with a gap at $x = 6$. The graph Y2 has two branches. There appears to be a vertical asymptote at $x = 6$, and both branches of Y2 appear to get close to the Y1 graph as x assumes large positive or negative values.

The graph of Y3 is similar to the graph of Y2 except the branches appear in the upper right and lower left.

Note that in Exercise 2 the quotient is the same in each case and only the remainders differ.

When the remainder is 0, the graph of Y1 is a graph of the linear quotient $y = x - 8$.

When the remainder is not 0 and for large positive or negative values of x, the graphs of Y2 and Y3 approach the line $y = x - 8$. As x approaches 6, the graphs of Y2 and Y3 are stretched away from the line $y = x - 8$ and approach the vertical asymptote at $x = 6$.

5. In both methods the first term of the quotient is found by finding the ? in $x * ? = x^3$.

In both methods we multiply the first term in the quotient by each term in the divisor.

In both methods we subtract the preceding result from the dividend.

The process is repeated to find the remaining terms of the quotient.

Chapter 11 Exploration

a. $I = \dfrac{a}{d^2}$

b. $a = 35{,}000$

c. $I \approx 155.6$ foot-candles

d. Either move closer to the light source or improve the light source.

Chapter 11 Review Exercises

1. Answers may vary.

a. $\dfrac{10}{12}, \dfrac{5x}{6x}$

b. $\dfrac{3x^4}{3xy^2}, \dfrac{x^3y^9}{y^{11}}$

c. $\dfrac{xz - 4z}{xz + 5z}, \dfrac{x^2 - 3x - 4}{x^2 + 6x + 5}$

2. In your calculator enter the first expression as Y1 and the second expression as Y2.

X	Y1	Y2
-4	-8	-8
3	-.125	-.125
10	.4	.4
-1	-1.25	ERROR

X=

$Y1 = (X - 4) / (X + 5)$,
$Y2 = (X^2 - 3X - 4) / (X^2 + 6X + 5)$

When $x = {}^-1$, the output of the first expression is $^-1.25$. The output of the second expression is undefined because of division by 0.

3. a. 6   b. xy^2 c. $x^2 - x$

4. a. $\dfrac{2x^3 + 3}{x^4}$

b. $\dfrac{^-2x - 3}{(x - 2)(x - 3)}$

c. $\dfrac{4x - y}{xy}$

d. $\dfrac{7x - 18}{(x + 1)(x - 4)}$

e. $\dfrac{3yz + 8}{y^2z^3}$

f. $\dfrac{3x + 8}{x(x + 2)^2}$

5. a. $\dfrac{2y}{3x^2}$

b. $\dfrac{x - 6}{x}$

c. $\dfrac{x + 3}{x - 3}$

d. $\dfrac{1}{x + 7}$

e. $^-1$

6. a. $\dfrac{4}{xy}$

b. $\dfrac{5x}{x + 3}$

c. $\dfrac{7}{2}$

d. $\dfrac{x + 8}{18x}$

7. a.

X	Y1	Y2
0	300	ERROR
10	350	35
20	400	20
30	450	15
40	500	12.5
50	550	11

X=

$Y1 = 300 + 5X, \; Y2 = (300 + 5X) / X$

b. The total cost is \$300, but the average cost is undefined because of division by 0.

c. The total cost increases at a constant rate. The average cost decreases, but the rate of decrease slows.

d.

X	Y1	Y2
100	800	8
1000	5300	5.3
10000	50300	5.03
100000	500300	5.003

X=

$Y1 = 300 + 5X, \; Y2 = (300 + 5X) / X$

The total cost continues to increase at a constant rate. The average cost approaches \$5 per item.

8.

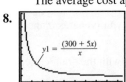

$y1 = \dfrac{(300 + 5x)}{x}$

It is a downward-sloping curve in the first quadrant. When x is close to 0, the curve falls steeply. Then it appears to level off.

9. Either graph with a MODE of Dot or graph with a friendly window such as $^-9.4 \le X \le 9.4$, $^-6.2 \le Y \le 6.2$.

10. a. The graph of $f(x) = \frac{1}{x}$ is shifted left 3 units.

b. The graph of $f(x)$ is shifted down 2 units.

c. The graph of $f(x)$ is reflected across the x-axis.

d. The graph of $f(x)$ is stretched away from the x-axis.

e. The graph of $f(x)$ is shifted right 2 units and shifted up 1 unit.

11. a. Horizontal asymptote: x-axis; vertical asymptote: $x = {}^-3$

b. Horizontal asymptote: $y = {}^-2$; vertical asymptote: y-axis

c. Horizontal asymptote: x-axis; vertical asymptote: y-axis

d. Horizontal asymptote: x-axis; vertical asymptote: y-axis

e. Horizontal asymptote: $y = 1$; vertical asymptote: $x = 2$

12. a. Domain: $\{x \mid x \ne {}^-3\}$; range: $\{y \mid y \ne 0\}$

b. Domain: $\{x \mid x \ne 0\}$; range: $\{y \mid y \ne {}^-2\}$

c. Domain: $\{x \mid x \ne 0\}$; range: $\{y \mid y \ne 0\}$

d. Domain: $\{x \mid x \ne 0\}$; range: $\{y \mid y \ne 0\}$

e. Domain: $\{x \mid x \ne 2\}$; range: $\{y \mid y \ne 1\}$

13. $x \approx {}^-.67$ or $x = 3$

14. $x = \frac{^-2}{3}$ or $x = 3$

15. a

16. a.

	Work	Time	Rate
Thaddeus	1 dinner	45 min	$\frac{1}{45}\frac{\text{dinner}}{\text{min}}$
Lynn	1 dinner	x min	$\frac{1}{x}\frac{\text{dinner}}{\text{min}}$
Together	1 dinner	20 min	$\frac{1}{20}\frac{\text{dinner}}{\text{min}}$

b. $\frac{1}{45} + \frac{1}{x} = \frac{1}{20}$

c. $x = 36$; working alone, Lynn prepares dinner in 36 minutes.

17. The Jacuzzi fills in 6 minutes with the drain closed.

18. a. $x - 3$

b. $\frac{2}{3} = \frac{9}{x-3}$

c. $x = \frac{33}{2} = 16.5$; the speed of the kayak in still water is 16.5 km/h.

d. The kayak returns downstream in $\frac{6}{13} \approx .46$ hours, or about 28 minutes.

19. The wind speed is 10 miles/hour.

20. a. As the price per gallon increases the number of gallons decreases. The product of the two quantities is constant.

b. $a = 20$. $20 is the fixed amount you have to spend on gas.

c. Gallons $= \frac{20}{\text{Price}}$ or $y = \frac{20}{x}$

d. You can purchase approximately 4.7 gallons of gasoline when the price is $4.25 per gallon.

21. a. $a = 24,000$ **b.** $y = 60$

22. a. $a = 3, y = .5$ **b.** $a = 12, x = 15$

c. $a = 90, y = 180$ **d.** $a = 250, x \approx 107.14$

23. a. $a = 1000$

b. The cost is approximately $142.86 per person when 7 students share the cottage.

24. The jogger completes the lap in approximately 122.7 seconds when his speed is 11 feet per second.

25. The astronaut weighs 16.4 pounds more on the earth than she does in an orbit 200 miles above the earth.

26. a. $x - 8$

b. $x - 8 + \frac{4}{x+5}$

c. $x - 8 - \frac{4}{x+5}$

27. a. $2x^2 + x - 5 + \frac{12}{x+2}$

b. $2x^2 - x + 3$

c. $x^3 + x^2 - x + 2 - \frac{3}{3x-1}$

Chapter 11 Test

1. $\dfrac{6x + 17}{(x+2)(x+3)}$

2. $\dfrac{-2x + 2}{(x-2)(x+2)(x-4)}$

3. $\dfrac{x+1}{x}$

4. $\dfrac{-x + 6}{x + 5}$

5. a. The graph of $f(x)$ is shifted right 4 units and up 5 units.

b. Horizontal asymptote: $y = 5$; vertical asymptote: $x = 4$

c. Domain: $\{x | x \neq 4\}$; range: $\{y | y \neq 5\}$

6. $x = \frac{-8}{3}$ or $x = 1$

7. Working alone, Ron completes the job in 10 hours.

8. The sieve fills in 4 hours when material is not allowed to pass through.

9. The speed of the motorboat is 9 miles/hour in still water.

10. $y = \frac{1}{6}$

11. The volume is 4.24 L.

12. The intensity of the light is 12 lux at a distance of 5 m.

Chapter 12 Inequalities

12.1 Exercises

1. a. Answers may vary; $x = -1, 2.5, 3, 5\frac{1}{4}$.

b. Yes. The phrase *never gets farther* than 4 blocks from her house means we include the endpoints of -2 and 6.

3. a. Answers may vary; 250 min and 300 min

b. $x = 200$ min is not a solution and $x = 400$ min is a solution.

5. a. $x < 4$ **b.** $x > 4$ **c.** $x \leq 4$

d. $x \geq 4$ **e.** $x \leq 4$ **f.** $x \geq 4$

g. $x \leq 4$ **h.** $x \geq 4$ **i.** $x > 4$

j. $x < 4$

7. a. ← —+———+—→ with -5 and 20 marked

b. ← —+———+—→ with -5 and 20 marked

9. Multiplying or dividing an inequality by a negative number reverses the inequality symbol.

a. $x \geq {}^-6$
b. $x < 14$
11. $x \geq \frac{-3}{8}$
13. $\{x | \frac{8}{3} < x \leq 5\}$

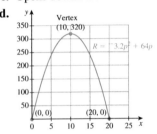

15. a. $80 + 2L$
b. $200 \leq 80 + 2L$ and $80 + 2L \leq 300$
c. and
d. $60 \leq L$ and $L \leq 110$. The length of the rectangle must be at least 60 m and no more than 110 m.

12.1 Skills and Review

17. $x = 8$
19. $x = 2$ or $x = \frac{8}{5}$
21. $y = {}^-1$
23. $x \approx 1.26$
25. a. $P = \$0$ or $P = \$20$
b. Vertex: $(10, 320)$
c. Opens downward
d.

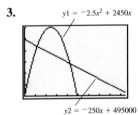

12.2 Exercises

1. a. At .55 second the fireworks have just come into good view. At 5.70 seconds the fireworks have just gone out of good view.
b. In the interval between 0 and .55 second, the fireworks are still below the level of the balcony.
c. In the interval between 5.70 and 6.25 seconds, the fireworks have fallen below the level of the balcony.

3.

Acme will lose money when their widget is priced less than \$234 or more than \$846. In set-builder notation, $\{x | 0 \leq x < 234$ or $846 < x\}$.

5.

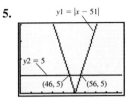

Percentages less than 46% or more than 56% are outside this candidate's margin of error. In set-builder notation, $\{x | 0 \leq x < 46$ or $56 < x \leq 100\}$.

7. $\{x | 0 \leq x \leq 4\}$
9. a. $\{x | x < {}^-4\}$; substitution of $x = {}^-5$, true; $x = 0$, false.
b. $\{x | x \geq {}^-4\}$; substitution of $x = 0$, true; $x = {}^-5$, false.
11. $\{x | x < {}^-3.39$ or $7.39 < x\}$
13. $\{x | x \leq {}^-2.24$ or $2.24 \leq x\}$
15. $\{x | x < {}^-2$ or $2 < x\}$

12.2 Skills and Review

17.

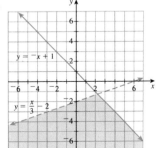

19. $x = \frac{2}{3} \approx .67$
21. $x = 25$
23. a. $f(g({}^-2)) = 50$
b. $f(g(x)) = 9x^2 - 6x + 2$
25. $x = {}^-4 + \sqrt{5}$ or $x = {}^-4 - \sqrt{5}$

12.3 Exercises

1. a, d
3. Answers may vary; two solutions: $(0, 99)$, $(20, 60)$, two nonsolutions: $(0, 100)$, $(49, 50)$.
5. a. ii   **b.** i   **c.** iii
7. $y < {}^-x - 2$; $y \leq 2x + 4$; $y \geq {}^-4$
9. $y < 4$; $y \geq {}^-4$; $x < {}^-1$; $x \geq {}^-5$
11.

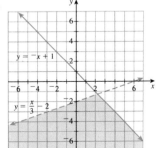

13.

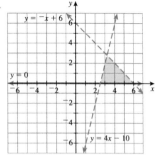

15. a. $x + y \leq 1; x \geq \frac{1}{4}; y < 2x; y \geq 0$

b.

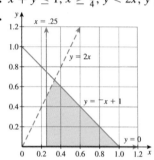

12.3 Skills and Review

17. $\{x \mid ^-3 \leq x \leq 11\}$

19. a. Let $x =$ the number of hours it takes the first painter to complete the job alone.

	Work	Time	Rate
First painter	1 job	x hours	$\frac{1}{x}$ job/hour
Second painter	1 job	$x + 2$ hours	$\frac{1}{x+2}$ job/hour
Together	1 job	5 hours	$\frac{1}{5}$ job/hour

b. $\frac{1}{x} + \frac{1}{x+2} = \frac{1}{5}$

c. $x \approx 9.1$ or $x \approx ^-1.1$

d. It takes the first painter 9 hours to complete the job alone.

21. $\dfrac{1}{(x + 5)(x - 4)}$

23. $x = 2$

25. a. y-intercept: $(0, ^-14)$

b. x-intercepts: $(^-2, 0), (7, 0)$

c. Vertex: $\left(\frac{5}{2}, \frac{^-81}{4}\right) = (2.5, ^-20.25)$

d.

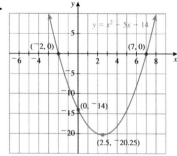

Chapter 12 Exploration

a. $x + y \leq 90$

b. $5x + 8y \geq 500$

c. $y \leq 30$

d.

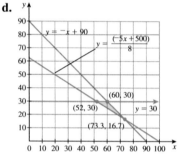

e. $(52, 30), (60, 30), \left(73\frac{1}{3}, 16\frac{2}{3}\right)$

Chapter 12 Review Exercises

1. $\{x \mid x \geq ^-3\}$

2. a. $\{x \mid x > 4\}$

b. $\{x \mid x \leq 1\}$

c. $\{x \mid x \leq ^-2\}$

d. $\{x \mid x > 3\}$

e. $\left\{x \mid x < \frac{1}{3}\right\}$

f. $\{x \mid x \leq 1\}$

3.

4. a. $\{x \mid 3 \leq x \leq 7\}$

b. $\{x \mid x < ^-3 \text{ or } 2 \leq x\}$

c. $\{x \mid ^-12 \leq x < ^-5\}$

d. $\{x < ^-1 \text{ or } x > 4\}$

e. $\{x \mid ^-2 \leq x < 5\}$

f. $\{x \mid 4 < x \leq 7\}$

5. $x \geq 100°F$

6. $\{x \mid x < 32 \text{ or } 75 < x\}$

7. a. $\frac{18+20+15+x}{4} = \frac{53+x}{4}$

b. $19 \le \frac{53+x}{4}$

c. $23 \le x$; the player must score at least 23 points in the fourth game to average at least 19 points per game.

d.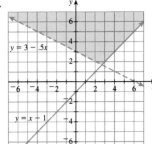

8. a. $50 \le 125 - 5x$ and $125 - 5x \le 100$

b. $5 \le x$ and $x \le 15$; the cover charge must be at least $5 and no more than $15.

c. $\{x \mid 5 \le x \le 15\}$

9. a.

b.

10. $\{x \mid .43 < x < 5.82\}$; substitution of $x = 3$, true; $x = 0$, false; $x = 6$, false.

11. a. 3   **b.** 1   **c.** 2

12. a. $\{x \mid {}^{-}3 < x < 3\}$ **b.** $\{x \mid x < 0 \text{ or } 8 < x\}$

c. $\{x \mid {}^{-}4 \le x \le 3\}$ **d.** $\{x \mid x \le {}^{-}4 \text{ or } 10 \le x\}$

e. $\{x \mid x < 4\}$ **f.** $\left\{x \mid 0 \le x \le \frac{25}{4}\right\}$

13. Any price between $13.59 and $30.25 generates revenue above $3000.

14. Remove grapefruits less than 3 inches in diameter or greater than 7 inches in diameter.

15. $\{s \mid 200 \le s \le 225\}$; the sides of the square lot are at least 200 feet and no more than 225 feet.

16. Only a and c are solutions.

17. Only b and d are solutions.

18.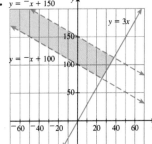

19.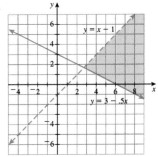

20.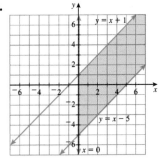

21.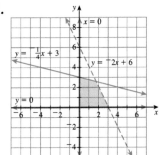

22. a. $x + y > 100$; $x + y < 150$; $y \ge 3x$

b.

c. Answers may vary; (25, 100) and $({}^{-}40, 150)$ are solutions. (75, 50) and (50, 0) are not solutions.

23. a. $2x + 2y > 60$; $2x + 2y \le 100$; $y \le 2.5x$; $y \ge 0$; $x \ge 0$

b.

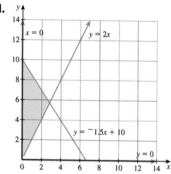

c. $(6, 30)$ is not a solution.

24. a. $30x + 20y \le 200$

b. $y \ge 2x$

c. There can't be a negative number of pants or shirts.

d.

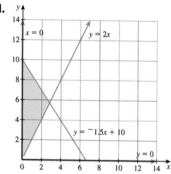

e. $(0, 10), (1, 8), (2, 7)$

Chapter 12 Test

1. $\{x | {}^-3 \le x < 8\}$

2. $\{x \le {}^-3 \text{ or } 5 < x\}$

3. $\{x < 2\}$; the opposing team may score 0 or 1 goal.

4. $40 \le x$ and $x \le 50$; the carpenter will need between 40 and 50 hours to complete the job.

5. $\{x | x > 1.59\}$

6. $\{x | {}^-.51 \le x \le 3.11\}$

7. $\{x | x < {}^-7 \text{ or } 2 < x\}$

8. The object is at least 40 m high anytime between 1.43 s and 4.29 s after release.

9.

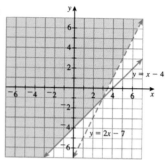

10.

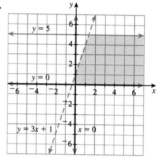

11. a. $x + y \le 250; y \ge 4x; x > 0; y > 0$

b.

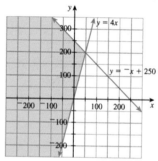

c. $(10, 240)$ is a solution.

12.

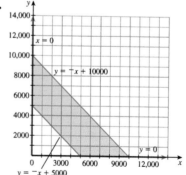

13. a. $x + y < 8$; $40x + 60y \geq 360$; $x \geq 0$; $y \geq 0$

b.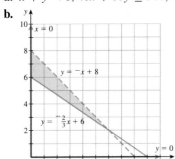

c. (4.5, 3) is a solution.

Index

Library of Functions

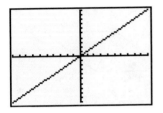

Basic Linear ($y = x$)

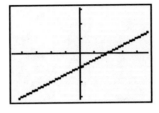

Linear ($y = mx + b$)

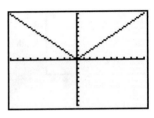

Absolute Value ($y = |x|$)

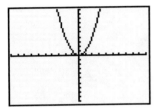

Basic Quadratic ($y = x^2$)

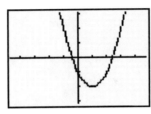

Quadratic ($y = ax^2 + bx + c$)

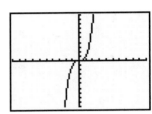

Basic Cubic ($y = x^3$)

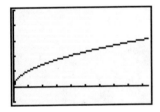

Square Root ($y = x^{1/2}$)

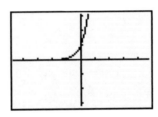

Exponential ($y = 10^x$)

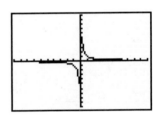

Basic Reciprocal ($y = 1/x$)

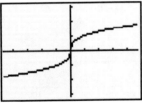

Cube Root ($y = x^{1/3}$)

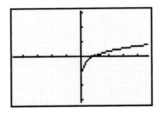

Logarithmic ($y = \log x$)

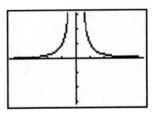

Inverse Square ($y = 1/x^2$)

Important Formulas

Area of Rectangle
$A = LW$

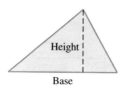

Area of Triangle
$A = \frac{1}{2}bh$

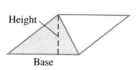

Area of Parallelogram
$A = bh$

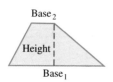

Area of Trapezoid
$A = \frac{1}{2}(b_1 + b_2)h$

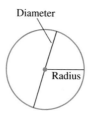

Circumference of Circle
$c = \pi d = 2\pi r$
Area of Circle
$A = \pi r^2$

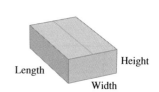

Volume of Rectangular Prism
$V = LWH$

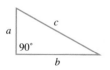

Pythagorean Theorem
$c^2 = a^2 + b^2$

$$\text{run} = x_2 - x_1$$
$$\text{rise} = y_2 - y_1$$

Run and Rise

$$\text{Distance} = \sqrt{\text{run}^2 + \text{rise}^2}$$

$$\text{Slope} = \frac{\text{rise}}{\text{run}}$$

Linear Equations
$y = mx + b$
$Ax + By = C$

Quadratic Equations
$ax^2 + bx + c = 0$

$$x = \frac{-b}{2a} \pm \frac{\sqrt{b^2 - 4ac}}{2a}$$

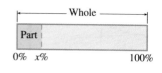

$$\text{Percent} = \frac{\text{Part}}{\text{Whole}}$$

Distance-Rate-Time

$$\text{Rate} = \frac{\text{Distance}}{\text{Time}}$$

Work Rate

$$\text{Work rate} = \frac{\text{Work}}{\text{Time}}$$

Compound Interest

$$A = A_0 \left(1 + \frac{r}{n}\right)^{nt}$$